Radiate Science knowledge with CGP...

OK, so there's a lot to learn in GCSE Combined Science — it is worth two GCSEs, after all.

Not to worry. This chunky CGP book explains all the facts, theory and practical skills you'll need, with essential exam practice questions on every page. It's a beautiful thing.

CGP — still the best! ☺

Our sole aim here at CGP is to produce the highest quality books — carefully written, immaculately presented and dangerously close to being funny.

Then we work our socks off to get them out to you — at the cheapest possible prices.

Contents

Published by CGP.

From original material by Richard Parsons.

Editors: Alex Billings, Mary Falkner, Katherine Faudemer, Emily Forsberg, Emily Garrett, Emily Howe, Duncan Lindsay, Ciara McGlade, Frances Rooney, Hayley Thompson, Sarah Williams.

Contributor: Paddy Gannon.

ISBN: 978 1 78294 565 9

With thanks to Susan Alexander, Matthew Benyohai, Sharon Keeley-Holden, David Paterson, Sarah Pattison, Camilla Simson and Karen Wells for the proofreading.

With thanks to Jan Greenway for the copyright research.

Data used for graph showing the prevalence of nonalcoholic fatty liver disease against the prevalence of obesity on page 20 from The Epidemiology of Nonalcoholic Fatty Liver Disease: A Global Perspective, Mariana Lazo, M.D., M.Sc.; Jeanne M. Clark, M.D., M.P.H Seminars in Liver Disease. 2008; 28(4): 339-350. www.thieme.com (reprinted by permission).

Data used for graph showing the risk of cardiovascular events against LDL levels on page 20 from P.M. Ridker, et al. Comparison of C-reactive protein and low density lipoprotein cholesterol levels in the prediction of first cardiovascular events. NEJM 2002; 347: 1557-65.

With thanks to HERVE CONGE, ISM/SCIENCE PHOTO LIBRARY for permission to reproduce the image on page 53.

Data provided to construct a graph on page 84 provided by The European Environment Agency.

Data provided to construct a graph on page 84 provided by the NASA GISS.

Printed by Elanders Ltd, Newcastle upon Tyne.
Clipart from Corel®

Cells and Genetic Material

All living things are made of <u>cells</u>. You are made up of billions of cells. So is a tree...

Cells Can be Eukaryotic or Prokaryotic

1) <u>Eukaryotic</u> cells are <u>complex</u>. All <u>animal</u> and <u>plant</u> cells are eukaryotic.

2) <u>Prokaryotic</u> cells are <u>smaller</u> and <u>simpler</u>. <u>Bacteria</u> are prokaryotic cells.

All Cells Contain Genetic Material

1) Cells contain a chemical called <u>DNA</u>. This is their <u>genetic material</u>.

2) DNA contains <u>instructions</u> that <u>control</u> what a cell does.
   It allows the whole organism to <u>develop</u> and <u>function</u> as it should.

3) DNA is <u>stored differently</u> in eukaryotic and prokaryotic cells (see below).

There's more about DNA on page 3.

Eukaryotic Cells Have a Nucleus

The different parts of a cell are called <u>sub-cellular structures</u>.
Most <u>animal</u> cells have these sub-cellular structures:

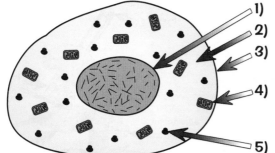

1) <u>Nucleus</u> — contains <u>DNA</u> (see page 3).

2) <u>Cytoplasm</u> — where most <u>chemical reactions</u> happen.

3) <u>Cell membrane</u> — holds the cell together and controls
   what goes <u>in</u> and <u>out</u>. It is <u>partially permeable</u>.

4) <u>Mitochondria</u> — contain the <u>enzymes</u> needed
   for most of the reactions of <u>aerobic respiration</u>.
   Respiration <u>releases energy</u> for the cell.

5) <u>Ribosomes</u> — join <u>amino acids</u> together to make <u>proteins</u>.

Plant cells usually have <u>all the bits</u> that <u>animal</u> cells have.
They also have:

1) A <u>cell wall</u> made of <u>cellulose</u>.
   It <u>supports</u> the cell and strengthens it.

2) <u>Chloroplasts</u> — where <u>photosynthesis</u> happens.
   Photosynthesis makes food for the plant (see page 28).
   Chloroplasts contain a substance called <u>chlorophyll</u>.

3) A <u>large vacuole</u> — stores <u>cell sap</u> (a solution of sugar and salts).

nucleus   ribosome   cell membrane   mitochondria

Prokaryotic Cells DON'T Have a Nucleus

1) <u>Prokaryotic cells</u> (such as bacteria) store their <u>genetic material</u> as:

   • <u>One</u> long circular <u>strand of DNA</u>. This floats around in the <u>cytoplasm</u>.

   • <u>Plasmids</u> — <u>small loops</u> of <u>extra</u> <u>DNA</u>.

2) Prokaryotes also have other <u>sub-cellular structures</u>, such as:

cell membrane   cell wall   ribosomes

Cell structures — become an estate agent...

On this page are typical cells with all the typical bits you need to know. Make sure you learn them all.

Q1   Give two ways in which genetic information may be stored in a prokaryotic cell.   [2 marks]

Cells and Microscopes

Without <u>microscopes</u> we would never have discovered cells. We can even use them to look <u>inside</u> cells.

Cells are Studied Using Microscopes

1) Microscopes use <u>lenses</u> to <u>magnify</u> things (make them look <u>bigger</u>).
2) <u>Light microscopes</u> can be used to look at cells.
They let us see <u>some sub-cellular structures</u>, e.g. <u>chloroplasts</u> and the <u>nucleus</u>.

There's more on sub-cellular structures on the previous page.

This is How to View a Specimen Using a Light Microscope

Preparing your specimen

1) Take a <u>thin slice</u> of your specimen (the thing you're looking at).
2) Take a clean <u>slide</u> and use a <u>pipette</u> to put one <u>drop of water</u> in the middle of it.
3) Then use <u>tweezers</u> to place your specimen on the slide.
4) You might need to add a drop of <u>stain</u> to make your specimen <u>easier to see</u>.
5) Carefully lower a <u>cover slip</u> onto the slide using a <u>mounted needle</u>. Try not to trap any <u>bubbles</u> under the cover slip.

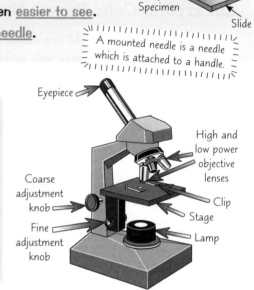

A mounted needle is a needle which is attached to a handle.

Viewing your specimen

1) <u>Clip</u> the slide onto the <u>stage</u>.
2) Select the <u>objective lens</u> with the <u>lowest</u> power.
3) Use the <u>coarse adjustment knob</u> to move the stage <u>up</u> to <u>just underneath</u> the objective lens.
4) <u>Look</u> down the <u>eyepiece</u>, then move the stage <u>down</u> until the specimen is <u>nearly in focus</u>.
5) <u>Move</u> the <u>fine adjustment knob</u>, until you get a <u>clear image</u>.
6) If you want to make the image bigger, use an objective lens with a <u>higher power</u> (and <u>refocus</u>).

This is How to Do a Scientific Drawing of a Specimen

1) Use a <u>sharp</u> pencil to draw clear <u>outlines</u> of the <u>main features</u>.
2) <u>Label</u> the <u>features</u> with <u>straight lines</u>. Make sure the lines <u>don't cross over</u> each other.
3) Don't do any <u>colouring</u> or <u>shading</u>.
4) The drawing should take up <u>at least half</u> the space available.
5) Include a <u>title</u>, the <u>magnification</u> used and a <u>scale</u>.

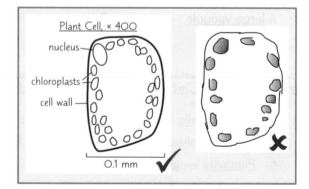

What, no colouring pencils? Scientists are spoilsports...

There's lots of important stuff here about how you use a light microscope to view specimens — so get learning.

Q1 A student prepares a slide with a sample of onion cells and places it on the stage of a light microscope. Describe the steps she should take to get a focused image of the cells. [4 marks]

DNA and Characteristics

Right, time to find out exactly what <u>DNA</u> is and why it's so <u>important</u>...

An Organism's DNA Makes Up its Genetic Material

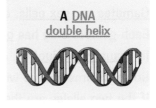

A <u>DNA</u>
<u>double helix</u>

1) DNA is a <u>polymer</u> — a molecule that's made up of <u>smaller</u>, <u>repeating units</u> called <u>monomers</u>.

2) DNA is made from monomers called <u>nucleotides</u>.

3) Each DNA molecule contains <u>two strands</u> of nucleotides, which coil together to form a <u>double helix</u> (a double-stranded spiral).

DNA is Stored in the Cell Nucleus as Chromosomes

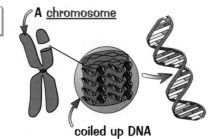

A <u>chromosome</u>

coiled up DNA

1) A chromosome is <u>one</u> very long <u>molecule of DNA</u> that's <u>coiled up</u>.

2) Chromosomes normally come in <u>pairs</u> — humans have <u>23 pairs</u>.

3) Each chromosome contains many <u>genes</u>. A <u>gene</u> is a <u>short section</u> of <u>DNA</u>.

Each Gene Codes for a Specific Protein

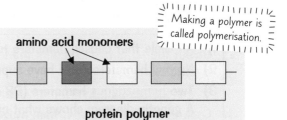

amino acid monomers

Making a polymer is called polymerisation.

protein polymer

1) Proteins are <u>polymers</u>.

2) They're made from <u>monomers</u> called <u>amino acids</u>.

3) A gene tells the cell to <u>put together</u> amino acids in a <u>particular order</u> to make a certain protein.

4) Proteins <u>control</u> different <u>characteristics</u>, e.g. eye colour.

5) Genes can exist in <u>different versions</u>. Each version gives a different form of a <u>characteristic</u>, like blue or brown eyes.

6) The different versions of the same gene are called <u>alleles</u> (or <u>genetic variants</u>).

7) Each chromosome in a pair carries the <u>same genes</u>, but they may each carry <u>different alleles</u>.

Genes and the Environment can Influence Characteristics

1) The <u>entire genetic material</u> in an organism is its <u>genome</u>.

2) The combination of <u>alleles</u> an organism has for each <u>gene</u> is called its <u>genotype</u>.

3) The <u>characteristics</u> the organism displays is called its <u>phenotype</u>.

4) An organism's genotype <u>affects</u> its <u>phenotype</u>.

5) An organism's phenotype is also <u>modified</u> (changed) by its <u>environment</u> (the conditions it lives in).

- For example, a plant grown in a nice sunny place could grow <u>leafy</u> and <u>green</u>.
- The same plant grown in darkness would grow <u>tall</u> and <u>spindly</u> and its leaves would turn <u>yellow</u> — so its characteristics would be affected by its environment.

Insert joke about genes and jeans here...

Phew. Lots of words to learn here. Make sure you know all about DNA, genes, etc. before you move on.

Q1   What is an organism's genome?   [1 mark]

Q2   What is an organism's: a) genotype,   b) phenotype?   [2 marks]

Genetic Diagrams

Genetic diagrams help to predict how characteristics will be passed on from parents to their offspring (children).

Organisms Have Two Alleles of Every Gene

There's more on genes, alleles and chromosomes on the previous page.

1) Gametes are sex cells, e.g. sperm and egg cells in animals.
2) Each gamete only has one copy of each chromosome. This means it only has one version of each gene.
3) In sexual reproduction, a sperm and an egg combine to produce a new organism.
4) So organisms end up with two versions of every gene (two alleles) — one from each gamete.
5) If the two alleles are the same, then the organism is homozygous.
6) If the two alleles are different, then the organism is heterozygous.
7) Some alleles are dominant (these are shown with a capital letter on genetic diagrams, e.g. 'C').
   Some alleles are recessive (these are shown by a small letter on genetic diagrams, e.g. 'c').
8) For an organism to show a recessive characteristic, both its alleles must be recessive (e.g. cc).
   But to show a dominant characteristic, only one allele needs to be dominant (e.g. either CC or Cc).

Genetic Diagrams Can Show How Characteristics are Inherited

1) Some characteristics are controlled by a single gene, e.g. blood group. You can use genetic diagrams to show how these characteristics are inherited (passed on from parents to offspring).
2) Here's an example. Remember, an organism's genotype is the alleles it has. Its phenotype is the characteristics it displays (see previous page).

1) An allele that causes hamsters to have superpowers is recessive ("b").
2) Normal hamsters don't have superpowers due to a dominant allele ("B").
3) Two homozygous hamsters (BB and bb) are crossed (bred together). A genetic diagram shows what could happen:

A hamster with the genotype BB or Bb will be normal. A hamster with the genotype bb will have superpowers.

Parents' phenotypes:	Normal	Superpowered

Parents' genotypes: BB bb

Gametes' genotypes: (each gamete just has one allele) B B b b

The lines show all the possible ways the parents' alleles could combine.

Offsprings' genotypes: Bb Bb Bb Bb

Each offspring must have one allele from each of its parents.

Offsprings' phenotypes: All the offspring are normal (boring).

4) A Punnett square is another type of genetic diagram.
5) This Punnett square shows a cross between two heterozygous hamsters (Bb and Bb):

gametes' genotypes are written at the top and side

offsprings' genotypes are shown in the squares

	B	b
B	BB	Bb
b	Bb	bb

• There's a 3 in 4 (75%) chance that offspring will be normal.
• There's a 1 in 4 (25%) chance that offspring will have superpowers.
• This gives a 3 normal : 1 superpowers ratio (3:1).

3) It's not always this simple. Most characteristics are actually controlled by several genes.

Your meanotype determines how nice you are to your sibling...

Genetic diagrams only tell you probabilities. They don't say what will definitely happen.

Q1 Height in pea plants is controlled by a single gene. The allele for tall pea plants (T) is dominant over the allele for short pea plants (t). A pea plant is heterozygous for this gene. Write down its genotype. [1 mark]

More Genetic Diagrams

Here's another page of funny diagrams with squares, circles and lines going everywhere.

Your Chromosomes Control Whether You're Male or Female

1) There are 23 pairs of chromosomes in every human body cell.
2) The 23rd pair is labelled XX or XY. These are the sex chromosomes.
3) They're the two chromosomes that decide whether you're male or female.
4) Males have an X and a Y chromosome (XY).
5) Females have two X chromosomes (XX).
6) The Y chromosome carries a gene which makes an embryo develop testes.
7) Here's a genetic diagram to show the chance of having a boy or a girl:

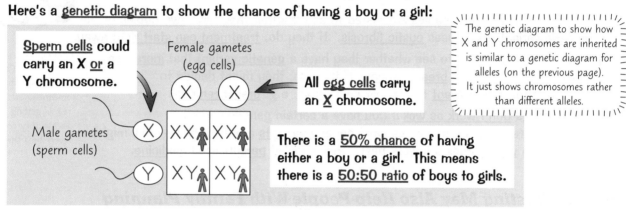

Sperm cells could carry an X or a Y chromosome.

Female gametes (egg cells)

All egg cells carry an X chromosome.

Male gametes (sperm cells)

There is a 50% chance of having either a boy or a girl. This means there is a 50:50 ratio of boys to girls.

The genetic diagram to show how X and Y chromosomes are inherited is similar to a genetic diagram for alleles (on the previous page). It just shows chromosomes rather than different alleles.

Family Trees Can Also Show Single Gene Inheritance

1) A family tree can show how genetic disorders are inherited.
2) Here's an example using cystic fibrosis — a genetic disorder of the cell membranes.

Genetic disorders are health conditions. They are often caused by inheriting faulty alleles.

1) The allele which causes cystic fibrosis is a recessive allele, 'f'.
2) People with two copies of the 'f' allele (genotype 'ff') will have the disorder.
3) People with only one copy of the recessive allele (genotype 'Ff') won't have the disorder — they're known as carriers.
4) Below is a family tree for a family that includes carriers of cystic fibrosis.
5) The horizontal lines (—) link parents. The vertical lines (|) link parents to their children.

John   Susan

Mark   Caroline   Eve   Phil

Will   new baby

?

Key
- ☐ Male
- ◯ Female
- ◼ ⬤ Has cystic fibrosis
- ◧ ◖ Carrier of cystic fibrosis
- ☐ ◯ Unaffected by cystic fibrosis

- Each half of a shape represents an allele.
- Purple = a recessive allele
- White = a dominant allele

unaffected by cystic fibrosis

F   f

F   FF   Ff
f   Ff   ff

carrier of cystic fibrosis

has cystic fibrosis

6) The new baby has two parents that are carriers (genotype 'Ff').
7) So, the new baby has a 1 in 4 chance of having cystic fibrosis.

Have you got the Y-factor...

I bet you're sick of genetic diagrams by now. Still, that family tree makes a nice change. Umm... sort of.

Q1   What does it mean if a person is described as being a carrier for a genetic disorder?   [1 mark]

Genome Research and Testing

Scientists might be able to use <u>genes</u> to <u>predict diseases</u> and provide us with <u>new and better drugs</u>.

Scientists Have Researched the Human Genome

An organism's genome is all of its DNA.

1) Scientists have identified <u>all of the genes</u> found in the <u>human genome</u>.

2) This could be really <u>useful</u> in <u>medicine</u>. E.g. by <u>comparing the genomes</u> of people with and without a certain disease, scientists can try to identify the <u>genetic variants</u> (<u>alleles</u>) involved in the disease.

3) <u>People</u> can then be <u>tested</u> for the genetic variants that are linked to a particular disease.

Genetic Testing Can Help To Improve Healthcare

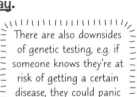

1) In the UK, all <u>newborn babies</u> are tested to see whether they have <u>two copies</u> of the <u>genetic variant</u> that causes <u>cystic fibrosis</u>. If they do, <u>treatment can start right away</u>.

2) <u>Women</u> can be tested to see whether they have a <u>genetic variant</u> that <u>increases their risk</u> of developing <u>breast cancer</u>. If they do, they might decide to have <u>treatment</u> to <u>prevent</u> the cancer developing, e.g. <u>breast removal</u>.

3) Some drugs <u>don't work as well</u> if you have a certain genetic variant. In the future, a doctor might see what <u>genetic variants</u> a patient has — this might show them <u>which drugs</u> will work <u>best</u>. This is called <u>personalised medicine</u>.

There are also downsides of genetic testing, e.g. if someone knows they're at risk of getting a certain disease, they could panic every time they feel ill.

Genetic Testing May Also Help People With Family Planning

A couple wanting to have a <u>baby</u> could use genetic testing to find out the risk of their <u>baby</u> having a particular <u>genetic disorder</u>. This could involve testing the <u>parents</u> and the <u>embryo</u> or <u>fetus</u>.

1) <u>Parent</u> — genetic tests could show whether one of the parents is a <u>carrier</u> (see previous page) for the condition.

2) <u>Embryo</u> — couples can have <u>fertility treatment</u> if they're struggling to have a baby. During fertility treatment, eggs are fertilised to make embryos in the lab. These embryos then have their <u>DNA tested</u>. Embryos <u>without</u> harmful genetic variants are <u>implanted</u> into the <u>womb</u> to <u>develop</u>.

3) <u>Fetus</u> — once a woman is pregnant, it is possible to get some of the <u>fetus' DNA</u> by taking a sample of the <u>amniotic fluid</u>. The parents can then find out if the fetus has a genetic variant linked to a <u>genetic disorder</u>. They can then decide if they want to <u>end</u> the pregnancy.

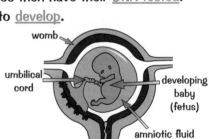
womb
umbilical cord
developing baby (fetus)
amniotic fluid

So, genetic testing allows couples to make <u>informed decisions</u> about <u>family planning</u>. But there are <u>risks</u>...

1) Testing <u>isn't 100% perfect</u>.
   - When <u>amniotic fluid</u> is tested, there's a <u>very small risk</u> it could cause a <u>miscarriage</u>.
   - Sometimes, a couple is told that their baby <u>has</u> a genetic disorder, but the test turns out to be <u>wrong</u> (a <u>false positive</u>). Or, they are told their baby <u>doesn't have</u> a disorder, but then the test is <u>wrong</u> (a <u>false negative</u>). This could cause <u>distress</u>.

2) Genetic testing can lead to <u>embryos</u> being <u>destroyed</u>. Some people think that any <u>potential life</u> should be allowed to <u>survive</u>, whatever disorders he or she may have.

3) There's also a worry that genetic testing is a '<u>slippery slope</u>'. Some people think parents will want to choose embryos that have the <u>characteristics</u> (e.g. hair colour) that they <u>prefer</u>.

Personalised medicine — write your name on the bottle...

Ah... nothing's ever straightforward, is it. Make sure you know the pros and cons of using genetic testing.

Q1   Describe a test that could be carried out to determine whether a fetus has a genetic disorder.   [2 marks]

Genetic Engineering

Genetic engineering is an area of science with <u>exciting possibilities</u>, but there might be <u>dangers</u> too...

Genetic Engineering Involves Changing an Organism's Genome

1) <u>Genetic engineering</u> is used to give organisms <u>new</u> and <u>useful characteristics</u>.

2) It involves <u>cutting a gene</u> out of one organism's genome and <u>putting it into</u> another organism's genome.

3) Organisms that have had a new gene <u>inserted</u> are called <u>genetically modified</u> (GM) organisms.

> Genetic engineering works because all organisms use the same molecule (DNA) to store their genetic material.

Genetic Engineering is Useful in Agriculture and Medicine

For example, in <u>agriculture</u> (farming):

> 'Resistant to' means 'not killed by'.

1) <u>Crops</u> can be genetically engineered to be <u>resistant to herbicides</u> (chemicals that kill plants).

2) This means that farmers can <u>spray</u> their crops to <u>kill weeds</u>, <u>without</u> affecting the crop itself.

3) This can <u>increase crop yield</u> (the amount of food produced). This can help to produce more food for the growing human population.

In <u>medicine</u>:

1) <u>Bacteria</u> can be genetically engineered to produce <u>human insulin</u>.

2) The bacteria can be grown in <u>large numbers</u>.

3) They can then be used to produce insulin for people with <u>diabetes</u> (see p.67).

But There are Some Concerns About Genetic Engineering

There are <u>concerns</u> about growing <u>genetically modified crops</u>:

1) <u>Genes</u> used in genetic engineering may get out into the <u>environment</u>. E.g. a herbicide resistance gene may be picked up by <u>weeds</u>, creating a new '<u>superweed</u>' that can't be killed.

2) Some people are worried that GM crops might have a <u>negative effect</u> on <u>food chains</u> or <u>human health</u>.

3) Some people think that more <u>long-term studies</u> need to be done to <u>fully understand</u> the risks.

There are <u>concerns</u> about using genetic engineering in <u>animals</u>:

I say it's great.

1) It can be hard to <u>predict</u> how changing an animal's genome will affect the animal.

2) Many genetically modified embryos <u>don't survive</u>.

3) Some genetically modified <u>animals</u> also suffer from <u>health problems</u> later in life.

There are also concerns about how genetic engineering may be used to alter <u>human genomes</u> in the <u>future</u>:

For example, there are fears it could lead to the creation of '<u>designer babies</u>', with parents <u>choosing</u> their child's <u>characteristics</u>.

If only there was a gene to make revision easier...

As with most new technologies, there are benefits and risks to genetic engineering. Make sure you learn them.

Q1   Explain one benefit of being able to genetically engineer herbicide-resistant crops.   [2 marks]

Health and Disease

Some grim reading coming up — it's time to find out about <u>diseases</u> and the <u>nasties</u> that can <u>cause</u> them...

Health Can be Affected by Disease

1) A <u>healthy</u> organism is one that is in a state of <u>well-being</u>
— it's <u>working</u> just as it <u>should</u> be, both <u>physically</u> and <u>mentally</u>.

2) A <u>disease</u> is a condition that disrupts the normal <u>structures</u> or <u>functions</u> of an organism.
It often damages cells. Most organisms will get a disease <u>at some point</u> in their life.

3) Many things can <u>cause</u> disease and ill health. For example:

- <u>infection</u> with a <u>pathogen</u> (see below).
- a <u>mutation</u> (change) in the organism's <u>genes</u> (see page 3).
- <u>trauma</u> (an <u>emotional shock</u> or a <u>physical injury</u>), e.g. being badly hurt may cause <u>depression</u>.
- <u>lifestyle</u> factors, e.g. eating too much food can lead to <u>obesity</u>.

Diseases Can be Communicable or Non-Communicable

Communicable Diseases

1) <u>Communicable</u> diseases are diseases that can <u>spread</u> between organisms.

2) They are caused by <u>pathogens</u> infecting the organism.

3) A <u>pathogen</u> is a type of <u>microorganism</u> (really tiny organism) that causes <u>disease</u>.

4) Types of pathogen include <u>bacteria</u>, <u>viruses</u>, <u>protists</u> and <u>fungi</u> (see next page).

Communicable diseases are also known as infectious diseases.

Non-communicable Diseases

1) <u>Non-communicable</u> diseases <u>cannot</u> be passed from one organism to another, e.g. cancers and diabetes.

2) They generally last for a <u>long time</u> and <u>progress slowly</u>.

3) They are often linked to <u>lifestyle factors</u> and <u>genes</u> (see pages 18-19).

1) Both types of disease cause <u>symptoms</u> — <u>changes</u> in the organism that suggest disease is present.
E.g. the main symptom of <u>chicken pox</u> is a spotty rash.

2) Symptoms may not be <u>obvious</u>, especially in the <u>early stages</u> of a disease.
E.g. once you're infected with the chicken pox virus, it takes around 14 days for the spots to appear.
The <u>time</u> between being <u>infected</u> with a pathogen and <u>showing</u> symptoms is called the <u>incubation period</u>.

Diseases May Interact With Each Other

Sometimes having <u>one disease</u> can make it <u>more</u> or <u>less likely</u> that you will suffer from <u>another disease</u>.
E.g.

1) <u>HPV</u> is a <u>virus</u> that can infect the <u>reproductive system</u>.
2) Some <u>HPV infections</u> can cause <u>cell changes</u>.
This can cause certain types of <u>cancer</u> to develop.

1) <u>Helminths</u> are a type of worm. Some helminths can cause <u>disease</u> if they get into your body.
2) However, being infected with a certain type of helminth may <u>reduce the development</u> of some other diseases, e.g. Crohn's disease (where the body attacks its <u>own cells</u> in the <u>gut</u>).

I have a communicable disease — it's telling me to go to bed...

Communicable diseases can be <u>passed</u> between people because they involve <u>pathogens</u>.

Q1   What is meant by the term 'non-communicable disease'?   [1 mark]

How Disease Spreads

There are loads of ways you can catch diseases. As if I wasn't feeling paranoid enough already...

Communicable Diseases are Caused by Pathogens

Pathogens are microorganisms that cause communicable diseases (see previous page). There are four types:

1) BACTERIA — these are very small cells (much, much smaller than your body cells).
They make you feel ill by producing toxins (poisons) that damage your cells and tissues.

2) VIRUSES — these are not cells. They're really tiny — even smaller than bacteria. They make copies of themselves inside the infected organism's cells. These cells then burst, releasing the viruses.

3) PROTISTS — these are eukaryotic (see page 1). They're usually single-celled.

4) FUNGI — some fungi have thread-like structures. These can grow and pierce human skin and the surface of plants, causing diseases. They can also produce spores. These can spread to other plants and animals.

Communicable Diseases are Spread in Different Ways

Pathogens infect both animals and plants. They can spread in different ways. For example:

1) Water

Some pathogens can be picked up by drinking or bathing in contaminated water. For example:

> Cholera is a bacterial infection. It causes diarrhoea and dehydration. It's spread by drinking water containing the diarrhoea of other sufferers.

Contaminated means it contains a pathogen.

2) Food

Some pathogens are picked up by eating contaminated food. For example:

1) Salmonella bacteria are found in some foods, e.g. raw meat.
2) If these foods are kept too long or not cooked properly the bacteria can cause food poisoning.

3) On Surfaces

Some pathogens can be picked up by touching contaminated surfaces. For example:

1) Tobacco mosaic disease affects many types of plants, e.g. tomatoes.
2) It's caused by a virus called tobacco mosaic virus (TMV).
3) This virus makes the leaves of plants patchy and discoloured.
4) The discolouration means the plant can't photosynthesise as well, so the virus affects its growth.
5) It's spread when infected leaves rub against healthy leaves.

1) Athlete's foot is a fungal disease.
2) It affects humans — it makes skin on the feet itch and flake off.
3) It's usually spread by touching the same things as an infected person, e.g. towels.

Ahh...Ahh... Ahhhhh Choooooooo — urghh, this page is catching...

Pathogens are usually really small — you often need a microscope to see them — but they spread themselves around pretty well. There's more about the different ways that diseases can spread coming up on the next page.

Q1 How is tobacco mosaic disease spread between plants? [1 mark]

More on How Disease Spreads

Brace yourself. Time for some more <u>ways</u> that communicable diseases can be <u>spread</u>. First up, body fluids...

1) Body Fluids

Some pathogens are spread by <u>body fluids</u> such as:

- <u>semen</u> — through <u>unprotected sex</u>
- <u>blood</u> — e.g. by <u>sharing needles</u> to inject drugs or by <u>contaminated blood transfusions</u>
- <u>breast milk</u> — by breast feeding

> Diseases that are spread through sexual contact are known as sexually transmitted infections or STIs.

1) <u>HIV</u> is a <u>virus</u> spread by <u>exchanging body fluids</u>.
2) The virus attacks the <u>immune system</u> (see page 12). At first it causes <u>flu-like symptoms</u>.
3) If the immune system isn't working properly, it <u>can't cope</u> with <u>other infections</u> or <u>cancers</u>.
4) At this stage, the virus is known as <u>late stage HIV</u>, or <u>AIDS</u>.

2) Animal Vectors

Animals that <u>spread disease</u> are called <u>vectors</u>.

1) <u>Malaria</u> is a disease caused by a <u>protist</u>.
2) <u>Mosquitoes</u> are <u>vectors</u> for malaria. They are insects that feed on <u>animals' blood</u>.
3) The malaria protist lives in the <u>blood</u> of infected animals.
4) A mosquito <u>picks up</u> the protist when it <u>bites</u> an <u>infected animal</u>.
   It then passes the protist on when it bites <u>another animal</u>.
5) Malaria causes <u>fever</u>. It can cause <u>death</u>.

3) Soil

Some <u>pathogens</u> live in <u>soil</u>. This means plants in the <u>contaminated</u> soil may be <u>infected</u>. For example:

1) <u>Crown gall disease</u> is caused by a type of bacterium.
2) These bacteria can live in <u>some soils</u> and on the <u>roots</u> of some plants.
3) If the bacteria enter a plant, they can cause <u>galls</u> (growths) on the plant.
4) The galls can <u>damage</u> the plant <u>tissue</u>. This can <u>slow</u> the flow of <u>water</u> through the plant.
5) This causes the plant to become <u>weaker</u> and it may eventually <u>die</u>.

4) Air

Some pathogens are carried in the <u>air</u>. For example:

1) <u>Chalara ash dieback disease</u> is caused by a fungus. It affects <u>ash trees</u>.
2) The fungus is spread from infected trees, through the <u>air</u>, by the <u>wind</u>.

1) The <u>influenza virus</u> causes <u>flu</u>.
2) When an infected person <u>coughs</u> or <u>sneezes</u>, <u>droplets</u> containing the virus go into the <u>air</u>.
3) Flu is spread when other people <u>breathe the droplets in</u>.

So there you have it — loads of different ways to get ill...

Animals, body fluids, air — there's no escape... Luckily, you've got defence systems to help you out (see p.11-12).

Q1   What type of pathogen causes crown gall disease?   [1 mark]

Defending Against Pathogens

Pathogens can be <u>anywhere</u>, so our bodies have to be <u>on guard</u> at all times to make sure they don't get in.

Humans Have a Pretty Clever Defence System

1) The body has got features that <u>stop</u> a lot of nasties entering the <u>blood</u>.

2) These are <u>non-specific</u> defences — they aren't produced in response to a <u>particular</u> pathogen. Non-specific defences are <u>always present</u>.

Physical Defences

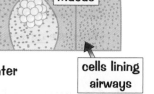

1) The airways are lined with <u>mucus</u> (snot) and <u>cilia</u> (hair-like structures). The mucus <u>traps</u> particles that could contain pathogens. The cilia <u>push</u> the <u>mucus</u> to the <u>back of the throat</u>, where it can be <u>swallowed</u>.

2) The <u>skin</u> acts as a <u>barrier</u> to pathogens. If it gets <u>cut</u>, pathogens could enter the <u>bloodstream</u> through the wound. This is where platelets come in...

3) <u>Platelets</u> in the blood clump together to 'plug' the wound. This is known as <u>blood clotting</u>. Blood clots <u>stop you losing</u> too much <u>blood</u>. They also help to prevent <u>microorganisms</u> from entering the blood.

- Platelets are <u>tiny fragments (bits) of cells</u>.
- They contain lots of <u>different substances</u> that are needed to help form the <u>clot</u>.
- They also have <u>proteins</u> on their surface. These help the platelets <u>stick</u> to each other to <u>plug</u> the wound.

platelets

Chemical Defences

1) <u>Eyes</u> produce <u>tears</u>, which contain an enzyme called <u>lysozyme</u>. Lysozyme breaks down <u>bacteria</u> on the surface of the eye.

2) <u>Saliva</u> (spit) contains molecules which <u>kill</u> pathogens that enter the mouth. This stops some of the pathogens from reaching the <u>stomach</u>.

3) The <u>stomach</u> produces <u>hydrochloric acid</u>. This <u>kills pathogens</u>.

Microbial Defences

1) Your <u>gut</u> naturally contains lots of <u>harmless bacteria</u>.

2) If <u>pathogens</u> enter your gut, they may <u>struggle to survive</u> because they have to <u>compete</u> with your natural bacteria.

Your gut means your intestines.

Drowning pathogens in soda — my preferred fizzy kill defence...

Make sure you learn all the different methods of defence on this page. Even if pathogens manage to make it past all of these defences, they've still got your immune system to deal with. There's more about this on the next page.

Q1   Explain how platelets help to defend the body against pathogens.   [2 marks]

The Human Immune System

Your immune system can <u>kill pathogens</u> before they have a chance to cause you serious problems.

Your Immune System Can Attack Pathogens

1) If pathogens do make it into your body, your <u>immune system</u> kicks in to destroy them.

2) The most important part of your immune system is the <u>white blood cells</u>.

3) Every type of cell has unique <u>molecules</u> on its surface called <u>antigens</u>. White blood cells have special <u>receptors</u> which help them to identify antigens on <u>pathogens</u>.

4) White blood cells recognise antigens on <u>pathogens</u> as <u>non-self</u> (foreign). They recognise antigens on <u>normal</u> body cells as <u>self</u>.

5) When white blood cells come across <u>non-self antigens</u>, an immune response is triggered.

6) There are <u>different types</u> of white blood cell — each works in a different way:

1. Consuming Pathogens

1) Some white blood cells have a <u>flexible membrane</u>.

2) They also contain lots of <u>enzymes</u>.

3) These features mean they can <u>ingest</u> (take in) and <u>digest</u> (break down) pathogens.

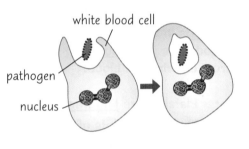

white blood cell

pathogen

nucleus

2. Producing Antibodies

1) When some white blood cells come across <u>antigens</u> on a <u>pathogen</u>, receptors on the white blood cell <u>bind</u> to the antigens.

2) The white blood cells then start to make <u>proteins</u> called <u>antibodies</u>.

3) Antibodies <u>bind</u> to the <u>antigens</u> on the pathogens.

4) The antibodies produced are <u>specific</u> to that type of antigen — they won't bind to any others.

5) Lots more of the antibodies are then made <u>quickly</u>. They flow all around the body to <u>find</u> all similar pathogens.

6) The <u>antibodies</u> may <u>disable</u> the pathogen (stop it from working). They may also '<u>tag</u>' the pathogens — this makes it easier for other white blood cells to <u>find</u> the pathogens and <u>destroy</u> them.

7) Some white blood cells (called <u>memory cells</u>) stay around in the blood. If the person is infected with the <u>same pathogen</u> again, the memory cells will <u>quickly</u> make the antibodies to kill it. This means the person is <u>naturally immune</u> to that pathogen and won't get ill.

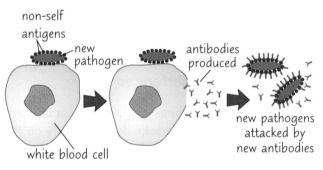

non-self antigens

new pathogen

white blood cell

antibodies produced

new pathogens attacked by new antibodies

3. Releasing Enzymes

Some white blood cells release <u>enzymes</u> that <u>break down</u> pathogens.

Fight disease — give your nose a blow with boxing gloves...

The <u>body</u> makes antibodies against the antigens on pathogens. There, don't say I never help you.

Q1   Give one role of antibodies in the immune response.   [1 mark]

Q2   Describe the role of memory cells in the immune response.   [2 marks]

Reducing and Preventing the Spread of Disease

The best way of dealing with disease is sometimes to just <u>avoid any contact</u> with pathogens in the first place...

The Spread of Disease Can Be Reduced or Prevented in Animals

1) The spread of a disease between <u>animals</u> (including <u>humans</u>) can cause a huge <u>loss</u> of <u>life</u>.

2) It can also lead to a <u>loss</u> of <u>food sources</u> (if animals kept for food are affected).

3) These things can <u>reduce</u> or <u>prevent</u> the spread of disease in animals:

BEING HYGIENIC

E.g. <u>washing hands</u> regularly to <u>remove pathogens</u>.

Many diseases are spread when a person touches a source of pathogens (e.g. door handle) and then touches their eyes, nose or mouth.

STERILISING WOUNDS IN THE SKIN

This <u>kills pathogens</u> near the wound so stops them entering the <u>blood</u>.

LIVING IN SANITARY CONDITIONS

1) This means having <u>clean drinking water</u> and a good system for <u>getting rid</u> of <u>sewage</u> (waste from toilets).

2) This can help to reduce the spread of pathogens present in <u>urine</u> or <u>faeces</u> (poo).

3) It can also help to reduce the spread of diseases that are spread in <u>water</u>, such as <u>cholera</u> (see page 9).

4) However, it can be <u>expensive</u> for a society to create sanitary conditions.

A society is a group of people that live in the same area and have the same laws. Laws give the society order.

DESTROYING INFECTED ANIMALS

1) E.g. farmers might <u>kill</u> animals that are infected with a disease.

2) This prevents <u>large numbers</u> of other animals from <u>getting the disease</u>.

3) However, this is very <u>costly</u> for the farmer.

RESTRICTING TRAVEL

1) Sometimes individuals should be prevented from <u>travelling</u>, and <u>spreading</u> a disease to new areas.

2) Although this is <u>good</u> for <u>society</u>, it means taking away an individual's <u>freedom of movement</u>.

VACCINATION (see page 15)

1) Vaccinating <u>people</u> and <u>animals</u> against disease means that they <u>won't</u> develop the infection.

2) However, some people may not want to be vaccinated, because of the <u>risks</u> involved (see p.15). A person's <u>choice</u> should be <u>balanced</u> with the benefit of vaccination to society.

THE USE OF CONTRACEPTION

Using <u>condoms</u> prevents <u>sexually transmitted infections</u> spreading between people during <u>sex</u>. <u>HIV</u> is an example of a sexually transmitted infection (see page 10).

The spread of disease — mouldy margarine...

Make sure you understand how each method above can prevent the spread of disease. However, you should also be aware of any costs linked to them — these can be costs to an individual or to society as a whole.

Q1   State two ways in which living in sanitary conditions can help to reduce the spread of disease.   [2 marks]

Reducing and Preventing the Spread of Disease

It's not just animals that get disease — plants can get poorly too...

The Spread of Disease Can Be Reduced or Prevented in Plants

1) Plant diseases can reduce the amount of food available for many organisms.
2) They can also damage habitats, e.g. if lots of trees got a disease it could damage a woodland habitat.
3) Here are some ways that the spread of disease in plants can be controlled:

CONTROLLING WHERE PLANTS ARE MOVED TO

This makes sure that infected plants don't come into contact with healthy plants.
E.g. garden centres are not allowed to sell plants which have crown gall disease (see p.10).

DESTROYING INFECTED PLANTS

1) This stops them from being able to infect other plants.
2) However, it can be costly to a farmer.

ONLY USING HEALTHY SOURCES OF SEEDS AND PLANTS

This stops the disease from being introduced into a population.

CROP ROTATION

1) Many pathogens will only infect one type of plant.
2) Changing the type of plants that are grown in a field each year stops pathogen populations getting too big.
3) However, it can be costly for farms if they have to grow different crops every year.

POLYCULTURE

1) Polyculture means growing different types plants in an area at the same time.
2) Pathogens that affect a specific type of plant will be less likely to spread — many plants close to an infected plant will be a different type, so they won't be affected by the pathogen.

no polyculture — all plants affected

polyculture — pathogen doesn't affect these plants

CHEMICAL CONTROL

1) Chemicals can be used to kill pathogens, e.g. fungicides can be used to kill fungi.
2) But chemical control could lead to resistant strains of the pathogen developing (see page 22).

BIOLOGICAL CONTROL

1) This is when another organism is used to control a pest or pathogen. For example, ladybirds eat aphids (an insect pest) so ladybirds can be released into an area to reduce aphid numbers.
2) However, in some cases, the control organism may become a pest itself and cause more problems.

Crop rotation — a perfect way to make plants dizzy...

Plant diseases can cause many problems. E.g. they can reduce the amount of food available for humans and other animals. Make sure you learn the different methods that can be used to stop plant diseases from spreading.

Q1   Give one benefit and one cost to a farmer of using a crop rotation system.   [2 marks]

Vaccinations

Before you get cracking on this page, take a look back at p.12 to remind yourself about the <u>immune response</u>.

Vaccinations Stop You Getting Infections

1) You can be <u>vaccinated</u> against some diseases, e.g. measles.
2) <u>Vaccination</u> usually involves injecting <u>dead</u> or <u>inactive</u> pathogens into the body. Dead or inactive pathogens don't cause you <u>any harm</u>.
3) The pathogens have <u>antigens</u>, so your white blood cells make <u>antibodies</u> to help destroy them.
4) Some white blood cells also become <u>memory cells</u>.
5) If <u>living pathogens</u> of the same type get into the body, the <u>memory cells</u> will quickly make antibodies to destroy them.
6) This means that you're <u>less likely</u> to get the disease.

> There's more on antibodies and memory cells on page 12.

7) <u>Big outbreaks</u> of disease can be <u>prevented</u> if <u>lots of people</u> are vaccinated. That way, even the people who <u>aren't vaccinated</u> are <u>unlikely</u> to catch the disease because there are <u>fewer people</u> able to pass it on.

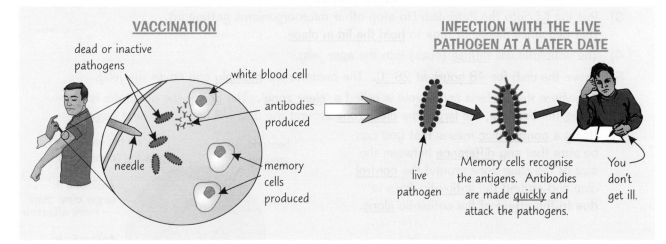

There are Pros and Cons of Vaccination

PROS
1) Vaccines have helped <u>control</u> lots of diseases that were once <u>common</u> in the UK (e.g. measles, mumps). Some of these diseases can make people <u>really ill</u>, or even <u>cause death</u>.
2) So, controlling these diseases has helped to <u>save lives</u> around the world.

CONS
1) Vaccines don't always work — sometimes they <u>don't</u> give you <u>immunity</u>.
2) You can sometimes have a <u>bad reaction</u> to a vaccine (although this is very <u>rare</u>).
3) It can be <u>expensive</u> to <u>make</u> vaccines and to vaccinate <u>lots of people</u>. Sometimes the <u>cost</u> of vaccine may <u>outweigh</u> its <u>benefit</u>, e.g. if the vaccine is for a disease that doesn't occur very <u>often</u> or the vaccine isn't very <u>effective</u>.

Take that, you evil antigen...

Deciding whether to have a vaccination means balancing risks — the risk of catching the disease if you don't have a vaccine, against the risk of having a bad reaction if you do. As always, you need to look at the evidence.

Q1   What do white blood cells produce in response to vaccinations?   [1 mark]

PRACTICAL Culturing Microorganisms

Here's how you can grow microorganisms and test how effective different antibiotics are at killing them.

You Can Investigate the Effect of Antibiotics on Bacterial Growth

Antibiotics are substances which kill bacteria.
You can test the action of antibiotics on bacteria grown on an agar plate.

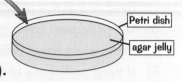

Petri dish
agar jelly

- To make an agar plate, hot agar jelly is poured into a Petri dish.
  Agar jelly contains all the nutrients bacteria need to grow.
- When the jelly's cooled and set, a liquid containing bacteria is spread evenly across the surface of the agar using sterile equipment (see below).

1) Once you have an agar plate coated in bacteria, take three discs of filter paper. Soak one disc in antibiotic A (disc A) and another in antibiotic B (disc B). The third disc (disc C) is a control disc (see below) — soak it in sterile water.

2) Place the discs on the jelly using sterile forceps (big tweezers).

3) Put the lid onto the Petri dish (to stop other microorganisms getting in). Use two small pieces of tape to hold the lid in place.

4) The antibiotic will diffuse (soak) into the agar jelly.

5) Leave the dish for 48 hours at 25 °C. The bacteria will multiply and cover the jelly.

6) Anywhere the bacteria can't grow is called a 'clear zone'. The better the antibiotic is at killing the bacteria, the larger the clear zone around the disc will be — see next page.

'Sterile' means totally clean.

7) Using a control disc means that you can be sure that any difference between the size of the clear zone around the control disc and around the antibiotic discs is due to the effect of the antibiotic alone.

No clear zone around an antibiotic disc means that the bacteria aren't affected by the antibiotic — they're resistant to it (see page 22).

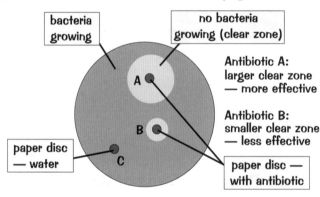

bacteria growing

no bacteria growing (clear zone)

Antibiotic A: larger clear zone — more effective

Antibiotic B: smaller clear zone — less effective

paper disc — water

paper disc — with antibiotic

You Need to Make Sure the Petri Dish Doesn't Get Contaminated

If unwanted microorganisms contaminate (get into) your dish it will affect your results. It could also result in the growth of pathogens. To avoid this, you should:

Techniques that prevent your dish from getting contaminated are called aseptic techniques.

1) Sterilise equipment before and after use, e.g. inoculating loops (wire loops) can be used to put the bacteria onto the agar plate. These should be sterilised by passing them through a hot flame.

2) Work near a Bunsen flame. Hot air rises, so microorganisms in the air should be drawn away from the culture.

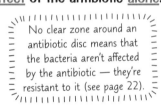

inoculating loop

3) The Petri dish should be stored upside down. This stops drops of condensation falling onto the agar surface.

Agar — my favourite jelly flavour after raspberry...

You really don't want to grow microorganisms that make you ill — that's partly why you need to keep things sterile.

Q1   Explain why it is important to use a control when investigating the effectiveness of different antibiotics on the growth of bacteria.

[1 mark]

Culturing Microorganisms 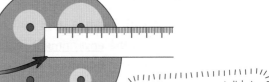 PRACTICAL

Once you've given your bacteria <u>time to grow</u> on your agar plate, you get to do the really fun stuff — a lovely bit of <u>maths</u>. Woo. Here's how you can <u>compare</u> your <u>clear zones</u>...

Calculate the Sizes of the Clear Zones to Compare Results

1) You can <u>compare</u> how <u>effective</u> different antibiotics are by looking at the <u>sizes</u> of the <u>clear zones</u>.

2) The <u>larger</u> the clear zone around a disc, the <u>more effective</u> the antibiotic is against the bacteria.

3) First you need to measure the clear zone's <u>diameter</u>. The diameter is just the distance <u>across</u> the middle.

4) Once you know the diameter, you can use <u>this equation</u> to calculate the <u>area</u> of a clear zone:

Don't open the Petri dish to measure the clear zones — they should be visible through the bottom of the dish.

This is the equation for the area of a circle. You're likely to use the units cm^2 or mm^2.

$$\text{Area} = \pi r^2$$

r is the radius of the clear zone — it's equal to half the diameter.

π is just a number. You should have a button for it on your calculator. If not, just use the value 3.14.

EXAMPLE:

The diagram below shows the clear zones produced by antibiotics A and B. Use the areas of the clear zones to compare the effectiveness of the antibiotics.

A — 14 mm   B — 20 mm

Diagram not to scale.

1) Divide the diameter of zone A by <u>two</u> to find the <u>radius</u>.

Radius of A = 14 ÷ 2 = 7 mm

2) Stick the radius value into the <u>equation</u> area = πr^2.

Area of A = π × 7^2 = 154 mm^2

3) <u>Repeat</u> steps 1 and 2 for zone B.

Radius of B = 20 ÷ 2 = 10 mm

4) <u>Compare</u> the <u>sizes</u> of the <u>areas</u>. 314 mm^2 is just over twice 154 mm^2, so you could say that:

Area of B = π × 10^2 = 314 mm^2

The clear zone of antibiotic B is roughly twice the size of the clear zone of antibiotic A, so antibiotic B is more effective than antibiotic A.

You Can Also Find the Area of a Colony

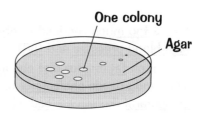
One colony
Agar

1) The equation above can also be used to calculate the <u>area</u> of a bacterial <u>colony</u> (a little cluster of bacteria).

2) You just need to measure the <u>diameter</u> of the colony you are interested in first.

My brother's football socks create a clear zone...

Make sure you know how to calculate the area of a clear zone.

Q1 A researcher was investigating the effect of three different antibiotics on the growth of bacteria. The diagram on the right shows the results.

a) Which antibiotic was most effective against the bacteria? [1 mark]

b) Calculate the size of the clear zone for Antibiotic C. Give your answer in mm^2. [2 marks]

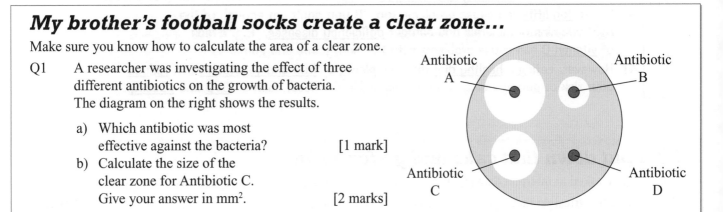

Antibiotic A   Antibiotic B
Antibiotic C   Antibiotic D

Non-Communicable Diseases

You may remember <u>non-communicable diseases</u> from page 8. Well, here's a bit more about them...

Lots of Factors Interact to Cause Non-Communicable Diseases

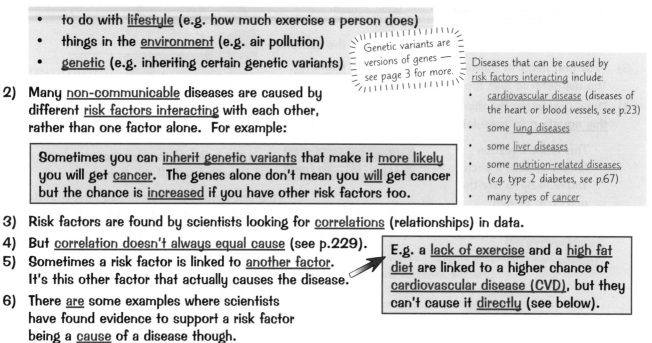

1) All diseases have <u>risk factors</u> — things that <u>increase</u> a person's <u>chance</u> of getting that disease. Risk factors can be:

- to do with <u>lifestyle</u> (e.g. how much exercise a person does)
- things in the <u>environment</u> (e.g. air pollution)
- <u>genetic</u> (e.g. inheriting certain genetic variants)

Genetic variants are versions of genes — see page 3 for more.

Diseases that can be caused by <u>risk factors interacting</u> include:
- <u>cardiovascular disease</u> (diseases of the heart or blood vessels, see p.23)
- some <u>lung diseases</u>
- some <u>liver diseases</u>
- some <u>nutrition-related diseases</u>, (e.g. type 2 diabetes, see p.67)
- many types of <u>cancer</u>

2) Many <u>non-communicable</u> diseases are caused by different <u>risk factors interacting</u> with each other, rather than one factor alone. For example:

> Sometimes you can <u>inherit genetic variants</u> that make it <u>more likely</u> you will get <u>cancer</u>. The genes alone don't mean you <u>will</u> get cancer but the chance is <u>increased</u> if you have other risk factors too.

3) Risk factors are found by scientists looking for <u>correlations</u> (relationships) in data.
4) But <u>correlation doesn't always equal cause</u> (see p.229).
5) Sometimes a risk factor is linked to <u>another factor</u>. It's this other factor that actually causes the disease.

> E.g. a <u>lack of exercise</u> and a <u>high fat diet</u> are linked to a higher chance of <u>cardiovascular disease (CVD)</u>, but they can't cause it <u>directly</u> (see below).

6) There <u>are</u> some examples where scientists have found evidence to support a risk factor being a <u>cause</u> of a disease though.

> E.g. the fact that <u>smoking</u> can cause <u>lung disease</u> and <u>lung cancer</u> (see next page).

Lifestyle Factors Can Increase the Risk of Non-Communicable Diseases

Exercise

1) Exercise <u>decreases</u> the amount of <u>stored</u> body <u>fat</u>. So people who exercise are <u>less likely</u> to suffer from <u>obesity</u> (see below) and <u>CVD</u>.
2) A <u>lack</u> of exercise increases the risk of <u>CVD</u> because it increases <u>blood pressure</u>.

Obesity is where you are more than 20% over the recommended body mass.

Diet

1) Eating <u>too much</u> can lead to <u>obesity</u>. Obesity is linked to <u>type 2 diabetes</u>, <u>high blood pressure</u> and <u>CVD</u>. It's also a risk factor for some <u>cancers</u>.
2) Too much <u>fat</u> in your diet can <u>increase</u> your <u>blood cholesterol level</u>. Your body needs <u>cholesterol</u> to function properly. However, <u>too much</u> of a type of <u>cholesterol</u> (known as 'bad' cholesterol) can cause <u>fat</u> to build up inside <u>arteries</u>. This can lead to <u>coronary heart disease</u>, a type of cardiovascular disease (see p.23).
3) Eating <u>too little</u> can cause problems too. If you don't get enough of the right vitamins or minerals you can get <u>deficiency diseases</u>. E.g. a lack of <u>vitamin C</u> can cause problems with the skin, joints and gums.
4) However, eating a <u>healthy diet</u> that has plenty of <u>fruit and vegetables</u> can <u>reduce</u> your risk of getting many non-communicable diseases, such as <u>CVD</u> and <u>obesity</u>.

Best put down that cake and go for a run...

You might be asked to interpret data about risk factors. Remember, correlation doesn't necessarily mean cause.

Q1   Give two lifestyle factors that can increase the risk of obesity.   [2 marks]

More on Non-Communicable Diseases

Sadly, you're not finished with risk factors just yet. Here are some more examples of lifestyle factors that can increase the risk of getting non-communicable diseases...

Alcohol and Smoking Can Also Lead to Non-Communicable Diseases

Alcohol

1) Alcohol is broken down by enzymes in the liver. Some of the products are toxic. If you drink too much alcohol over a long period of time, these products can cause a liver disease called cirrhosis.

2) Drinking too much alcohol increases blood pressure. This can lead to CVD.

3) Many cancers have been linked to drinking too much alcohol.

Smoking

Burning cigarettes produce things such as nicotine, carbon monoxide and tar.
These can cause problems such as:

1) CVD — carbon monoxide reduces the amount of oxygen that can be carried in the blood. If the heart muscle doesn't get enough oxygen it can lead to a heart attack (see page 23). Nicotine causes the heart to contract more often. This increases blood pressure, which increases the risk of CVD.

2) Cancer — tar from cigarette smoke is full of toxic chemicals. Some of these can cause cancer.

3) Lung diseases — cigarette smoke can damage the lining of the tubes in the lungs.

4) Smoking when pregnant can cause lots of health problems for the unborn baby.

Lifestyle Factors Cause Different Trends

Global

Non-communicable diseases are more common in developed countries than in developing countries. However, these diseases are now becoming much more common in developing countries too. These trends can be linked to lifestyle and income. For example:

- Lack of exercise and drinking more alcohol are linked with higher income.

- Deaths related to smoking are more common in poorer countries.

- In developed and developing countries, obesity is linked with higher incomes. This is because people can afford lots of high-fat food. However, obesity is now linked with lower incomes too, as people are eating cheaper, less healthy foods.

> In developed countries, people generally have a higher income (more money) and a higher standard of living than people in developing countries.

National

Non-communicable diseases are the biggest cause of death in the UK.
However, there are differences across the country. For example:

- People from poorer areas are much more likely to smoke, have a poor diet, and not exercise than those who have more money. This means that heart disease, obesity, type 2 diabetes, and cancer are more common in those areas.

- People from poorer areas are also more likely to suffer from alcohol-related disorders.

Local

- People's lifestyle choices affect non-communicable diseases at the local level.

- If you choose to smoke, drink, not exercise or have a poor diet, then the risk increases.

Too many exams are a risk factor for stress...

Trends in non-communicable diseases are often to do with income, because it can have a big effect on lifestyle.

Q1   Give two non-communicable diseases that drinking too much alcohol is a risk factor for.   [2 marks]

Interpreting Data on Disease

In the exam, you could be given some data about the <u>causes</u>, <u>spread</u>, <u>effects</u> or <u>treatment</u> of disease. You'll need to be able to <u>interpret</u> the data (i.e. work out what it's showing) — this page should help you.

You Need to be Able to Interpret a Scatter Diagram

A <u>variable</u> is a <u>factor</u> that can <u>change</u>. A <u>scatter diagram</u> allows you to easily spot if there's a <u>correlation</u> (relationship) between two variables. For example:

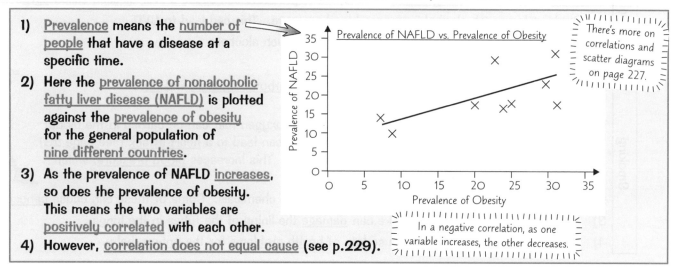

1) <u>Prevalence</u> means the <u>number of people</u> that have a disease at a specific time.
2) Here the <u>prevalence of nonalcoholic fatty liver disease (NAFLD)</u> is plotted against the <u>prevalence of obesity</u> for the general population of <u>nine different countries</u>.
3) As the prevalence of NAFLD <u>increases</u>, so does the prevalence of obesity. This means the two variables are <u>positively correlated</u> with each other.
4) However, <u>correlation does not equal cause</u> (see p.229).

There's more on correlations and scatter diagrams on page 227.

In a negative correlation, as one variable increases, the other decreases.

Data Can be Shown in Lots of Ways

In the exam you might have to <u>convert</u> between different forms of data.
E.g. you might get a <u>table</u> of data (like this) and be asked to <u>draw a bar chart</u> using the data (like this).

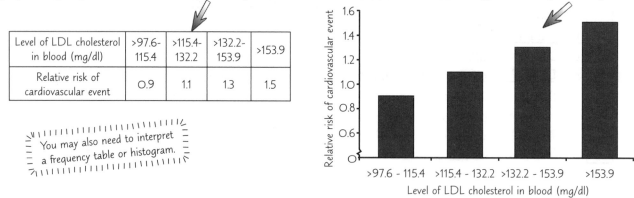

Level of LDL cholesterol in blood (mg/dl)	>97.6-115.4	>115.4-132.2	>132.2-153.9	>153.9
Relative risk of cardiovascular event	0.9	1.1	1.3	1.5

You may also need to interpret a frequency table or histogram.

Health Data Has to be Collected Carefully

1) When studying <u>health and disease</u>, it isn't possible to collect all of the <u>potential data</u> (data can't be collected from <u>every</u> member of the population). Instead data has to be collected from a <u>sample</u> that <u>represents</u> the full <u>potential</u> data set.
2) The <u>bigger</u> the sample <u>size</u> the <u>better</u> — it's <u>more likely</u> that more of the different <u>characteristics</u> present in the <u>whole</u> population will be <u>included</u> in a bigger sample.
3) The sample should also be <u>random</u> so it represents the population <u>as a whole</u>.

If a sample doesn't represent the population as a whole, it's said to be biased.

Scatter diagrams — graphs with lightly sprinkled kittens...

Don't be frightened by questions where you need to interpret data. Take your time and make sure you understand what the data's showing. Pay close attention to the units used, the titles in tables and the axes labels on graphs.

Q1   Explain why a large sample size is better than a small one when collecting health data.   [1 mark]

Investigating Pulse Rate

So, a fun experiment to do now — grab your <u>headband</u> and <u>leg warmers</u> and let's get started...

Regular Exercise Can Reduce the Risk of Some Non-Communicable Diseases

1) Your <u>resting heart rate</u> is how quickly your heart beats when you're <u>at rest</u>.
<u>Recovery rate</u> is the time taken for your heart rate to return to its <u>normal resting rate</u> after exercise.

2) A <u>high</u> resting heart rate and a <u>slow</u> recovery rate have both been linked to
an <u>increased risk</u> of developing some <u>non-communicable diseases</u>, e.g. <u>cardiovascular disease</u>.

3) <u>Regular exercise</u> can <u>reduce</u> a person's <u>resting heart rate</u> and <u>speed up</u> their <u>recovery rate</u>.
So regular exercise could help to <u>reduce</u> the chance of developing some non-communicable diseases.

4) Scientists are able to <u>investigate</u> the effect of <u>regular exercise</u> on heart rate using <u>long term studies</u>.

5) These studies can involve <u>measuring</u> a person's heart rate <u>during</u> and <u>after</u> exercise.
You can do <u>similar tests</u> yourself...

You Can Investigate The Effect of Exercise on Pulse Rate

To do this experiment you need to know how to <u>measure</u> your <u>pulse rate</u>.
You can measure it by putting <u>two fingers</u> on the inside of your <u>wrist</u> or
on your <u>neck</u> and counting the number of pulses in <u>1 minute</u>.

Your pulse rate is a way of measuring your heart rate.

1) Measure and record your <u>pulse rate</u> at <u>rest</u>.
2) Then do 3 minutes of <u>gentle exercise</u>, e.g. walk around your school field.
3) Measure and record your pulse rate again <u>immediately after</u> the exercise.
4) Then take <u>regular measurements</u> of your pulse rate until it has gone back to its <u>resting rate</u>.
Record the time that this takes — this is your <u>recovery rate</u>.
5) Repeat steps 2-4 two times more, but <u>increase the difficulty</u> of the exercise each
time (e.g. jog round the field for 3 minutes, then run round it for 3 minutes).
6) Produce a <u>bar chart</u> of your results to show how <u>pulse rate</u>
is affected by the <u>difficulty of the exercise</u>.
7) Do the same to show how <u>recovery rate</u> is affected by the difficulty of exercise.
8) You could collect results from your <u>whole class</u>. For each person you'd need to
work out the <u>percentage change</u> in <u>pulse rate</u> and <u>recovery rate</u> for <u>each exercise</u>.
9) You'd also need to calculate the <u>average</u> percentage change in
pulse rate and recovery rate for the <u>whole class</u>.
10) Remember to <u>control any variables</u> during the experiment,
e.g. if you're using results from the whole class, make sure everyone's
done the <u>same exercise activities</u> and for the <u>same length of time</u>.

See page 34 for how to calculate percentage change.

If looking at what you truly love can make your heart beat faster...

...then chocolate cake must be really good for me. Unless you've been living in a cave for the past few years, you should be well aware that regular exercise is a good thing. Make sure you know how you can investigate the effect of exercise on pulse rate and recovery rate.

Q1   What is meant by the term 'recovery rate'?   [1 mark]

Treating Disease

Your body does lots of things to try to fight against diseases, but sometimes it needs a little help...

Medicines Can Get Rid of Symptoms or Treat the Cause of Disease

1) A medicine is a substance that helps to control or treat a disease.

2) Some medicines just tackle the symptoms of a disease.
They reduce how bad the symptoms are or how long they last.

> Painkillers (e.g. aspirin) are medicines that reduce pain (a symptom of disease).

3) Other medicines treat the cause of the disease.
Some of these work by killing or disabling pathogens.
E.g:

> Remember, a pathogen is a microorganism that can cause disease.

| Antibiotics | Antibiotics can be used to treat bacterial infections. They kill bacteria without killing your own body cells. |

| Antivirals | 1) Antivirals can be used to treat viral infections. They are difficult to make because viruses use your cells to reproduce — it's hard to target the virus without damaging your cells. |
| | 2) Most antivirals don't kill the viruses but stop them from reproducing. |

4) Doctors prescribe medicines — this means they say which medicines a patient can have.
They need to think about these things when deciding what to prescribe:

- Risks — some people may react badly to a medicine, e.g. some people are allergic to penicillin.
- Costs — some medicines can be very expensive, especially if they need to be taken for a long time.
- Effectiveness (how well it works) — some medicines may not be fully effective.

Doctors need to weigh up the possible benefits of medicines against the risks and costs.

5) Patients also have to consent (agree) to the treatment.

Overuse of Antibiotics May Make Some Diseases Difficult to Treat

1) Some bacteria are resistant to (not killed by) certain antibiotics (see p.69).

2) Antibiotic-resistant strains (types) of bacteria have increased.
This is because antibiotics are not always used properly.

> For example, people don't always finish the full course of antibiotics they've been given. This means that the most resistant bacteria may survive.
> These bacteria are then able to grow and reproduce.

3) Antibiotic-resistant strains of bacteria can be very dangerous.
So, doctors have to think carefully when prescribing antibiotics.

4) They have to balance their patient's well-being with the well-being of other people in society.
They may not prescribe antibiotics if they're not really needed, e.g. for minor infections.

GCSEs are like antibiotics — you have to finish the course...

Kapow, down with you nasty pathogens — we will kill you all. Ahem, sorry. You'd best learn this lot.

Q1   Name the type of pathogen that antibiotics kill.   [1 mark]

Treating Cardiovascular Disease

Cardiovascular disease is a big, big problem in the UK. The good news is there are lots of ways to treat it.

Cardiovascular Disease Affects Your Heart and Blood Vessels

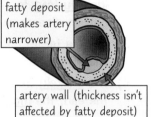
See pages 60-61 for more on blood vessels and the heart.

1) Cardiovascular disease (CVD) is any disease to do with your heart and blood vessels.
2) Too much cholesterol (a fatty substance) in the blood can cause fatty deposits to build up in arteries (a type of blood vessel). This makes the arteries narrower and reduces blood flow.
3) Sometimes bits of the fatty deposits can break off and block blood flow.
4) A blood clot can also form at the site of the deposit and block blood flow.
5) The coronary arteries supply the heart muscles with blood. If blood flow to the heart muscles is blocked, it can cause a heart attack.
6) If blood flow to the brain is blocked, it can cause a stroke.

fatty deposit (makes artery narrower)

artery wall (thickness isn't affected by fatty deposit)

Lifestyle Changes Can be Used to Reduce the Risk of CVD

1) Making lifestyle changes can help to reduce the risk of developing CVD in the first place. These include:

- exercising regularly
- losing weight if necessary
- stopping smoking
- eating a healthy diet that is low in saturated fat
- reducing stress

2) For people who already have CVD, these lifestyle changes are often still recommended.

Some Drugs Can Reduce the Risk of a Heart Attack or Stroke

1) Some people may need to take medicines to treat CVD. Here are some examples:

- Statins — reduce the amount of cholesterol in the bloodstream.
- Anticoagulants — make blood clots less likely to form.
- Antihypertensives — reduce blood pressure.

2) All of these medicines can have negative side effects, e.g. antihypertensives can cause fainting.

Some People With CVD Need Surgery

1) Here are some examples of things surgeons can do to treat CVD:

- Put in stents — these are tubes that are put inside arteries. They keep arteries open, making sure that blood can flow to the heart muscles.
- Coronary bypass surgery — a piece of healthy blood vessel is put into the heart. This lets blood flow around a blocked vessel.
- A heart transplant — the whole heart is replaced with a donor heart (a heart from another person).

fatty deposit

stent pushes artery wall out, squashing fatty deposit

more space in centre of artery

2) Surgery is risky. For example, there's a risk the person could get an infection or lose a lot of blood.

Look after yerselves me hearties...

Treatments can be risky and expensive, so it's better to stop CVD from developing in the first place. But when treatment is needed, doctors need to weigh up the likely effectiveness of each treatment against its cost and risks.

Q1   Give one disadvantage of treating CVD with surgery.   [1 mark]

Developing New Medicines

New medicines are constantly being developed. This page tells you all about how that happens...

Possible New Medicines Have to be Discovered First

1) Medicines work on targets, e.g. a gene or protein linked to a disease.

2) Studying the genomes (see page 3) and proteins of organisms can help to identify targets. E.g. studying the genomes of people with and without a certain disease may help scientists to find gene variants linked to the disease.

Scientists can also look at the genomes and proteins of pathogens when identifying targets for new medicines.

3) Once a target has been identified, scientists have to find a chemical substance that will have the effect they want on the target. They do this by screening huge libraries of chemicals.

4) It's unlikely that screening will find a chemical that will work perfectly as a medicine. Instead, the most suitable chemicals are selected and changed. Then they are tested.

There are Lots of Tests to Help Develop Possible Medicines

All new medicines have to go through testing before they can be used to treat patients.

Preclinical testing:

1) Drugs are first tested on cultured human cells (cultured means that they've been grown in a lab).

2) Next the drug is tested on live animals.

3) These tests check whether the drug is effective (produces the effect you're looking for). They also test whether the drug is safe.

Clinical testing:

1) If the drug passes the tests on animals then it's tested on human volunteers in a clinical trial.

2) First, the drug is tested on healthy volunteers. This is to make sure that it's safe, i.e. it doesn't have any harmful side effects when the body is working normally.

3) If the results are good, the drug can be tested on people with the disease. This is to test the drug's effectiveness and its safety.

4) For many clinical tests, patients are randomly put into two groups. One is given the new drug, the other is given a placebo (a substance that looks like the drug being tested but doesn't do anything).

5) The doctor compares the two groups of patients to see if the drug makes a real difference.

6) Clinical trials can be blind — the patient doesn't know whether they're getting the drug or the placebo.

7) In fact, they're often double-blind — neither the patient nor the doctor knows who's taken the drug and who's taken the placebo until all the results have been gathered.

There are ethical issues around giving a placebo to people with the disease instead of a possible treatment. E.g. people taking a placebo will continue to suffer from symptoms of the disease during the trial. So not all trials use placebos.

8) Trials can also be open-label — the doctor and the patient know who is receiving the drug. These might be used when comparing the effectiveness of two very similar drugs.

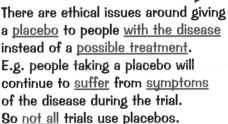

Medicines are tested — just like a GCSE student...

Testing, retesting and then... yep, more testing. You'd know all about that anyway, it's just like being in school...

Q1   Explain how a double-blind trial would be carried out.   [2 marks]

Revision Questions for Chapters B1 & B2

Well that's <u>the first two chapters</u> done and dusted. Now time to see how much you've <u>learnt</u>.
- Try these questions and <u>tick off each one</u> when you <u>get it right</u>.
- When you've done <u>all the questions</u> for a topic and are <u>completely happy</u> with it, tick off the topic.

Cells, Genetic Material and Microscopy (p.1-2) ☑

1) State whether each of the following is a eukaryotic cell or a prokaryotic cell:
   a) animal cell   b) bacterial cell   c) plant cell. ☑
2) Where is genetic material stored in a eukaryotic cell? ☑
3) Why are samples sometimes stained before viewing under a light microscope? ☑

DNA and Characteristics (p.3) ☑

4) Why is DNA described as a polymer? ☑
5) What is: a) a gene   b) an allele? ☑
6) What interacts with an organism's genotype to determine its phenotype? ☑

Genetic Diagrams (p.4-5) ☑

7) What does it mean if an organism is homozygous? ☑
8) In a genetic diagram, is a capital letter used to represent a dominant or recessive allele? ☑
9) What is the 23rd pair of chromosomes labelled as in a human female? ☑

Genome Research and Genetic Engineering (p.6-7) ☑

10) What is personalised medicine? ☑
11) Give one risk of carrying out genetic testing on a fetus' DNA. ☑
12) Describe two concerns people may have about using genetically modified crops. ☑

Health, the Spread of Disease and Defence Against Pathogens (p.8-12) ☑

13) What is a pathogen? ☑
14) Give an example of a disease that is spread through: a) water   b) the air. ☑
15) Describe how the skin acts as a defence against pathogens. ☑
16) Give three ways in which white blood cells help to defend the body against pathogens. ☑

More on the Spread of Disease and Culturing Microorganisms (p.13-17) ☑

17) Explain why restricting the travel of infected individuals can help to prevent the spread of disease. ☑
18) How does polyculture help to reduce the spread of disease in plants? ☑
19) Give one risk of using vaccinations as a way of protecting people from diseases. ☑
20) Why might there be a clear zone around a disc soaked in antibiotic on an agar plate of bacteria? ☑

Non-Communicable Diseases, Interpreting Data, and Pulse Rate (p.18-21) ☑

21) What is meant by a risk factor for a non-communicable disease? ☑
22) Give one non-communicable disease which may be associated with smoking. ☑
23) What is meant by a positive correlation? ☑
24) What is meant by a person's resting heart rate? ☑

Treating Disease (p.22-24) ☑

25) What do antiviral drugs do? ☑
26) Give an example of a surgical procedure which can help to treat cardiovascular disease. ☑
27) What is a placebo? ☑

Chapter B2 — Keeping Healthy

Enzymes

Chemical reactions are what make you work. And enzymes are what make them work.

Enzymes Are Catalysts Produced by Living Things

1) Enzymes are biological catalysts.

2) This means they speed up chemical reactions in living organisms.

3) A substrate is a molecule that gets changed in a chemical reaction.

> Enzymes catalyse reactions in both plants and animals — including photosynthesis in plants (see p.28).

4) Every enzyme has an active site — the part where it joins on to its substrate to catalyse the reaction.

5) Enzymes are substrate specific — this means that they usually only work with one substrate.

6) This is because the substrate has to fit into the active site for the enzyme to work.

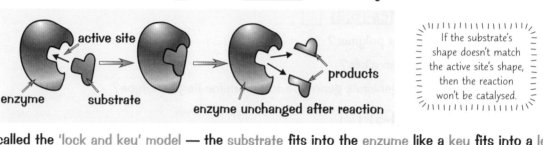

> If the substrate's shape doesn't match the active site's shape, then the reaction won't be catalysed.

7) This is called the 'lock and key' model — the substrate fits into the enzyme like a key fits into a lock.

Temperature Affects Enzyme Shape and Activity

1) A higher temperature increases the rate of an enzyme-catalysed reaction at first.

2) The enzymes and substrate have more energy, so move about more. They're more likely to collide (bump into each other) and react.

3) But if it gets too hot, some of the bonds holding the enzyme together break.

4) This changes the shape of the enzyme's active site. This means the substrate won't fit any more.

5) If this happens, the enzyme is said to be denatured. It can't catalyse the reaction at all.

6) All enzymes have an optimum temperature — this is the temperature at which they work best.

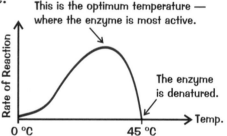

This is the optimum temperature — where the enzyme is most active.

The enzyme is denatured.

> When an enzyme is denatured, it's destroyed. It won't go back to its usual shape.

pH Also Affects Enzyme Shape and Activity

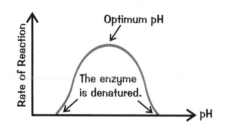

Optimum pH

The enzyme is denatured.

1) If pH is too high or too low, it affects the bonds holding the active site together.

2) This changes the shape of the active site and denatures the enzyme.

3) All enzymes have an optimum pH that they work best at.

4) The optimum pH is often neutral pH 7, but not always.

Substrate Concentration Also Affects the Rate of Reaction

1) The higher the substrate concentration, the faster the reaction.

2) This is because it's more likely that the enzyme will meet up and react with a substrate molecule.

3) This is only true up to a point though.

4) After that, there are so many substrate molecules that all the active sites on the enzymes are full.

5) At this point, adding more substrate molecules makes no difference.

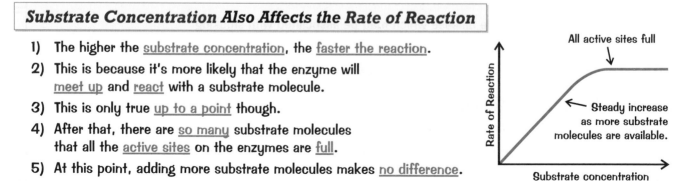

All active sites full

Steady increase as more substrate molecules are available.

Substrate concentration

Enzymes

PRACTICAL

You'll soon know how to investigate the effect of temperature on the rate of enzyme activity. It's thrilling stuff.

You Can Investigate How Temperature Affects Enzyme Activity

1) The experiments below show two different ways of investigating how temperature affects enzyme activity.

2) You could adapt these experiments to investigate other factors instead (e.g. pH or substrate concentration).

You can use buffer solutions to alter the pH of the enzyme and substrate mixtures.

You Can Measure How Fast a Product Appears...

1) The enzyme catalase breaks down hydrogen peroxide into water and oxygen.

2) You can collect the oxygen and measure how much is produced in a set time.

3) Use a pipette to add a set amount of hydrogen peroxide to a boiling tube.

4) Put the tube in a water bath at 10 °C.
(Keep the boiling tube in the water bath for five minutes.)

5) Set up the rest of the apparatus as shown.

6) Add a source of catalase to the hydrogen peroxide. Quickly attach the bung.

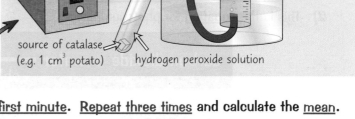

water bath at constant temperature   measuring cylinder

delivery tube

amount of oxygen produced per minute is measured

source of catalase (e.g. 1 cm³ potato)   hydrogen peroxide solution

7) Record how much oxygen is produced in the first minute. Repeat three times and calculate the mean.

8) Repeat at 20 °C, 30 °C and 40 °C.

9) Control any variables (e.g. pH, the potato used, the size of the potato pieces, etc.) to make it a fair test.

A variable is a factor in an investigation that can change or be changed. There's more on variables and fair tests on p.223.

10) Calculate the mean rate of reaction at each temperature. Do this by dividing the mean volume of oxygen produced (in cm³) by the time taken (i.e. 60 s). The units will be cm³/second.

...Or How Fast a Substrate Disappears

1) The enzyme amylase helps to break down starch to maltose.

2) It's easy to detect starch using iodine solution — if starch is present, the iodine solution will change from browny-orange to blue-black.

3) Set up the apparatus as shown.

4) Put a drop of iodine solution into each well on the spotting tile.

5) Every ten seconds, drop a sample of the mixture into a well using a pipette. Record the time when the iodine solution remains browny-orange (i.e. when there's no more starch).

6) Repeat with the water bath at different temperatures. Remember to control all of the variables each time.

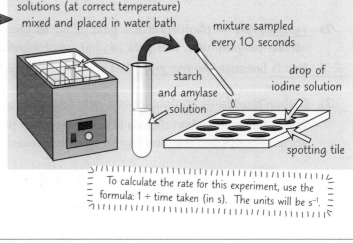

solutions (at correct temperature) mixed and placed in water bath

mixture sampled every 10 seconds

starch and amylase solution

drop of iodine solution

spotting tile

To calculate the rate for this experiment, use the formula: 1 ÷ time taken (in s). The units will be s⁻¹.

If only enzymes could speed up revision...

The key thing with experiments is to only change the thing you're testing — and absolutely nothing else. Sorted.

Q1   An enzyme-controlled reaction was carried out at 25 °C. After 60 seconds, 33 cm³ of product had been released. Calculate the rate of reaction in cm³/second.   [1 mark]

Photosynthesis

Photosynthesis is one the most important reactions on Earth. Here's a whole page on it...

Plants and Algae Make Their Own Food by Photosynthesis

1) During photosynthesis, energy from the Sun is used to make glucose (a type of sugar).
2) Some of the glucose is used in respiration (see page 50).
3) Some is converted to starch and stored.
4) The rest is used to make larger molecules that the plants or algae need to grow, e.g. proteins, lipids and carbohydrates.
5) These molecules make up the organism's biomass. Biomass means 'the mass of living material'.

Some prokaryotes can also photosynthesise, although they don't have chloroplasts (see below).

Photosynthesis Happens Inside Chloroplasts

1) Chloroplasts are tiny structures (see page 1) inside some cells. They contain:
   • enzymes that catalyse the reactions in photosynthesis,
   • chlorophyll, which absorbs light.
2) This is the equation for photosynthesis:

$$\text{carbon dioxide} + \text{water} \xrightarrow[\text{chlorophyll}]{\text{LIGHT}} \text{glucose} + \text{oxygen}$$

3) Photosynthesis is endothermic. This means that energy is taken in during the process.
4) Lots of chemical reactions happen during photosynthesis, but it takes place in two main stages:
   • First, energy transferred by light to the chlorophyll is used to split water into oxygen gas and hydrogen ions. The oxygen is released as a waste product.
   • Carbon dioxide gas then combines with the hydrogen ions to make glucose.

Three Things Can Affect the Rate of Photosynthesis

These factors are known as limiting factors — they can stop photosynthesis from happening any faster.

1) Light intensity — photosynthesis gets faster as light intensity (the strength of light) increases. This is because a higher light intensity provides more energy.

2) Temperature — photosynthesis gets faster as temperature increases, but only up to a certain temperature. If it gets too hot, photosynthesis slows down and can stop altogether. This is because the enzymes that control photosynthesis denature (see page 26).

3) Carbon dioxide — photosynthesis gets faster as carbon dioxide concentration increases. This is because carbon dioxide is a substrate for photosynthesis — and the rate of an enzyme-controlled reaction increases with increasing substrate concentration (see page 26).

The carbon dioxide concentration in the air is quite low — so on a warm, sunny day, the limiting factor is often carbon dioxide concentration.

My brain is my limiting factor — it stops me thinking any faster...

You must learn the photosynthesis equation. Learn it so well that you'll still remember it when you're 109.

Q1   Greenhouses are used to increase the temperature for growing plants.
      Explain why it might be a problem for plants if a greenhouse gets too hot.   [2 marks]

Investigating Photosynthesis PRACTICAL

By now, you should know that <u>light</u> and <u>carbon dioxide</u> are needed for <u>photosynthesis</u>.
But in science, you <u>don't</u> really <u>know anything</u> until you've done some <u>experiments</u> to prove it...

The Starch Test Shows Whether Photosynthesis is Taking Place

1) <u>Glucose</u> is <u>stored</u> by plants as <u>starch</u>.
2) If a plant can't <u>photosynthesise</u>, it can't make <u>starch</u> — you can use this to show that <u>light</u> and <u>carbon dioxide</u> (<u>CO$_2$</u>) are needed for photosynthesis.
3) First, you need to know how to <u>test a leaf</u> for starch:

   - Start by dunking the leaf in <u>boiling water</u> (hold it with forceps). This <u>stops</u> any <u>chemical reactions</u> happening inside the leaf.
   - Put the leaf in a boiling tube with some <u>ethanol</u>.
   - Heat the boiling tube gently in an <u>electric water bath</u>. This gets rid of any <u>chlorophyll</u> and makes the leaf a <u>white-ish</u> colour.
   - <u>Rinse</u> the leaf in <u>cold water</u>, then add a few drops of <u>iodine solution</u>.
   - If <u>starch</u> is <u>present</u> the leaf will turn <u>blue-black</u>.

Ethanol is highly flammable — keep it away from naked flames, e.g. Bunsen burners.

You Can Use the Starch Test to Show Light is Needed for Photosynthesis

1) <u>Place two plants</u> in the <u>dark</u> for 48 hours. This will make them <u>use up</u> their <u>starch stores</u>.
2) Keep one plant <u>in the dark</u> and move the other one <u>into the light</u>.
3) After a few days, do the <u>starch test</u> on a leaf from each plant.
4) The leaf from the plant moved to the <u>light</u> should turn <u>blue-black</u>. The leaf from the plant kept in the dark <u>won't</u>.
5) This shows that <u>light is needed</u> for photosynthesis because <u>no starch</u> has been made in the leaf grown <u>without light</u>.

You Can Use the Starch Test to Show CO$_2$ is Needed for Photosynthesis

1) Take a <u>plant</u> that's been kept in the <u>dark</u> (this is so that the plant has <u>used up</u> all its stores of <u>starch</u>).
2) Set up the plant in the apparatus shown in the <u>diagram</u>. The <u>soda lime</u> absorbs <u>carbon dioxide</u> out of the air.
3) Leave the plant for 24 hours, then <u>test</u> a leaf for <u>starch</u>.
4) It <u>won't</u> turn <u>blue-black</u>.
5) This shows that <u>no starch</u> has been made in the leaf, which means that <u>CO$_2$ is needed</u> for photosynthesis to happen.

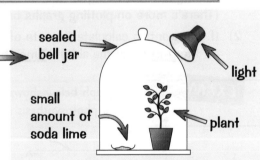

sealed bell jar
light
small amount of soda lime
plant

For both of these tests, it's important that any variables that could affect the results, e.g. the temperature, are controlled.

I'm working on sunshine — woah oh...

The starch test is dead easy to carry out. Remember that <u>iodine</u> is used and it turns <u>blue-black</u> if starch is present.

Q1 A destarched plant is left on a sunny windowsill for three days.
After this time, a leaf from the plant was tested for starch with iodine solution.
a) Describe the likely result of the test. [1 mark]
b) Explain why the test is likely to have this result. [2 marks]

Investigating the Rate of Photosynthesis

If you've always wanted to investigate how <u>different factors</u> affect the <u>rate</u> of photosynthesis, you're in luck...

You Can Investigate the Effect of Light Intensity on the Rate of Photosynthesis

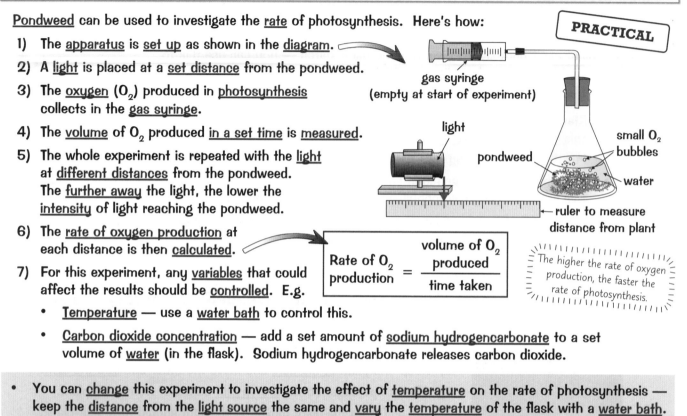

<u>Pondweed</u> can be used to investigate the <u>rate</u> of photosynthesis. Here's how:

1) The <u>apparatus</u> is <u>set up</u> as shown in the <u>diagram</u>.

2) A <u>light</u> is placed at a <u>set distance</u> from the pondweed.

3) The <u>oxygen</u> (O_2) produced in <u>photosynthesis</u> collects in the <u>gas syringe</u>.

4) The <u>volume</u> of O_2 produced <u>in a set time</u> is <u>measured</u>.

5) The whole experiment is repeated with the <u>light</u> at <u>different distances</u> from the pondweed. The <u>further away</u> the light, the lower the <u>intensity</u> of light reaching the pondweed.

6) The <u>rate of oxygen production</u> at each distance is then <u>calculated</u>.

7) For this experiment, any <u>variables</u> that could affect the results should be <u>controlled</u>. E.g.

- <u>Temperature</u> — use a <u>water bath</u> to control this.

- <u>Carbon dioxide concentration</u> — add a set amount of <u>sodium hydrogencarbonate</u> to a set volume of <u>water</u> (in the flask). Sodium hydrogencarbonate releases carbon dioxide.

PRACTICAL

gas syringe
(empty at start of experiment)

light

pondweed

small O_2 bubbles

water

ruler to measure distance from plant

$$\text{Rate of } O_2 \text{ production} = \frac{\text{volume of } O_2 \text{ produced}}{\text{time taken}}$$

The higher the rate of oxygen production, the faster the rate of photosynthesis.

- You can <u>change</u> this experiment to investigate the effect of <u>temperature</u> on the rate of photosynthesis — keep the <u>distance</u> from the <u>light source</u> the same and <u>vary</u> the <u>temperature</u> of the flask with a <u>water bath</u>.

- To investigate the effect of changing the <u>CO_2 concentration</u>, <u>vary</u> the amount of <u>sodium hydrogencarbonate</u> instead.

Only change one variable at a time.

You Can Calculate Rate from a Graph

1) Once you've written your results in a table, you can <u>plot</u> them in a <u>graph</u>. (There's more on plotting graphs on p.226.)

2) If you want to calculate the rate of photosynthesis from your graph, <u>volume of oxygen</u> should go on the <u>y-axis</u> (up the side). <u>Time</u> should go on the <u>x-axis</u> (across the bottom).

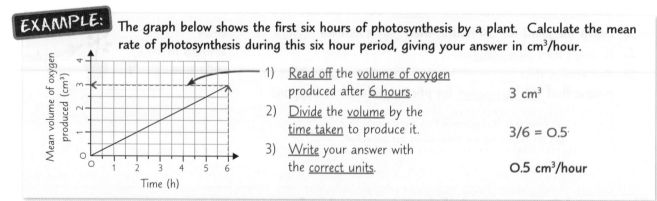

EXAMPLE:

The graph below shows the first six hours of photosynthesis by a plant. Calculate the mean rate of photosynthesis during this six hour period, giving your answer in cm³/hour.

Mean volume of oxygen produced (cm³)

Time (h)

1) <u>Read off</u> the <u>volume of oxygen</u> produced after <u>6 hours</u>.   3 cm³

2) <u>Divide</u> the <u>volume</u> by the <u>time taken</u> to produce it.   3/6 = 0.5

3) <u>Write</u> your answer with the <u>correct units</u>.   0.5 cm³/hour

That was intense — but I see light at the end of the tunnel...

Instead of measuring the volume of oxygen produced by the pondweed, you could count the bubbles produced.

Q1   A student is investigating the effect of temperature on the rate of photosynthesis of some pondweed. Describe how she would control the light intensity reaching the plant.   [1 mark]

Diffusion, Osmosis and Active Transport

Substances can move in and out of cells by <u>diffusion</u>, <u>osmosis</u> and <u>active transport</u>...

Diffusion — Don't be Put Off by the Fancy Word

1) <u>Diffusion</u> is the <u>movement</u> of particles from where there are <u>lots</u> of them to where there are <u>fewer</u> of them. Here's the fancy <u>definition</u>:

> <u>DIFFUSION</u> is the <u>spreading out</u> of <u>particles</u> from an area of <u>higher concentration</u> to an area of <u>lower concentration</u>.

2) Diffusion continues until the concentration of the particles is <u>even</u> in <u>both areas</u>.

3) This diagram shows what's happening when the smell of perfume <u>diffuses</u> through the <u>air</u> in a room:

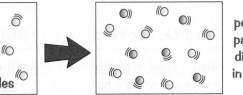

perfume particles diffused in the air

Osmosis Involves Water Molecules

> <u>OSMOSIS</u> is the movement of <u>water molecules</u> across a <u>partially permeable membrane</u> from an area of <u>higher water concentration</u> to an area of <u>lower water concentration</u>.

1) A <u>partially permeable</u> membrane is a membrane with very <u>small holes</u> in it.

2) <u>Small molecules</u> can pass through the holes, but <u>bigger</u> molecules <u>can't</u>.

3) <u>Cell membranes</u> are partially permeable membranes.

4) Water molecules pass <u>both ways</u> through a partially permeable membrane during osmosis.

5) But the <u>overall movement</u> of water molecules is from the area with <u>more water molecules</u> to the area with <u>fewer water molecules</u>.

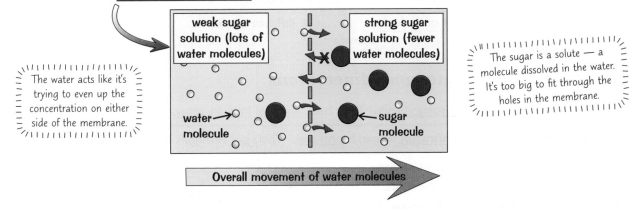

The water acts like it's trying to even up the concentration on either side of the membrane.

The sugar is a solute — a molecule dissolved in the water. It's too big to fit through the holes in the membrane.

Overall movement of water molecules

Active Transport Works The Opposite Way to Diffusion

> <u>ACTIVE TRANSPORT</u> is the <u>movement of particles</u> across a membrane from an area of <u>lower concentration</u> to an area of <u>higher concentration</u>. It uses <u>energy</u>.

1) Active transport moves particles in the <u>opposite direction</u> to <u>diffusion</u>.

2) Scientists say that active transport moves particles <u>against</u> a <u>concentration gradient</u>.

3) This requires <u>energy</u> (unlike diffusion). The energy is released by <u>respiration</u> (see p.50).

Revision by diffusion — you wish...

Hopefully there'll have been an overall movement of information from this page into your brain...

Q1   Give two differences between the processes of diffusion and active transport.   [2 marks]

Transport in Plants and Prokaryotes

Diffusion, osmosis and active transport are at work in all living organisms, including plants and prokaryotes.

Cells Need to Take in Substances and Get Rid of Waste

1) All cells need to take in substances in order to function. They also need to get rid of waste.
2) Substances move into and out of cells across their partially permeable cell membranes (see p.1).
3) Prokaryotes (see p.1) are only one cell big — so substances can diffuse straight into and out of them from their environment.
4) Plants are multicellular (made of many cells). They have special features to help exchange substances.

CO_2 and O_2 Move Through Stomata and Cell Membranes in Plants

1) When a plant is photosynthesising, it uses up lots of carbon dioxide (CO_2). This means there's hardly any CO_2 inside the leaf.
2) There's much more CO_2 in the air though — so CO_2 moves from the air into the leaf by diffusion.
3) It then diffuses from the air spaces inside the leaf into the leaf cells (through the cells' partially permeable cell membranes).
4) Oxygen (O_2) is a waste product of photosynthesis. It diffuses out of the leaf cells and into the air.
5) Both of these gases move through tiny pores (holes) in the leaf called stomata.

When prokaryotes photosynthesise, CO_2 diffuses directly into the cell. O_2 diffuses out.

air space

Oxygen diffuses out of the leaf

CO_2 diffuses into leaf

stomata

Root Hairs Take in Water and Mineral Ions

1) Plants need water for photosynthesis. They need mineral ions to grow.

For example, they need nitrogen to make proteins. They get nitrogen from nitrate ions (NO_3^-).

2) The cells on plant roots grow into long 'hairs' which stick out into the soil.
3) Each branch of a root will be covered in millions of these tiny hairs.
4) This gives the plant a large surface area for absorbing water and mineral ions from the soil.
5) Water moves into plant root hair cells by osmosis.
6) Mineral ions (like nitrate ions) move into root hair cells by active transport.

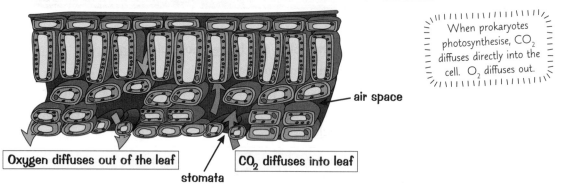

soil

mineral ions

root hair cell

higher concentration

mineral ions

lower concentration

7) This is because there's usually a higher concentration of mineral ions in the root hair cells than in the soil.
8) Root hair cells use molecules of ATP (see p.50) to provide the energy needed to transport the ions.

Active transport — get on your bike...

All cell membranes are partially permeable — this allows control over what goes in and out of the cell.

Q1   Explain what feature allows plant roots to absorb lots of water and mineral ions from the soil.   [2 marks]

Investigating Diffusion and Osmosis

For all you non-believers — here are a few <u>experiments</u> you can do to see <u>diffusion</u> and <u>osmosis</u> in action.

You Can Investigate Diffusion in a Non-Living System

<u>Phenolphthalein</u> is a <u>pH indicator</u> — it's <u>pink</u> in alkaline solutions and <u>colourless</u> in acidic solutions.
You can use it to investigate <u>diffusion</u> in <u>agar jelly</u>:

1) First, you need some agar jelly made up with <u>phenolphthalein</u> and dilute <u>sodium hydroxide</u>.

2) Dilute sodium hydroxide is an <u>alkali</u>, so the jelly should be <u>pink</u>.

3) Add some dilute <u>hydrochloric acid</u> to a <u>beaker</u>.

4) Measure out and cut some <u>cubes</u> from the jelly — then put them in the beaker of acid.

5) If the cubes are <u>left</u> for a while, they'll eventually turn <u>colourless</u>.

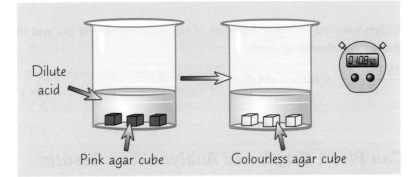

Dilute acid

Pink agar cube   Colourless agar cube

6) The cubes turn colourless because the <u>acid diffuses into</u> the jelly and <u>neutralises</u> the sodium hydroxide.

7) Use a <u>stopwatch</u> to <u>time how long</u> this takes.

8) You could investigate how <u>changing</u> the <u>concentration</u> of the <u>acid</u> (e.g. between 0.1 and 1 M) affects the rate of diffusion. Keep everything apart from the concentration of acid the same.

'M' is a unit of concentration.

You Can Do an Experiment to Investigate Osmosis

Sucrose is a type of sugar.

1) Start by preparing <u>sucrose solutions</u> of different concentrations.

2) Next, use a cork borer to cut a <u>potato</u> into <u>cylinders</u> of the <u>same length</u> and <u>width</u>.

3) Divide the cylinders into <u>groups of three</u> and use a <u>mass balance</u> to measure the <u>mass</u> of each <u>group</u>.

4) Place <u>one group</u> in each solution.

The beaker labelled 0.0 M is pure water. It doesn't have any sucrose in it, so the concentration of sucrose is zero. Concentration can also be given as mol/dm³.

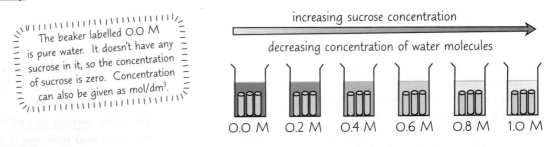

increasing sucrose concentration

decreasing concentration of water molecules

0.0 M   0.2 M   0.4 M   0.6 M   0.8 M   1.0 M

5) <u>Leave</u> the cylinders in the solution for <u>at least 40 minutes</u>.

6) <u>Remove</u> the cylinders and pat dry <u>gently</u> with a paper towel.

7) <u>Weigh</u> each <u>group</u> again and record your results.

8) The <u>only</u> thing that you should <u>change</u> in this experiment is the <u>concentration</u> of the <u>sucrose solution</u>.

9) Everything else (e.g. the volume of the solution) must be kept the <u>same</u> or your results <u>won't be valid</u>.

10) Once you've got your results you can calculate the <u>percentage change in mass</u> for the cylinders in each beaker. There's more on this on the next page.

There's more on valid results on page 223.

Investigating Diffusion and Osmosis

Once you've <u>carried out</u> your experiment and got your <u>results</u>, it's time to do some <u>calculations</u>...

You Need to Calculate the % Change in Mass of Your Potato Cylinders...

1) Once you've got the results from your osmosis experiment, <u>calculate</u> the <u>percentage change in mass</u> for each group of cylinders.

2) Use this formula to find the percentage change in mass:

$$\text{percentage change} = \frac{\text{final mass} - \text{starting mass}}{\text{starting mass}} \times 100$$

Calculating percentage change allows you to compare cylinders that didn't have the same starting mass.

EXAMPLE:

A group of cylinders weighed 13.2 g at the start of the experiment. At the end they weighed 15.1 g. Calculate the percentage change in mass.

$$\text{percentage change} = \frac{15.1 - 13.2}{13.2} \times 100 = +14.4\%$$

The positive result tells you the potato cylinders gained mass. If the answer was negative then the potato cylinders lost mass.

...Then You Can Plot a Graph and Analyse Your Results

The graph you plot should look a bit like this:

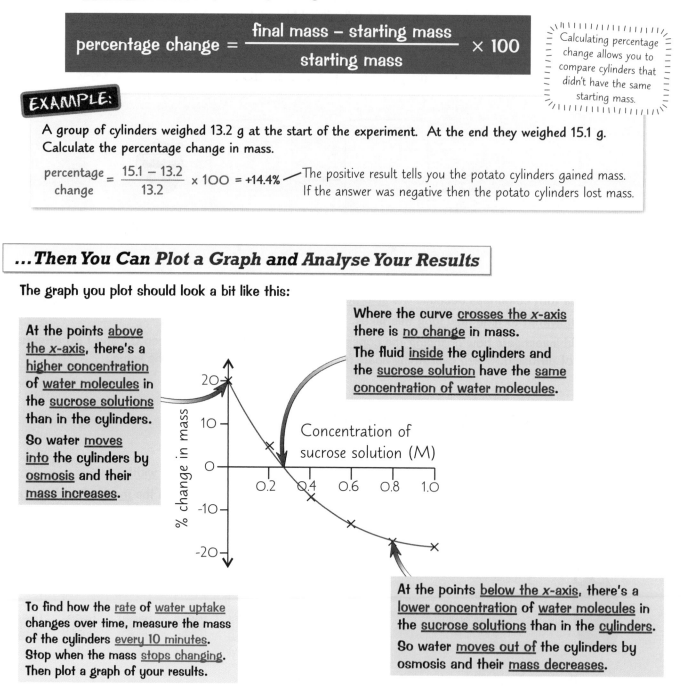

At the points <u>above</u> the x-axis, there's a <u>higher concentration</u> of <u>water molecules</u> in the <u>sucrose solutions</u> than in the cylinders.

So water <u>moves</u> <u>into</u> the cylinders by <u>osmosis</u> and their <u>mass increases</u>.

Where the curve <u>crosses the x-axis</u> there is <u>no change</u> in mass. The fluid <u>inside</u> the cylinders and the <u>sucrose solution</u> have the <u>same concentration of water molecules</u>.

At the points <u>below the x-axis</u>, there's a <u>lower concentration</u> of <u>water molecules</u> in the <u>sucrose solutions</u> than in the <u>cylinders</u>. So water <u>moves out of</u> the cylinders by osmosis and their <u>mass decreases</u>.

To find how the <u>rate</u> of <u>water uptake</u> changes over time, measure the mass of the cylinders <u>every 10 minutes</u>. Stop when the mass <u>stops changing</u>. Then plot a graph of your results.

So that's how they make skinny fries...

The osmosis experiment here used sucrose, but you could do the experiment with different solutes (e.g. salt).

Q1 A group of potato cubes were placed in a sucrose solution and left for one hour. The cubes weighed 13.3 g at the start of the experiment and 11.4 g at the end. Calculate the percentage change in mass. [2 marks]

Q2 Potato cylinders in a salt solution with a concentration of 0.3 mol/dm³ do not change mass. What does this tell you about the concentration of the solution in the potato cells? [1 mark]

Chapter B3 — Living Together — Food and Ecosystems

Xylem and Phloem

Plants don't have <u>blood vessels</u>. Instead, they have <u>xylem</u> and <u>phloem tubes</u> to get stuff to the right places.

Phloem Tubes Transport Food

1) Phloem tubes are made of <u>living cells</u> called <u>sieve tube elements</u>.
2) There are <u>end walls</u> between the sieve tube elements. These have <u>pores</u> (small holes) to allow stuff to flow through.
3) Sieve tube elements <u>don't have</u> a <u>nucleus</u>.
4) They <u>can't survive on their own</u>, so they have <u>companion cells</u> to help them function.
5) Plants make <u>sugars</u> in their <u>leaves</u> during <u>photosynthesis</u>.
6) Phloem tubes <u>transport</u> these <u>sugars</u> to areas of the plant that <u>don't photosynthesise</u> (e.g. the <u>roots</u>).
7) This process is called <u>translocation</u>.

> Sugars enter the phloem by active transport. They are pushed around by water that enters the phloem by osmosis.

Xylem Tubes Take Water Up

1) Xylem tubes are made of <u>dead cells</u>.
2) The cells are joined together with a <u>hole</u> down the <u>middle</u>.
3) There are no <u>end walls</u> between the cells.
4) The cells are <u>strengthened</u> with a material called <u>lignin</u>.
5) Xylem tubes carry <u>water</u> and <u>mineral ions</u> from the <u>roots</u> to the <u>stem</u> and <u>leaves</u>.
6) The movement of water from the <u>roots</u>, through the <u>xylem</u> and out of the <u>leaves</u> is called the <u>transpiration stream</u> (see below).

Water and minerals

Transpiration is the Loss of Water from the Plant

1) Transpiration is caused by <u>evaporation</u> and <u>diffusion</u> of water from a plant's surface (mainly the leaves).
2) Here's how it happens:

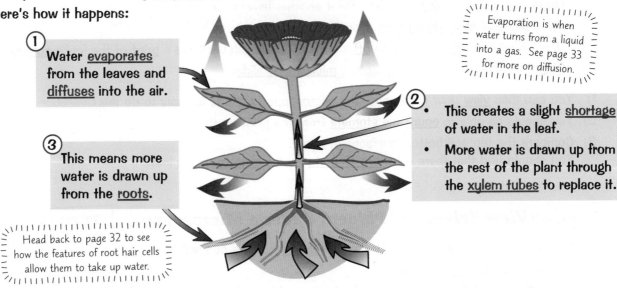

① Water <u>evaporates</u> from the leaves and <u>diffuses</u> into the air.

> Evaporation is when water turns from a liquid into a gas. See page 33 for more on diffusion.

② • This creates a slight <u>shortage</u> of water in the leaf.
• More water is drawn up from the rest of the plant through the <u>xylem tubes</u> to replace it.

③ This means more water is drawn up from the <u>roots</u>.

> Head back to page 32 to see how the features of root hair cells allow them to take up water.

3) There's a constant <u>stream of water</u> through the plant. This is called the <u>transpiration stream</u>.

Don't let revision stress you out — just go with the phloem...

Phloem transports substances in <u>both</u> directions, but xylem only transports things upwards — xy to the sky.

Q1   Describe the structure of xylem.   [3 marks]

Stomata

You've not learnt about transpiration 'til you've learnt about stomata (sadly)...

Stomata are Involved in Transpiration

1) Stomata are tiny pores (holes) on the surface of a plant (see page 32).
2) They're mostly found on the lower surface of leaves.
3) Stomata can open and close.
4) When they are open, carbon dioxide and oxygen can diffuse in and out of a leaf. Water vapour can also diffuse out of the leaf during transpiration (see the previous page).
5) This is how stomata open and close:

> Stomata are surrounded by guard cells. These change shape to control the size of the pore:
>
> When the guard cells are swollen, the stomata are OPEN.
>
> guard cells   stomata
>
> When the guard cells are limp, the stomata are CLOSED.

6) Stomata close when water supplies start to dry up.
7) Stomata also close as it gets darker. This is because photosynthesis can't happen in the dark, so the plant doesn't need the stomata to be open to let carbon dioxide in.
8) This helps plants to save water.

You Can View Stomata Under a Microscope | PRACTICAL |

Stomata can be observed using a light microscope. You can make a slide to view them on like this:

- Paint a thin layer of clear nail varnish onto the leaf you want to look at. Leave the varnish to dry for a bit. Paint another layer over the top.
- Put a piece of clear sticky tape over the top of the painted leaf.
- Use the tape to peel the varnish off slowly. The varnish will have a print of the leaf's surface.
- Stick the tape with the varnish onto a microscope slide.

1) You can then view your slide under the microscope (see p.2 for how to do this).
2) You should be able to count the stomata from the print on the varnish.
3) Compare the top and bottom surfaces of a leaf. You should find that there are more stomata on the bottom of the leaf.

You Can View Xylem and Phloem Under a Microscope | PRACTICAL |

1) Leave a plant stem upright in a beaker of eosin dye. The dye will travel up the stem.
2) This will stain the xylem red.
3) A thin section of the stem can then be taken and looked at on a slide under a microscope.

See p.2 for how to prepare a slide.

I say stomaaarta, you say stomaaayta...

I can't think of anything more exciting than counting stomata. But then, I don't have much of an imagination.

Q1   Explain why stomata open during the day.   [2 marks]

Chapter B3 — Living Together — Food and Ecosystems

Transpiration Rate

Remember, transpiration is the <u>loss of water</u> from a plant's surfaces (see page 35).
The <u>faster</u> the rate of <u>transpiration</u>, the <u>faster</u> the rate of <u>water uptake</u> by the plant.

Transpiration Rate is Affected by These Factors:

LIGHT INTENSITY

1) The <u>brighter</u> the light, the <u>faster</u> transpiration happens.
2) Bright light makes <u>photosynthesis</u> happen <u>faster</u>, so the <u>leaves</u> need more <u>water</u>.
3) This means more water is <u>drawn up</u> from the <u>roots</u>.
4) Bright light also causes the <u>stomata</u> to <u>open</u> to let <u>carbon dioxide in</u>.
5) This allows <u>more water vapour</u> to <u>diffuse out</u>.

TEMPERATURE

1) The <u>warmer</u> it is, the <u>faster</u> transpiration happens.
2) When it's warm, the water molecules in the leaves have <u>more energy</u>. This means they move out of the stomata <u>more quickly</u>.

Like light intensity, an increase in temperature also makes photosynthesis happen faster.

AIR MOVEMENT

1) The <u>more windy</u> it is, the <u>faster</u> transpiration happens.
2) <u>Fast</u> moving air means that water vapour around the leaf is <u>swept away</u>.
3) This means there's a <u>higher concentration</u> of water vapour <u>inside</u> the leaf compared to <u>outside</u>. So water vapour moves <u>out</u> of the leaf quickly by <u>diffusion</u> (see p.31).

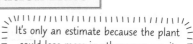

You Can Measure Loss of Mass to Estimate Transpiration Rate

1) When a plant <u>loses water</u>, it <u>loses mass</u>.
2) So if you measure <u>how much mass</u> a plant loses in a <u>set amount of time</u>, you can <u>estimate transpiration rate</u>.

It's only an estimate because the plant could lose mass in other ways, e.g. it loses oxygen during photosynthesis.

- Take a <u>plant</u> in a <u>pot</u> of damp soil. Put the pot in a <u>bag</u> and <u>tie it shut</u> around the <u>stem</u>.
- <u>Weigh</u> the plant and its pot. <u>Record</u> the <u>mass</u>.
- <u>Leave</u> the plant in a well-lit place for <u>24 hours</u>.
- <u>Weigh</u> the plant <u>again</u>. You should notice that it has <u>decreased in mass</u>.
- <u>Divide</u> the <u>mass lost</u> (in grams) by the <u>time taken</u> to lose it (in days).
- This will give you an <u>estimate</u> of the <u>transpiration rate</u> (in grams/day).

3) You can <u>compare</u> how much mass a plant loses in the <u>light</u> with how much it loses in the <u>dark</u>.
4) To compare them fairly, you need to <u>calculate</u> the <u>percentage change in mass</u> — see page 34 for more.

So, blowing on a plant makes it thirsty...?

Sunny, warm and windy — the perfect conditions for transpiration and for hanging out your washing.

Q1   Explain how air movement affects the rate of transpiration from a plant.   [4 marks]

Using a Potometer

It's time for another <u>experiment</u> — you get to use a piece of equipment you've probably never heard of...

A Potometer can be Used to Measure Water Uptake

1) A <u>potometer</u> is a special piece of equipment.
2) It measures <u>water uptake</u> by a plant.
3) Here's what you do:

- Set up the equipment as in the diagram.
- Record the <u>starting position</u> of the <u>air bubble</u>.
- Start a <u>stopwatch</u>.
- As the plant takes up water, the air bubble gets <u>sucked</u> along the tube.
- Record <u>how far</u> the air bubble moves in a <u>set time</u>.
- Then you can <u>estimate</u> the <u>transpiration rate</u>.

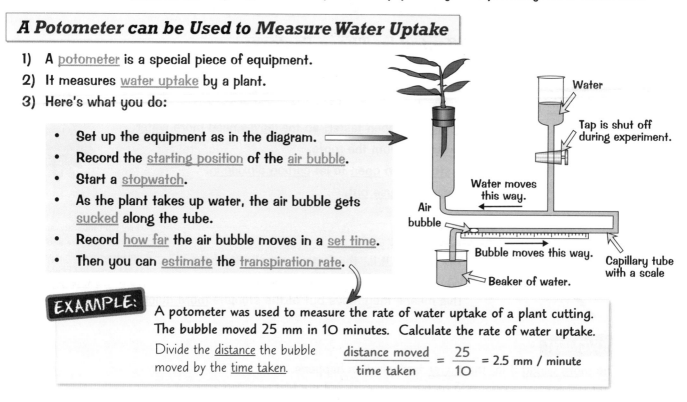

Water

Tap is shut off during experiment.

Water moves this way.

Air bubble

Bubble moves this way.

Capillary tube with a scale

Beaker of water.

EXAMPLE: A potometer was used to measure the rate of water uptake of a plant cutting. The bubble moved 25 mm in 10 minutes. Calculate the rate of water uptake.

Divide the <u>distance</u> the bubble moved by the <u>time taken</u>.

$$\frac{\text{distance moved}}{\text{time taken}} = \frac{25}{10} = 2.5 \text{ mm / minute}$$

You Can Use a Potometer to Estimate Transpiration Rate

1) When a plant <u>loses water</u> in transpiration, it <u>takes up more water</u> to <u>replace</u> it (see page 35).
2) So <u>measuring water uptake</u> with a potometer gives you an <u>estimate</u> of the <u>plant's transpiration rate</u>.
3) It's <u>not</u> a completely <u>accurate</u> estimate though.
4) That's because the water taken up by the plant <u>isn't</u> all lost through transpiration.
5) For example:

- some water is <u>used up</u> in <u>photosynthesis</u>,
- some water is lost from parts of the <u>potometer</u> that <u>aren't sealed</u>.

You Can See How Environmental Conditions Affect Water Uptake

You can use a potometer to <u>estimate</u> how <u>light intensity</u>, <u>temperature</u> or <u>air movement</u> affect the <u>rate of water uptake</u>. Here's how:

1) <u>Light intensity</u> — You could use a <u>lamp</u> to <u>increase</u> the <u>light intensity</u> that hits the plant.
2) <u>Temperature</u> — You could <u>change</u> the temperature by putting the potometer in a <u>warmer or cooler room</u>.
3) <u>Air movement</u> — You could use a <u>fan</u> to <u>increase</u> the air movement around the plant.

Just remember to <u>only change one variable at a time</u> and keep the rest <u>the same</u>.

Potometer — a useless tool for measuring pans...

Using a potometer can be kind of tricky. So, if you're doing this experiment in class, make sure to follow all the instructions your teacher gives you, so that you get some nice, solid results at the end.

Q1 A student is investigating the effect of light intensity on the rate of water uptake by a plant. Give two variables he should keep the same.

[2 marks]

Ecosystems and Interactions Between Organisms

Ecosystems might all look pretty wild, but everything is actually quite <u>organised</u>.

Ecosystems are Organised into Different Levels

Ecosystems have <u>different levels</u> of <u>organisation</u>:

1) <u>Individual</u> — A <u>single</u> organism.
2) <u>Population</u> — <u>All</u> the organisms of <u>one species</u> in a <u>habitat</u>.
3) <u>Community</u> — All the organisms of <u>different species</u> living in a habitat.
4) <u>Ecosystem</u> — A community of <u>organisms</u> along with all the <u>non-living conditions</u> (see next page).

> A habitat is the place where an organism lives, e.g. a field.

> A species is a group of similar organisms that can reproduce with each other to give offspring that can also reproduce.

Organisms Compete for Resources to Survive

1) Organisms need <u>resources</u> (things from their <u>environment</u>) in order to <u>survive</u> and <u>reproduce</u>:

- <u>Plants</u> need <u>light</u>, <u>space</u>, <u>water</u> and <u>minerals (nutrients)</u>. They also need <u>seed dispersers</u> (organisms that spread their seeds) and <u>pollinators</u> (e.g. bees).
- <u>Animals</u> need <u>space (territory)</u>, <u>shelter</u>, <u>food</u>, <u>water</u> and <u>mates</u>.

> The size of a population is limited by competition for these factors as well as predation (see below).

2) Organisms <u>compete with other species</u> (and members of their own species) for the <u>same resources</u>.

- For example, <u>red and grey squirrels</u> live in the <u>same habitat</u> and eat the <u>same food</u>.
- The <u>grey</u> squirrels are <u>better at competing</u> for these resources than the red squirrels.
- This means there's <u>not enough food</u> for the <u>reds</u>. So the <u>population</u> of red squirrels is <u>decreasing</u>.

Environmental Changes Affect Communities in Different Ways

1) The <u>environment</u> that plants and animals live in <u>changes all the time</u>.
2) These changes are caused by <u>biotic</u> (living) factors and <u>abiotic</u> (non-living) factors (see next page).
3) For some species these changes may cause the <u>population size</u> to <u>increase</u>.
   For other species the population size may <u>decrease</u>.
   The <u>distribution</u> of populations (where they live) may also change.

Biotic Factors Include...

> Competition (see above) is also a biotic factor. A new competitor could affect population sizes.

Availability of Food

In a year when <u>lots of berries</u> grow, the population of <u>blackbirds</u> might <u>increase</u>.
This is because there'll be <u>enough food</u> for all of them, so they're more likely to <u>survive</u> and <u>reproduce</u>.

Number of Predators

If the <u>number of lions</u> (predator) <u>decreases</u> then the number of <u>gazelles</u> (prey) might <u>increase</u>.
This is because <u>fewer</u> of them will be <u>eaten</u> by the lions.

Presence of Pathogens

A <u>new pathogen</u> (p.9) may cause populations to <u>decrease</u> due to <u>illness</u>.

The availability of food — a major factor in mood swings

This bit's not quite over yet. Turn the page to find out how <u>abiotic</u> factors can affect communities.

Q1   Give two biotic factors that could affect the community in an ecosystem.   [2 marks]

Abiotic Factors and Investigating Distribution

You've learned a bit about <u>biotic factors</u>, but don't forget the <u>abiotic factors</u> in an ecosystem.

Abiotic Factors Can Also Affect Communities

<u>Changes</u> in <u>abiotic factors</u> can affect <u>communities</u>. For example:

Abiotic factors are non-living factors — see previous page.

Environmental conditions

1) Changes in temperature may affect the <u>distribution</u> of organisms (where they live).

2) <u>Light intensity</u>, <u>moisture level</u> and <u>soil pH</u> can also affect the distribution of organisms.

Toxic chemicals

Toxic chemicals can lead to many <u>problems</u> in ecosystems. For example:

There's more on food chains on page 44.

1) <u>Bioaccumulation</u>:
   * This is when toxic chemicals (e.g. pesticides) <u>build up</u> the further along a food chain you go.
   * This means that <u>organisms</u> at the <u>top</u> of the chain get a <u>toxic dose</u> (enough to <u>harm</u> them).

2) <u>Eutrophication</u>:
   * This happens when <u>fertilisers</u> from farms enter <u>lakes</u> and <u>ponds</u>.
   * This can cause <u>increased growth</u> of <u>algae</u>.
   * The algae <u>block sunlight</u> from plants in the water, which die.
   * Microorganisms feeding on the dead plants use up <u>oxygen</u> in the water. This leads to the <u>death</u> of other organisms (e.g. fish).

Use a Quadrat to Study The Distribution of Small Organisms

PRACTICAL

To compare how <u>common</u> an organism is in <u>two sample areas</u>, follow these steps:

1) Place a <u>quadrat</u> on the ground in your <u>first</u> sample area.
   Quadrats need to be placed <u>at random</u> so that you get a <u>sample</u> which shows the general features of the whole area. For more about random sampling take a look at page 242.

2) <u>Count</u> all the organisms you're interested in <u>within</u> the quadrat.

3) <u>Repeat</u> steps 1 and 2 lots of times.

4) <u>Work out</u> the <u>mean</u> number of organisms per quadrat.

This is a quadrat.

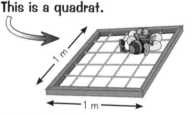

1 m × 1 m

EXAMPLE: Anna counted the number of daisies in 7 quadrats.
She recorded the following results: 18, 20, 22, 23, 23, 23, 25

$$\text{Mean} = \frac{\text{total number of organisms}}{\text{number of quadrats}} = \frac{18 + 20 + 22 + 23 + 23 + 23 + 25}{7} = \frac{154}{7} = 22 \text{ daisies per quadrat}$$

5) <u>Repeat</u> steps 1 to 4 in the <u>second</u> sample area.

6) <u>Compare</u> the two means. E.g. you might find 2 daisies per m² in the shade, and 22 daisies per m² (lots more) in an open field.

You can also use quadrats to estimate the abundance (population size) in the area you're studying — see the next page for more.

Drat, drat and double drat — my favourite use of quadrats...

Quadrats are great for investigating organisms that don't move, such as plants. Be careful with the living things in any habitat you're studying, e.g. don't trample all over plants and be careful with animals that you come across.

Q1 What is meant by bioaccumulation? [1 mark]

Investigating Ecosystems *PRACTICAL*

Here's how to study the <u>abundance</u> of organisms.

Estimate Population Sizes by Scaling Up from a Small Sample Area

1) Once you have counted the number of organisms in <u>several quadrats</u> (see previous page) you can work out the <u>population size</u> of the organisms in a <u>habitat</u>.

2) <u>Divide</u> the <u>area</u> of the <u>habitat</u> by the <u>quadrat size</u>. Then <u>multiply</u> this figure by the <u>mean number</u> of organisms per quadrat.

EXAMPLE:

Students used 0.5 m^2 quadrats to randomly sample daisies in a field. They found a mean of 10 daisies per quadrat. The field's area was 800 m^2. Estimate the population of daisies in the field.

1) Divide the area of the habitat by the quadrat size. $800 \div 0.5 = 1600$

2) Multiply this by the mean number of organisms per quadrat. $1600 \times 10 = 16\ 000$ daisies in the field

Use Capture-Mark-Release-Recapture to Estimate Population Sizes

1) <u>Capture</u> a <u>sample</u> of the population.
2) <u>Mark</u> the animals in a <u>harmless</u> way.
3) <u>Release</u> all the animals back into the environment.
4) Leave some <u>time</u> for the animals to <u>mix</u> with the rest of the population. Then <u>recapture</u> another sample of the population.
5) <u>Count</u> how many of this sample are marked.
6) Then <u>estimate</u> population size with this equation:

$$\text{Population Size} = \frac{\text{number in first sample} \times \text{number in second sample}}{\text{number in second sample previously marked}}$$

EXAMPLE:

A pitfall trap was set up in an area of woodland. 30 woodlice were caught in an hour. They were marked on their shell and then released back into the environment. The next day, 35 woodlice were caught in an hour — only 5 of these were marked. Estimate the population size.

All you need to do is put the numbers into the population size equation (shown above).

Population size = $(30 \times 35) \div 5 = 210$ woodlice

number in the first sample | number in the second sample | number in the second sample previously marked

A pitfall trap is a container with steep sides and an open top. It is sunk into the ground and used to trap insects on the ground.

The population size of my chocolate mice has fallen...

When using the capture-recapture method you have to assume some things. For example, that marking the animals hasn't affected their chance of survival (e.g. by making it more likely that they'll be seen and get eaten).

Q1   Capture-mark-release-recapture was used to estimate a population of crabs. In the first sample 22 were caught. A second sample had 26 crabs, 4 of which were marked. Estimate the population size.   [2 marks]

PRACTICAL More on Investigating Ecosystems

Yep, there's still some more to learn about this stuff. Coming up we have <u>keys</u> and <u>transects</u> — lovely.

Keys are Used to Identify Creatures

1) A <u>key</u> is a <u>set of questions</u> that you can use to figure out what an <u>unknown organism</u> is.

2) Each <u>question</u> asks you something about your organism. You are given different <u>options</u> for the answers.

3) You go through the questions until you're just <u>left with one</u> possible species your organism could be.

<u>Part of a key</u> is shown on the right. It can be used to identify <u>types of organisms</u> that might be found on a <u>woodland floor</u>.

Some keys use statements, rather than questions.

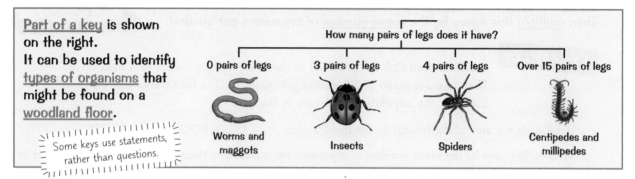

How many pairs of legs does it have?

0 pairs of legs — Worms and maggots
3 pairs of legs — Insects
4 pairs of legs — Spiders
Over 15 pairs of legs — Centipedes and millipedes

Transects are Used to Investigate Distribution

1) The <u>distribution</u> of organisms often <u>changes gradually</u> across an area. You can investigate this using a <u>line</u> called a <u>transect</u>.

2) For example, a transect could be used to investigate how the distribution of a <u>plant species</u> changes from a <u>hedge</u> towards the <u>middle</u> of a field.

3) When you sample along the length of a transect using a <u>quadrat</u> (see p.40) this is called a <u>belt transect</u>.

4) To do a <u>belt transect</u> follow the steps below:

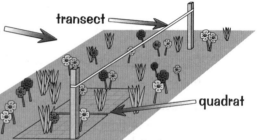

transect

quadrat

- Mark out a <u>line</u> in the area you want to study using a <u>tape measure</u>.
- Place a <u>quadrat</u> at the <u>start</u> of the <u>line</u>. <u>Count</u> and <u>record</u> the organisms you find in the quadrat.
- Then, take samples by <u>moving</u> your quadrat <u>along the line</u>. You can put each quadrat down <u>straight after</u> the one before (this might take ages though). Or you can <u>leave gaps</u> between each quadrat, e.g. just put a quadrat down every 2 m.
- <u>Repeat</u> your transect at least <u>twice</u> more at different places within the area you want to study.

5) It might be <u>difficult</u> to count all the <u>individual organisms</u> in the quadrat (e.g. if they're grass plants).

6) In this case you can calculate the <u>percentage cover</u>.

7) This means estimating the percentage <u>area</u> of the quadrat covered by a particular type of organism, e.g. by <u>counting</u> the number of little squares covered by the organisms.

8) You can investigate how <u>abiotic factors</u> affect the <u>distribution</u> and <u>abundance</u> of organisms in the habitat (see next page). You can do this by measuring abiotic factors at <u>points</u> along the <u>transect</u>.

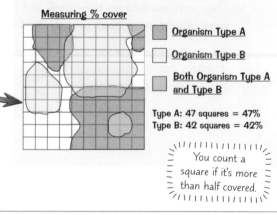

Measuring % cover

Organism Type A
Organism Type B
Both Organism Type A and Type B

Type A: 47 squares = 47%
Type B: 42 squares = 42%

You count a square if it's more than half covered.

Identification keys — not much use when you're locked out...

Keys help you identify organisms you've found when sampling. This is pretty important when you want to talk about the different organisms that you've seen — it's not much use saying you found six slimy things in a pond...

Q1   Describe how to carry out a belt transect.   [3 marks]

Investigating Factors Affecting Distribution

The way organisms are <u>distributed</u> depends on a number of different <u>factors</u>. Prepare to learn all about them.

The Distribution of Organisms is Affected by Biotic and Abiotic Factors

1) Both <u>biotic</u> and <u>abiotic</u> factors can affect the <u>distribution of organisms</u>.
   For example:

See pages 39-40 for more on biotic and abiotic factors.

   - <u>BIOTIC</u> — a <u>new species</u> might move into an area. The new species might be <u>better at competing</u> for food than species already living there — so the old species might <u>move somewhere else</u>.
   - <u>ABIOTIC</u> — daisies might be <u>more common</u> in an <u>open area</u> of a field compared to under trees. This could be because there's <u>more light</u> in the open area.

2) You can <u>measure abiotic factors</u> that you think might be affecting distribution.

PRACTICAL

There's more on measuring temperature on p.236 and pH on p.237.

   1) Use a <u>thermometer</u> to measure the <u>temperature</u> in different places.
   2) Use a <u>soil moisture meter</u> to measure the level of <u>moisture</u> in some soil.
   3) Use a <u>light meter</u> to measure <u>light intensity</u>. Hold the meter at the level of the organisms you're investigating (e.g. <u>ground level</u> for daisies). Make sure it's at the <u>same height</u> and <u>angle</u> for every reading you take.
   4) Measure <u>soil pH</u> using <u>indicator liquid</u> (e.g. Universal indicator). The indicator <u>changes colour</u> depending on the pH of the soil. You can compare the colour to a chart to find the pH of the soil. <u>Electronic pH monitors</u> can also be used. They will give more accurate pH value for the sample.

The Distribution of Living Indicators Can Be Used to Assess Pollution

1) Some <u>organisms</u> are very <u>sensitive to changes</u> in their environment. They can be studied to see how polluted an area is. These organisms are known as <u>living indicators</u>. For example:

PRACTICAL

   - If you find <u>stonefly larvae</u> or <u>freshwater shrimps</u> in a river, it <u>indicates</u> that the <u>water is clean</u>.
   - <u>Blood worms</u> and <u>sludge worms</u> indicate <u>highly polluted water</u>.
   - Different types of lichen are sensitive to pollution in the air. If there are <u>lots of lichen species</u> in an area, then the air is clean.

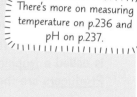
freshwater shrimp

2) When investigating living indicators, you need to <u>sample</u> them.
3) Sampling methods will <u>vary</u> depending on the <u>organism</u> you're interested in and <u>where</u> it is found.
4) For example, <u>aquatic organisms</u> could be caught with a <u>net</u> which is swept through the water.
5) <u>Lichens</u> (which grow on trees and rocks and don't move about) could be sampled using <u>quadrats</u> or <u>transects</u> (see pages 40-42).

Aquatic organisms are ones that live in water.

Teenagers are living indicators — not found in clean rooms...

Some organisms can only live in clean, unpolluted places. Others can live in polluted places.
So, these organisms can be used to tell how polluted a place is. Pretty clever, isn't it?

Q1   A local park has many species of lichen. Explain what this indicates about the air quality.   [2 marks]

Chapter B3 — Living Together — Food and Ecosystems

Food Chains and Food Webs

If you like <u>food</u>, and you like <u>chains</u>, then <u>food chains</u> might just blow your mind. Steady now, here we go...

Food Chains Show What's Eaten by What in an Ecosystem

1) <u>Food chains</u> always start with a <u>producer</u>.
Producers <u>make</u> (produce) <u>their own food</u> using energy from the Sun.

2) Producers are usually <u>green plants</u> — they make <u>glucose</u> by <u>photosynthesis</u> (see p.28).

3) Some of this glucose is used to make the plant's <u>biomass</u> — its <u>mass</u> of <u>living material</u>.

4) Biomass is <u>passed along</u> a food chain when an organism <u>eats</u> another organism.
This means that these photosynthetic organisms <u>support nearly all life on Earth</u>.

5) <u>Consumers</u> are organisms that <u>eat other organisms</u>:
- <u>Primary</u> consumers eat <u>producers</u>.
- <u>Secondary</u> consumers eat <u>primary</u> consumers.
- <u>Tertiary</u> consumers eat <u>secondary</u> consumers.

6) Here's an example of a <u>food chain</u>:

7) Each stage in a food chain is called a <u>trophic level</u>.
<u>Producers</u> are the <u>first</u> trophic level.

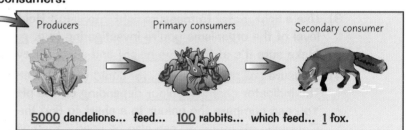

5000 dandelions... feed... 100 rabbits... which feed... 1 fox.

Food Webs Show How Food Chains are Linked

1) There are many different species within an environment. That means that there are <u>lots of different</u> possible <u>food chains</u>. You can draw a <u>food web</u> to show them (a diagram of what eats what).

2) All the species in a food web are <u>interdependent</u> — they <u>depend</u> on each other for survival.

3) The <u>transfer of biomass</u> is one way in which organisms are <u>interdependent</u>.
The <u>direction</u> of biomass transfer is shown by the <u>arrows</u> in a food chain or web.

4) Because the species are <u>interdependent</u>, a change in the size of one population will affect the sizes of other populations in the community.

The transfer of biomass is the movement of living material along a food chain when organisms eat each other.

The diagram on the right shows part of a <u>food web</u> from a <u>stream</u>.
If all the <u>stonefly larvae</u> die, then for example:
- there would be <u>less food</u> for <u>waterboatmen</u>, so their population might <u>decrease</u>.
- the <u>blackfly larvae</u> would not have to <u>compete</u> with the <u>stonefly larvae</u> for <u>food</u> (algae) so their population might <u>increase</u>.

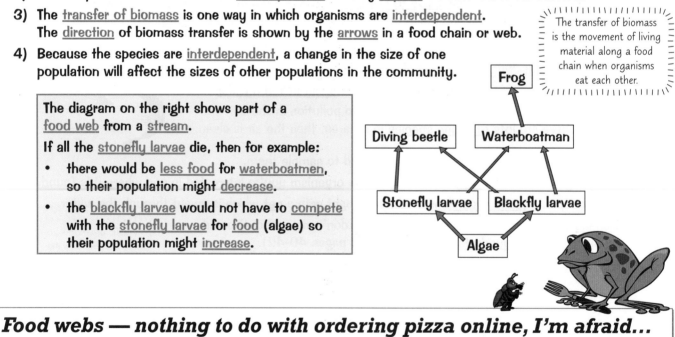

Food webs — nothing to do with ordering pizza online, I'm afraid...

Food webs are handy for looking at relationships between individual species. Unfortunately you hardly ever see simple food webs in the real world — they're normally as tangled together and interlinked as a bowl of spaghetti.

Q1 The diagram on the right shows part of a food web. Using the diagram, suggest what might happen to the number of hawks if the number of mice increased.

[1 mark]

Making and Breaking Biological Molecules

Organisms can break big molecules down into smaller ones and build small molecules back up into bigger ones. It's pretty clever stuff, and all given a helping hand by our good friends, enzymes (see page 26).

Carbohydrates, Lipids and Proteins are Organic Molecules

1) Organisms need to take in organic molecules. Organic molecules are molecules that contain carbon.

2) The large molecules shown below and the smaller molecules they're made up from are all organic:

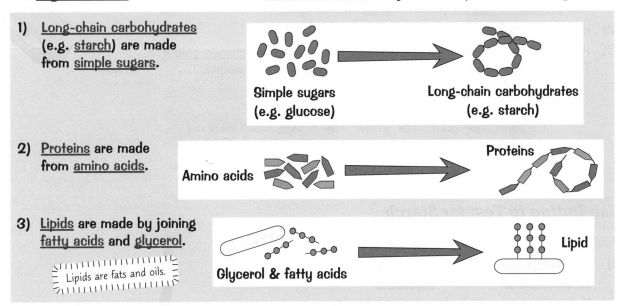

1) Long-chain carbohydrates (e.g. starch) are made from simple sugars.

   Simple sugars (e.g. glucose) → Long-chain carbohydrates (e.g. starch)

2) Proteins are made from amino acids.

   Amino acids → Proteins

3) Lipids are made by joining fatty acids and glycerol.

   Lipids are fats and oils.

   Glycerol & fatty acids → Lipid

Plants Build Up Organic Molecules in their Biomass

1) Producers take in the elements they need from their environment, e.g. plants take in carbon from the air and nitrogen compounds from the soil.

2) Producers use carbon (along with oxygen and hydrogen) to make glucose during photosynthesis (see page 28).

3) Glucose is then used to make other small organic molecules, e.g. other sugars, fatty acids and glycerol.

4) Glucose is also joined with nitrate ions to make amino acids.

5) These small molecules are then used to create larger organic molecules, e.g. long-chain carbohydrates, lipids and proteins.

6) These larger molecules are used to build structures like cell membranes and organelles.

Breaking down and building up molecules involves enzymes — see page 26.

Animals Break these Molecules Down, then Build them Up Again

1) Consumers can only get carbon and nitrogen compounds by eating producers or other consumers.

2) They take in large organic molecules from other organisms when they eat them.

3) Digestion breaks down these large molecules into smaller ones. These can be absorbed by the consumer.

4) The small molecules are then transported to the consumer's cells. They are then built up into larger molecules (proteins, etc.) again. These form the biomass of the consumer.

What do you call an acid that's eaten all the pies — a fatty acid...

Make sure you learn the diagrams at the top of the page really well (I mean, really, really well). And remember that when the bigger organic molecules get broken down, the arrow just goes the opposite way.

Q1   Name the molecules that result from the breakdown of: a) carbohydrates, b) proteins.   [2 marks]

Testing for Biological Molecules

You need to know how you can test for biological molecules using different chemicals. The tests are all qualitative — you can tell whether or not a substance is present in a sample, but not how much is present.

You Can Test for Sugars Using Benedict's Reagent

There are different types of sugar molecules. Some are called reducing sugars. Here's how to test for them:

1) Add Benedict's reagent (which is blue) to a sample.

2) Heat it in a water bath that's set to 75 °C.

3) If the sample contains a reducing sugar, the solution will change colour. The colour change depends on how much sugar is in the sample:

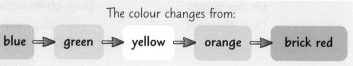

The colour changes from:

blue ⇒ green ⇒ yellow ⇒ orange ⇒ brick red

Use Iodine to Test for Starch

Just add iodine solution to the test sample.

1) If starch is present, the sample changes from browny-orange to a dark, blue-black colour.

2) If there's no starch, it stays browny-orange.

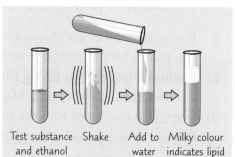
iodine → food sample — no starch / starch present

Use the Emulsion Test for Lipids

1) Shake the test substance with ethanol for about a minute until it dissolves. Then, pour the solution into water.

2) If there are any lipids present, they will show up as a milky emulsion.

3) The more lipid there is, the more noticeable the milky colour will be.

An emulsion is when one liquid doesn't dissolve in another — it just forms little droplets.

Test substance and ethanol — Shake — Add to water — Milky colour indicates lipid

The Biuret Test is Used for Proteins

1) Add 2 cm³ of biuret solution to your test sample. Mix the contents of the tube by gently shaking it.

2) If there's no protein, the solution will stay blue.

3) If the sample contains protein, the solution will turn purple.

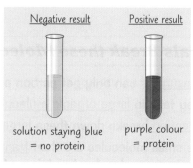
Negative result — Positive result
solution staying blue = no protein — purple colour = protein

The Anger Test — annoy test subject. Red face = anger present...

OK, so this stuff isn't thrilling. But learning it is better than being dissolved in a giant vat of vinegar...

Q1   A solution that has been mixed with biuret solution turns purple. What conclusion would you draw from this test?

[1 mark]

Cycles in Ecosystems

All the <u>nutrients</u> in our environment are constantly being <u>recycled</u> —
there's a nice balance between what <u>goes in</u> and what <u>goes out</u> again.

Materials are Constantly Recycled in an Ecosystem

There's more on ecosystems on page 39.

1) <u>Living things</u> need materials such as <u>carbon</u>, <u>water</u> and <u>nitrogen</u> to <u>survive</u>.

2) But there <u>isn't</u> an <u>endless supply</u> of these materials — so they're <u>recycled</u> through an ecosystem.

3) As materials are recycled, they pass through the <u>biotic</u> (living) parts of the ecosystem — these include <u>animals</u>, <u>plants</u> and <u>microorganisms</u>.

4) Materials are also recycled through the <u>abiotic</u> (non-living) parts of the ecosystem — for example, the <u>air</u> and <u>soil</u>.

The Carbon Cycle Shows How Carbon is Recycled

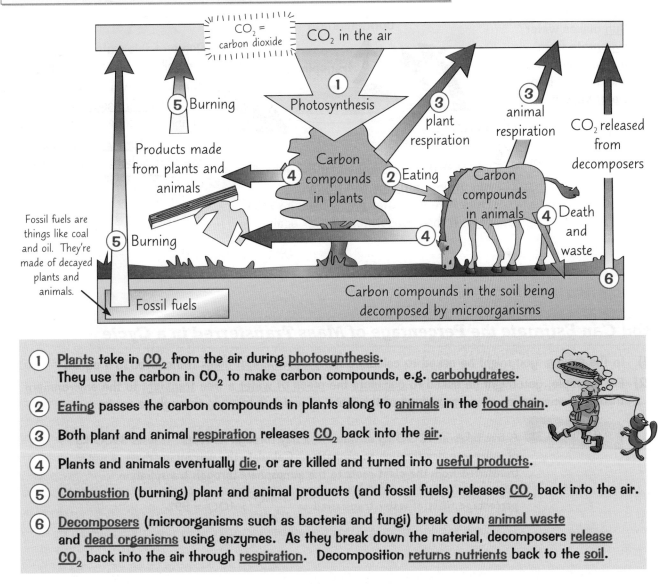

(1) <u>Plants</u> take in <u>CO_2</u> from the air during <u>photosynthesis</u>. They use the carbon in CO_2 to make carbon compounds, e.g. <u>carbohydrates</u>.

(2) <u>Eating</u> passes the carbon compounds in plants along to <u>animals</u> in the <u>food chain</u>.

(3) Both plant and animal <u>respiration</u> releases <u>CO_2</u> back into the <u>air</u>.

(4) Plants and animals eventually <u>die</u>, or are killed and turned into <u>useful products</u>.

(5) <u>Combustion</u> (burning) plant and animal products (and fossil fuels) releases <u>CO_2</u> back into the air.

(6) <u>Decomposers</u> (microorganisms such as bacteria and fungi) break down <u>animal waste</u> and <u>dead organisms</u> using enzymes. As they break down the material, decomposers <u>release</u> <u>CO_2</u> back into the air through <u>respiration</u>. Decomposition <u>returns nutrients</u> back to the <u>soil</u>.

A Carbon Cycle — a great gift for bike lovers...

The <u>biotic</u> parts of the ecosystem shown in the big diagram above are the horse, tree and microorganisms in the soil. The <u>abiotic</u> parts include the air and the soil. Make sure you don't mix the two terms up.

Q1   Name two processes which release carbon dioxide into the atmosphere.   [2 marks]

More on Cycles in Ecosystems

Like carbon, water on planet Earth is constantly recycled. This is lucky for us because without water, we wouldn't survive. And I don't just mean there'd be no paddling pools, ice lollies or bubble baths...

The Water Cycle Means Water is Endlessly Recycled

1) All living things need water to survive.

2) The water cycle constantly recycles water so that we don't run out of it.

3) This is the water cycle:

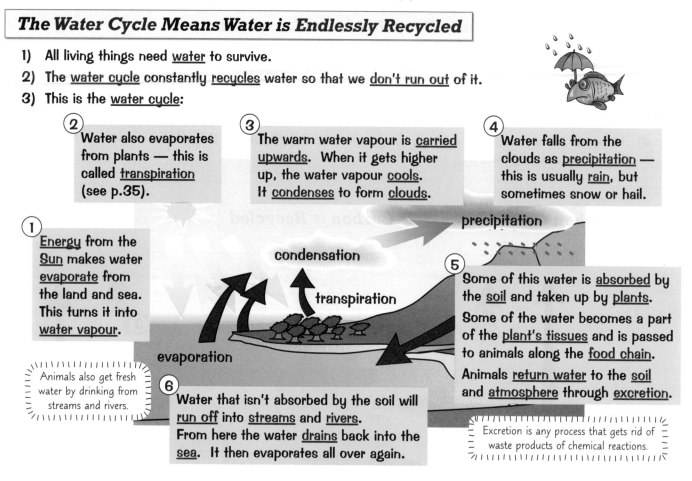

② Water also evaporates from plants — this is called transpiration (see p.35).

③ The warm water vapour is carried upwards. When it gets higher up, the water vapour cools. It condenses to form clouds.

④ Water falls from the clouds as precipitation — this is usually rain, but sometimes snow or hail.

① Energy from the Sun makes water evaporate from the land and sea. This turns it into water vapour.

Animals also get fresh water by drinking from streams and rivers.

⑤ Some of this water is absorbed by the soil and taken up by plants.
Some of the water becomes a part of the plant's tissues and is passed to animals along the food chain.
Animals return water to the soil and atmosphere through excretion.

⑥ Water that isn't absorbed by the soil will run off into streams and rivers. From here the water drains back into the sea. It then evaporates all over again.

Excretion is any process that gets rid of waste products of chemical reactions.

You Can Estimate the Percentage of Mass Transferred in a Cycle

1) In the exams, you might be asked to calculate the percentage of mass transferred in a cycle.

2) For example, you might be asked to calculate the mass of water a tree transfers to the environment through transpiration as a percentage of the mass of water it takes in through its roots:

> **EXAMPLE:** A tree takes in 4000 kg of water in a day through its roots. It loses 3960 kg of water in a day through transpiration. Calculate the percentage mass of water transferred from the plant roots to the atmosphere through transpiration.
>
> percentage mass of water transferred $= \dfrac{3960}{4000} \times 100 = 99\%$

Come on out, it's only a little water cycle, it won't hurt you...

The most important thing to remember is that it's a cycle — a continuous process with no beginning or end. Water that falls to the ground as rain (or any other kind of precipitation) will eventually end up back in the clouds again.

Q1   In the water cycle, how does water move from the land into the air?   [1 mark]

Revision Questions for Chapter B3

It's time to say goodbye to Chapter B3 — but not before a healthy dose of questions to test yourself with...
- Try these questions and <u>tick off each one</u> when you <u>get it right</u>.
- When you've done <u>all the questions</u> for a topic and are <u>completely happy</u> with it, tick off the topic.

Enzymes (p.26-27) ☑

1) What part of an enzyme makes it specific to a particular substrate? ☑
2) Explain how temperature affects enzyme activity. ☑
3) State two ways in which you could measure the rate of an enzyme-controlled reaction. ☑

Photosynthesis (p.28-30) ☑

4) Where in a plant cell does photosynthesis take place? ☑
5) What is the equation for photosynthesis? ☑
6) What effect would a low carbon dioxide concentration have on the rate of photosynthesis? ☑
7) Describe an investigation you could do to measure the effect of light intensity on photosynthesis. ☑

Methods of Transport and Transport in Plants (p.31-38) ☑

8) Define the following terms: a) diffusion,   b) osmosis,   c) active transport. ☑
9) If a potato cylinder is placed in a solution with a very high sucrose concentration, what will happen to the mass of the potato cylinder over time? Explain why. ☑
10) What is translocation? ☑
11) Which type of plant transport vessel is made up of dead cells? ☑
12) How do stomata open and close? ☑
13) Give three factors that affect the rate of transpiration. ☑
14) What can a potometer be used to measure? ☑

Ecosystems and Interactions Between Organisms (p.39-44) ☐

15) Give two resources that plants compete for in ecosystems. ☑
16) What is eutrophication? ☑
17) Briefly describe how you could use quadrats to investigate the population size of a species. ☑
18) Why might you need to use a key when investigating organisms? ☑
19) What is a living indicator and why might you sample one? ☑
20) How do food webs show interdependence? ☑

Biological Molecules (p.45-46) ☑

21) Name a big molecule that's formed from simple sugars. ☑
22) Which two molecules are produced when lipids are broken down? ☑
23) How would you test for the presence of lipids in a sample? ☑

Cycles in Ecosystems (p.47-48) ☑

24) Name the process that takes in carbon from the air. ☑
25) What is the role of microorganisms in the carbon cycle? ☑
26) Explain how evaporation, condensation and precipitation are involved in the water cycle. ☑

Respiration

You need energy to keep your body going. Energy comes from food, and it's transferred by respiration.

Respiration is NOT "Breathing In and Out"

The molecule that is broken down in respiration is called the substrate.

1) Respiration is the process of transferring energy from a molecule such as glucose (a sugar).
2) Consumers (animals) produce glucose by breaking down the biomass they get when they eat other organisms (see page 44).
3) Respiration involves several chemical reactions. It is exothermic — that means it releases energy.
4) The energy transferred by respiration can't be used directly by cells — so it's used to make a substance called ATP. ATP stores the energy.
5) The energy is used for processes including:
   * breaking and making molecules,
   * active transport (see page 31)
   * contracting muscles (in animals)

Producers (such as plants — see page 44) make their own glucose for respiration through photosynthesis (see page 28).

6) These processes are needed for organisms to stay alive, so respiration happens in all cells all the time.

Aerobic Respiration Needs Plenty of Oxygen

1) "Aerobic" just means "with oxygen".
2) So, aerobic respiration is respiration with oxygen.
3) Aerobic respiration produces lots of ATP — 32 molecules per molecule of glucose.
4) The products of breaking down glucose are combined with oxygen to make carbon dioxide and water.
5) Here is the equation for aerobic respiration:

Carbon dioxide is a waste product of aerobic respiration.

$$\text{glucose + oxygen} \longrightarrow \text{carbon dioxide + water}$$

mitochondria

6) In prokaryotic cells (microorganisms such as bacteria) all aerobic respiration reactions happen in the cytoplasm.
7) In eukaryotic cells (plant and animal cells), aerobic respiration happens in the mitochondria (see p.1) and in the cytoplasm.

You Can Investigate the Effect of Different Substrates on Respiration Rate

1) Put a set volume and concentration of substrate solution in a test tube.
2) Put the test tube in a water bath set to 25 °C.
3) Add a set mass of live yeast to the test tube and stir for 2 minutes.
4) Attach the test tube to a gas syringe.
5) Measure the volume of CO_2 produced in a set amount of time.
6) Calculate the rate of respiration using this equation:

$$\text{rate of respiration} = \frac{\text{volume of } CO_2 \text{ produced}}{\text{time}}$$

bung

gas syringe

test tube

water bath

yeast and substrate solution

7) Repeat the experiment with a different substrate and compare the two rates.

Respiration transfers energy — but this page has worn me out...

Thank goodness for respiration — transferring the energy stored in my tea and biscuits to my brain cells. Great.

Q1   Give the word equation for aerobic respiration.   [2 marks]

More on Respiration

Now on to another type of respiration — <u>anaerobic respiration</u>.

Anaerobic Respiration Doesn't Use Oxygen At All

1) "<u>An</u>aerobic" just means "<u>without</u> oxygen".

2) So <u>anaerobic respiration</u> happens when there is <u>very little or no oxygen</u>. For example:

- <u>Human cells</u> — During <u>hard exercise</u> the body <u>can't</u> get enough <u>oxygen</u> to the <u>muscle cells</u> for aerobic respiration. They have to start <u>respiring anaerobically</u> as well.
- <u>Plant root cells</u> — If the <u>soil</u> a plant's growing in becomes <u>waterlogged</u> (full of water) there'll be <u>no oxygen</u> for the <u>roots</u>. This means that the root cells will have to <u>respire anaerobically</u>.
- <u>Bacterial cells</u> — Bacteria can get <u>under</u> your <u>skin</u> through <u>puncture wounds</u>. There's <u>very little oxygen</u> under your skin, so only bacteria that can <u>respire anaerobically</u> can <u>survive</u> there.

3) Anaerobic respiration transfers much <u>less energy per glucose molecule</u> than aerobic respiration.

4) The process of anaerobic respiration is slightly <u>different</u> in <u>different organisms</u>:

Animals and Some Bacteria Produce Lactic Acid

In <u>animals</u> and <u>some bacteria</u>, glucose is only <u>partially broken down</u> during anaerobic respiration. <u>Lactic acid</u> is formed as a <u>waste product</u>. Here's the word equation:

$$glucose \longrightarrow lactic\ acid$$

Plants and Some Microorganisms Produce Ethanol and Carbon Dioxide

When <u>plants</u> and <u>some microorganisms</u> (including <u>yeast</u>) respire anaerobically, they produce <u>ethanol</u> and <u>carbon dioxide</u>. Again, the glucose is only <u>partially</u> broken down. This is the <u>word equation</u>:

$$glucose \longrightarrow ethanol + carbon\ dioxide$$

Anaerobic respiration in yeast is known as fermentation.

You Need to Compare Aerobic and Anaerobic Respiration

This handy table shows the <u>differences</u> and <u>similarities</u> between <u>aerobic</u> and <u>anaerobic</u> respiration.

	Aerobic	Anaerobic
Conditions	Oxygen present	Not enough oxygen present
Inputs	Glucose and oxygen	Glucose
Outputs	Carbon dioxide and water	In animals and some bacteria — lactic acid In plants and some microorganisms (e.g. yeast) — ethanol and carbon dioxide
ATP yield	High — 32 ATP made per molecule of glucose	Much lower — 2 ATP made per molecule of glucose

The yield is the amount of ATP produced by the reaction overall.

My friend Anna O'Robic is quite odd — I only see her at the gym...

Make sure you know those word equations and can compare the processes of aerobic and anaerobic respiration.

Q1 Name the product(s) of anaerobic respiration in plants. [1 mark]

The Cell Cycle and Mitosis

In order to survive and grow, our cells have got to be able to <u>divide</u>. And that means our DNA as well.

New Cells are Needed for Growth and Repair

1) The body cells in multicellular organisms <u>divide</u> to <u>produce more cells</u>. This means that organisms can <u>grow</u> and <u>replace</u> damaged cells.

2) Cells <u>grow</u> and <u>divide</u> over and over again — this is called the <u>cell cycle</u>. There are <u>two main parts</u>:

interphase

The Cell Cycle

mitosis

① <u>Interphase</u>
1) During interphase the cell <u>grows</u>. It also <u>increases</u> the amount of <u>sub-cellular structures</u> such as <u>mitochondria</u> and <u>ribosomes</u>.
2) It then <u>copies</u> its DNA, so there's <u>one copy</u> for each cell.
3) The DNA forms <u>X-shaped</u> chromosomes. Each 'arm' of a chromosome is an <u>exact copy</u> of the other.

Chromosomes are long lengths of coiled DNA — see page 3.

The left arm has the same DNA as the right arm of the chromosome.

② <u>Mitosis</u> — this is when a cell reproduces itself.

The cell has <u>two copies</u> of its DNA.

The chromosomes <u>line up</u> at the centre of the cell. <u>Cell fibres</u> pull them apart. The <u>two arms</u> of each chromosome go to <u>opposite ends</u> of the cell.

<u>Membranes</u> form around each of the sets of chromosomes. These become the <u>nuclei</u> of the two new cells.

Nuclei is just the word for more than one nucleus.

Lastly, the <u>cytoplasm</u> divides.

You now have <u>two new cells</u> containing exactly the same DNA — they're <u>genetically identical</u> to <u>each other</u> and to the <u>parent cell</u>.

3) You can <u>estimate</u> how many cells there will be after a set amount of time.

Just use this formula:

number of cells = 2^n

n = number of divisions

E.g. a cell divides <u>once</u> every <u>30 minutes</u>. After <u>4 hours</u> there will have been roughly <u>8 divisions</u>. So there will be roughly 2^8 = <u>256 cells</u>.

This is only an estimate though. The cells might not keep dividing at the same rate for four hours because the conditions might change (e.g. a lack of food). Also, some of the cells might die.

Cancer is a Case of Uncontrolled Cell Division

1) <u>Changes</u> in a person's <u>DNA</u> can cause a cell to <u>divide uncontrollably</u>.
2) This can result in the growth of a <u>mass of abnormal cells</u> called a <u>tumour</u>.
3) If the tumour <u>invades and destroys</u> surrounding tissue it is called <u>cancer</u>. Cancer is a <u>non-communicable disease</u> (see page 8).

A cell's favourite computer game — divide and conquer...

Mitosis can seem tricky at first. But don't worry — just go through it slowly, one step at a time.

Q1   Describe what happens during the interphase stage of the cell cycle.   [3 marks]

Microscopy

Biologists <u>love microscopes</u>, which is why they're making a <u>second appearance</u> in this book...

Cells are Studied Using Microscopes

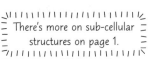
There's more on sub-cellular structures on page 1.

1) Microscopes use <u>lenses</u> to <u>magnify</u> things (make them look <u>bigger</u>).

2) Microscope technology has <u>got better</u> over time. This has allowed <u>new observations</u> to be made.

3) <u>Light microscopes</u> can be used to look at cells.
They let us see <u>some sub-cellular structures</u>, e.g. <u>chloroplasts</u> and the <u>nucleus</u>.

4) <u>Electron microscopes</u> were invented <u>after</u> light microscopes.

5) Electron microscopes can make specimens look <u>bigger</u> and show <u>more detail</u> than light microscopes.

6) This has given us a <u>better understanding</u> of <u>how cells work</u>. E.g. it has allowed scientists to understand how the internal <u>structures</u> of mitochondria and chloroplasts relate to their <u>functions</u>.

You can Observe Stages of Mitosis Using a Light Microscope

PRACTICAL

1) You saw how to use a <u>light microscope</u> to <u>observe cells</u> on page 2.

2) <u>Chromosomes</u> can be <u>stained</u> so you can see them under a microscope. This means you can watch what happens to them <u>during mitosis</u>.

3) These are some <u>cells</u> from a <u>plant root tip</u> shown under a light microscope.

4) The cells are squashed underneath a <u>cover slip</u>. This makes it easier to see the <u>chromosomes</u>.

5) You can see that there are cells at different stages of the <u>cell cycle</u> and <u>mitosis</u>.

Cell in late stage of mitosis — the nucleus has divided.

Cells in early stage of mitosis — the chromosomes are being pulled apart.

Most of the cells shown are in interphase — the chromosomes are all spread out and just look like one big blob.

HERVE CONGE, ISM/SCIENCE PHOTO LIBRARY

You Can Estimate the Size of Cells Under a Microscope

Sometimes, you might want to <u>estimate</u> the <u>relative sizes</u> of two cells. Here's how:

EXAMPLE:

Look at the plant cells on the right.
Estimate how many times bigger Cell 2 is than Cell 1.

There are different ways to answer this.

1) If you compare the cells, you can see that Cell 2 is about <u>twice the height</u> and <u>twice the width</u> of Cell 1. So Cell 2 is roughly <u>2 x</u> as <u>tall</u> or <u>wide</u> as Cell 1.

2) So you can estimate that the <u>area</u> of Cell 2 is 2^2 or <u>4 x</u> as great as Cell 1, and the <u>volume</u> is 2^3 or <u>8 x</u> as great.

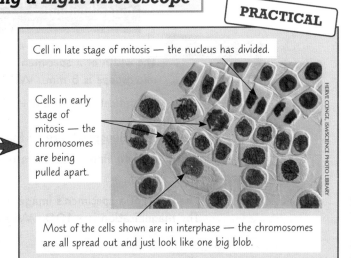

Cell 1   Cell 2

I take my microscope everywhere — good job it's a light one...

We're not done with microscopy yet I'm afraid. Do this question, then move on to the next page.

Q1 Explain how electron microscopes have given us a greater understanding of how cells work. [2 marks]

More Microscopy

Sometimes you need to do a bit of <u>maths</u> with microscope images. It's time to get your <u>numbers head on</u>...

Magnification is How Many Times Bigger the Image is

1) You can work out the <u>total magnification</u> of an image under a microscope using this formula:

> **total magnification = eyepiece lens magnification × objective lens magnification**

> **EXAMPLE:**
> What's the total magnification of an image viewed with an eyepiece lens magnification of × 10 and an objective lens magnification of × 40?
>
> total magnification = 10 × 40 = × 400

2) You can also work out the magnification of an image if you <u>don't know</u> what <u>lenses</u> were used.

3) You need to be able to <u>measure the image</u>, and you also need to know the <u>actual size</u> of the specimen.

4) This is the <u>formula</u> you need:

> **magnification = $\dfrac{\text{measured size}}{\text{actual size}}$** — Both measurements should have the same units (see below).

> **EXAMPLE:**
> The width of a specimen is 0.02 mm. The width of its image under a microscope is 8 mm. What magnification was used to view the specimen?
>
> magnification = 8 mm ÷ 0.02 mm = × 400

5) If you're working out the <u>measured size</u> or the <u>actual size</u> of the object, use the <u>formula triangle</u> below.

6) <u>Cover</u> the thing you want to find. The parts you can <u>see</u> are the formula you need to use.

> **EXAMPLE:**
> The width of a specimen's image underneath a microscope is 3 mm. The magnification is × 100. What is the actual width of the specimen?
>
> Cover up 'actual size' on the formula triangle.
> This leaves the formula: measured size ÷ magnification
>
> So, the actual width = 3 mm ÷ 100 = 0.03 mm

What are you looking at?

Formula triangle: **measured size** over **magnification** × **actual size**

You Might Need to Convert Units

1) <u>Millimetres</u> (mm), <u>micrometres</u> (μm) and <u>nanometres</u> (nm) are <u>units</u> used when measuring very small objects, e.g. cells.

2) This diagram shows you how to <u>convert between these</u> units to write the <u>same value</u> using different units.

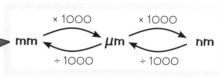

mm → μm → nm (× 1000 each way; ÷ 1000 back)

3) E.g. to write <u>0.007 mm</u> in μm, you <u>times it</u> by 1000 to get <u>7 μm</u>.

Mi-cros-copy — when my twin gets annoyed...

Make sure you memorise the formula triangle on this page — it's like learning three formulas all in one go.

Q1   Calculate the actual length of a cell with a measured size of 0.7 mm under a magnification of × 400. Write your answer in μm.   [3 marks]

Sexual Reproduction and Meiosis

Ever wondered how <u>sperm</u> and <u>egg cells</u> are made? Well today's your lucky day.

Sexual Reproduction Involves Gametes

1) <u>Gametes</u> are 'sex cells'. In <u>animals</u> they're <u>sperm</u> and <u>egg</u> cells.
2) During <u>sexual reproduction</u>, an egg and a sperm cell <u>combine</u>. This is called <u>fertilisation</u>.
3) This forms a <u>new cell</u> called a <u>zygote</u>.
4) <u>Gametes</u> only have <u>one copy</u> of each <u>chromosome</u>.
5) The chromosomes from both gametes <u>pair up</u> in the zygote.
   So zygotes have <u>two copies</u> of each <u>chromosome</u> (the <u>full set</u>).

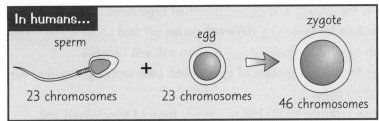

Gametes are Produced by Meiosis

1) Meiosis is a type of <u>cell division</u>.
2) It produces <u>four gametes</u> from each parent cell.

parent cell

① • Before meiosis can <u>begin</u>, the cell goes through <u>interphase</u>.
• The DNA in the parent cell is <u>copied</u>.
  It makes <u>X-shaped chromosomes</u>.
• <u>Half</u> of the chromosomes have come from the organism's <u>father</u> and half have come from the organism's <u>mother</u>.

② • The cell <u>divides</u>.
• Each new cell gets <u>half</u> of the chromosomes.

③ • Each cell divides <u>again</u>.
• The <u>X-shaped chromosomes</u> are <u>pulled apart</u>.
• You end up with <u>four</u> new <u>daughter cells</u>.
  These are the <u>gametes</u>.
• Each gamete:
   • has only <u>one copy</u> of each chromosome,
   • is <u>genetically different</u> (each has a <u>different mix</u> of chromosomes from the organism's mother and father).

gametes

Identical twins are genetically identical because they come from a single zygote that splits in two, then develops into two separate individuals.

Now that I have your undivided attention...

In humans, meiosis only occurs in the reproductive organs, when gametes are made.

Q1   Explain why gametes need to have half the number of chromosomes of a normal body cell.   [2 marks]

Chapter B4 — Using Food and Controlling Growth

Stem Cells

Your body is made up of all sorts of <u>weird and wonderful cells</u>. This page tells you where they all <u>came from</u>...

Stem Cells can Differentiate into Different Types of Cells

1) A <u>zygote</u> is formed from fertilisation (see previous page). It divides by <u>mitosis</u> to form an <u>embryo</u>.
2) The cells in an embryo are <u>all the same</u>. They're called <u>embryonic stem cells</u>.
3) The cells in an embryo are <u>unspecialised</u>.
4) After the embryo has divided into eight cells, most of the cells <u>differentiate</u> (change) to become <u>specialised cells</u>.
5) Embryonic stem cells can produce <u>any kind</u> of specialised cell at all.
6) This is important in the <u>growth</u> and <u>development</u> of organisms.
7) Stem cells differentiate by <u>switching</u> different genes <u>off</u> and <u>on</u>.
8) This decides which <u>type</u> of <u>specialised cell</u> a stem cell will become.
9) This allows <u>tissues</u> to form — groups of specialised cells working together for a <u>particular function</u>.
10) <u>Adults</u> also have <u>stem cells</u>.
11) Adult stem cells can produce <u>many</u> but <u>not every</u> type of specialised cell.
12) In animals, adult stem cells are used to <u>replace damaged cells</u>, e.g. to make new skin cells.

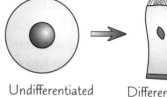

Undifferentiated stem cell

Differentiated ciliated epithelial cell (see p.11).

Meristems Contain Plant Stem Cells

1) <u>Plants</u> have tissues called <u>meristems</u>.
2) Meristems are found in the areas of a plant that are <u>growing</u>, e.g. the tips of the <u>roots and shoots</u>.
3) Only <u>meristems</u> have cells that divide by <u>mitosis</u>. They produce <u>stem cells</u> that can divide and form <u>any cell type</u> in the plant.

meristems

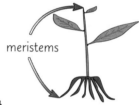

Stem Cells Can be Used in Medicine

1) Doctors already use <u>adult stem cells</u> to cure some <u>diseases</u>.
2) Scientists think that <u>embryonic</u> stem cells could be really useful in <u>medicine</u> too.
3) Stem cells can be <u>taken</u> from human embryos and made to <u>differentiate</u> into <u>specialised cells</u>.
4) Stem cells could be used to <u>grow</u> specialised cells to replace <u>damaged</u> tissue or cells in a patient. For example, it might be possible to grow new <u>heart muscle cells</u> to help someone with <u>heart disease</u>.
5) But there are <u>risks</u> with using stem cells that scientists need to learn more about. For example:

- <u>Tumours</u> — the stem cells may <u>divide uncontrollably</u> in the patient and form a <u>tumour</u> (growth).
- <u>Infection and disease</u> — the stem cells may contain a <u>virus</u> which could be <u>passed on</u> to the patient.

6) Research using <u>embryonic stem cells</u> also raises <u>ethical issues</u>.
7) For example, using embryonic stem cells means that an embryo is <u>destroyed</u>. Some people think that human embryos <u>shouldn't</u> be used as each is a <u>potential human life</u>.
8) Because of this, the use of human embryonic stem cells in <u>scientific research</u> and <u>medicine</u> is <u>regulated</u> by the <u>government</u> in most countries, including the UK.

A merry stem.

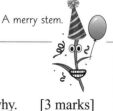

Cheery cells, those merry-stems...

Turns out stem cells are pretty nifty. Now, let's see if you're specialised to answer this question...

Q1   If the tip is cut off a plant shoot, the tip can be used to grow a whole new plant. Suggest why.   [3 marks]

Revision Questions for Chapter B4

Hurrah. It's the <u>end</u> of <u>Chapter B4</u>. Better get this one last page over with.

- Try these questions and <u>tick off each one</u> when you <u>get it right</u>.
- When you've done <u>all the questions</u> for a topic and are <u>completely happy</u> with it, tick off the topic.

<u>Respiration (p.50-51)</u> ☐

1) What is respiration? ☑
2) Is respiration an exothermic or an endothermic reaction? ☑
3) Name the type of respiration that requires oxygen. ☑
4) Briefly describe an experiment to investigate the effect of different substrates on the rate of respiration in yeast. ☑
5) Describe a situation when:
   a) a plant root would have to respire anaerobically.
   b) bacteria would have to respire anaerobically. ☑
6) Give an example of when lactic acid would be produced as a product of respiration. ☑
7) Which form of respiration has a greater ATP yield per glucose molecule? ☑

<u>The Cell Cycle, Mitosis and Microscopy (p.52-54)</u> ☑

8) What is the cell cycle? ☑
9) What are the two main parts of the cell cycle? ☑
10) What major illness can result from uncontrolled cell division? ☑
11) Give an advantage of electron microscopes over light microscopes. ☑
12) Why is it useful to squash a plant root tip if you want to view the cells dividing by mitosis under a light microscope? ☑
13) Write the formula you would use to find the actual size of a specimen using the magnification used and the size of the image seen through a microscope lens. ☑
14) Describe how you would convert a measurement from mm to μm. ☑

<u>Sexual Reproduction, Meiosis and Stem Cells (p.55-56)</u> ☑

15) Name the gametes in humans. ☑
16) Describe how gametes are formed by meiosis. ☑
17) What is a stem cell? ☑
18) How are embryonic stem cells different to adult stem cells? ☑
19) Which parts of a plant contain stem cells? ☑
20) What are the potential benefits of stem cells being used in medicine? ☑

Exchange of Materials

As you might remember from Chapter B3, all organisms need to <u>exchange</u> things with their <u>environment</u>...

Organisms Exchange Substances with their Environment

All organisms must <u>take in</u> the substances they need from the environment and <u>get rid</u> of <u>waste products</u>. For example:

1) Cells need <u>oxygen</u> for <u>aerobic respiration</u> (see p.50). <u>Carbon dioxide</u> is produced as a waste product. Oxygen and carbon dioxide move between <u>cells</u> and the <u>environment</u> by <u>diffusion</u> (see p.31).

2) <u>Water</u> is needed for many chemical reactions. Dissolved <u>food molecules</u> (e.g. glucose and amino acids) are needed for <u>synthesis reactions</u> (see p.45). Water and dissolved food molecules are <u>absorbed</u> into the blood from the <u>digestive system</u>.

3) <u>Urea</u> is a waste product. It diffuses from <u>cells</u> into the <u>blood</u>. It is then <u>filtered out</u> of the blood by the <u>kidneys</u> and <u>removed</u> from the body as <u>urine</u>.

> CO_2 and urea need to be removed before they reach toxic levels.

You Can Calculate an Organism's Surface Area to Volume Ratio

1) A <u>ratio</u> shows <u>how big</u> one value is <u>compared</u> to another.

2) So, a <u>surface area to volume ratio</u> shows how big a shape's <u>surface</u> is compared to its <u>volume</u>.

3) Here's one way of calculating an <u>organism's</u> surface area to volume ratio:

- A 2 cm × 4 cm × 4 cm <u>block</u> can be used to <u>estimate</u> the surface area to volume ratio of this <u>hippo</u>.
- The <u>area</u> of a square or rectangle is found by the equation: LENGTH × WIDTH.
  - The <u>top and bottom surfaces</u> of the block have a <u>length of 4 cm</u> and a <u>width of 4 cm</u>.
  - There are <u>four sides</u> to the block. They each have a <u>length of 4 cm</u> and a <u>height of 2 cm</u>.
  - So the hippo's <u>total surface area</u> is:
    (4 × 4) × 2 (top and bottom surfaces)
    + (4 × 2) × 4 (four sides)
    = <u>64 cm²</u>.

- The <u>volume</u> of a block is found by the equation: LENGTH × WIDTH × HEIGHT. So the hippo's <u>volume</u> is 4 × 4 × 2 = <u>32 cm³</u>.

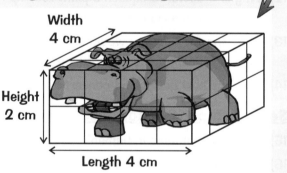

Width 4 cm

Height 2 cm

Length 4 cm

The surface area to volume ratio (<u>SA : V</u>) of the hippo can be written as <u>64 : 32</u>. To get the ratio so that volume is equal to <u>one</u>, <u>divide both sides</u> of the ratio by the <u>volume</u>. So the SA : V of the hippo is <u>2 : 1</u>.

4) The <u>larger</u> the organism, the <u>smaller</u> its surface area is compared to its volume.

> **Example:** SA : V of hippo = 2 : 1   SA : V of mouse = 6 : 1
> The <u>mouse</u> has a larger surface area compared to its volume.

> Simplifying ratios so that the volume is equal to one means that you can easily compare the surface area to volume ratios of different organisms.

5) The <u>smaller</u> its <u>surface area</u> compared to its <u>volume</u>, the <u>harder</u> it is for an organism to <u>exchange substances</u> with its environment.

Not that I'm suggesting putting animals in boxes...

Have a go at this question to make sure you understand how to calculate surface area to volume ratios.

Q1   A bacterial cell can be represented by a 1 μm × 1 μm × 2 μm block. Calculate the cell's surface area to volume ratio. Give your ratio in its simplest whole number form.   [3 marks]

Human Exchange Surfaces

The human body has <u>special surfaces</u> for <u>exchange</u> to make sure that we can take in <u>enough</u> substances.

Multicellular Organisms Need Exchange Surfaces

Single-celled organisms have a large surface area to volume ratio, so they can exchange everything they need across their surface.

1) <u>Multicellular organisms</u> have a <u>small</u> surface area to volume ratio.
2) They normally <u>can't</u> exchange <u>enough substances</u> across their <u>outside surface</u> alone.
3) So, multicellular organisms have <u>specialised exchange surfaces</u> — for example, the <u>alveoli</u>.
4) Humans have a <u>circulatory system</u> to <u>move substances</u> between exchange surfaces and the rest of the body (see pages 60-62).
5) The circulatory system <u>shortens the distance</u> that substances have to <u>diffuse</u> to and from cells.
6) All of the movement into, out of and around the <u>human body</u> depends on the <u>gaseous exchange</u>, <u>circulatory</u>, <u>digestive</u> and <u>excretory systems</u> all <u>working together</u>.

Oxygen and Carbon Dioxide Diffuse Between Alveoli and Capillaries

The lungs contain millions of little <u>air sacs</u> called <u>alveoli</u>. Here's how <u>gas exchange</u> happens in the alveoli:

1) The alveoli fill up with <u>air</u> from the <u>environment</u> when you <u>breathe in</u>.
2) This air has <u>lots of oxygen</u> but <u>very little carbon dioxide</u>.
3) The alveoli are surrounded by lots of <u>capillaries</u> (see page 61), which carry <u>blood</u>.
4) Blood arriving at the alveoli has <u>lots of carbon dioxide</u> (CO_2) and <u>not much oxygen</u> (O_2).
5) The <u>oxygen</u> diffuses from the <u>air into the blood</u>.
6) The <u>carbon dioxide</u> diffuses from the <u>blood into the air</u>.
7) The alveoli are specialised for the <u>diffusion</u> of O_2 and CO_2. They have:
   - A <u>large</u> surface area.
   - A <u>good blood supply</u>.
   - Very <u>thin walls</u> (made of cells with <u>partially permeable</u> cell membranes) so gases don't have <u>far</u> to <u>diffuse</u>.

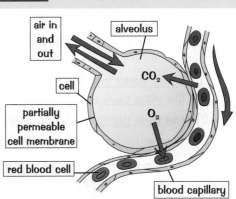

Dissolved Food and Water are Absorbed in the Digestive System

1) <u>Digested food</u> is absorbed in the <u>small intestine</u>.
2) The inside of the small intestine is covered in millions of <u>villi</u>.
3) These villi increase the <u>surface area</u> of the small intestine.
4) This means that food is <u>quickly absorbed</u> into the blood.
5) The digested food moves into the blood by <u>diffusion</u> and <u>active transport</u> (see page 31).
6) Villi have a <u>single</u> layer of surface cells and a <u>good blood supply</u>. This means that absorption of molecules is <u>quick</u>.
7) Their surface cells have <u>partially permeable cell membranes</u>. These <u>control the movement</u> of molecules.
8) <u>Water</u> is <u>absorbed</u> into the blood from the <u>large intestine</u> by <u>osmosis</u>.

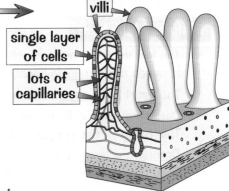

Al Veoli — the Italian gas man...

Here's a little fact that needs wedging firmly into your brain — a big surface area means a faster rate of diffusion.

Q1   Give one way in which alveoli are adapted for gas exchange.   [1 mark]

The Circulatory System

In humans, it's the job of the circulatory system to move substances around the body.

Blue = deoxygenated blood.
Red = oxygenated blood.

Humans Have a DOUBLE Circulatory System

This means that the heart pumps blood around the body in two circuits:

1) In the first circuit, the heart pumps deoxygenated blood (blood without oxygen) to the lungs. The blood picks up oxygen in the lungs.

2) Oxygenated blood (blood with oxygen) then returns to the heart.

3) In the second circuit, the heart pumps oxygenated blood around all the other organs of the body. This delivers oxygen to the body cells.

4) Deoxygenated blood then returns to the heart.

5) As it is pumped around the body, the blood travels through blood vessels near exchange surfaces. This includes the villi (where it picks up food and water — see previous page) and the kidneys (where it is filtered and urea is removed).

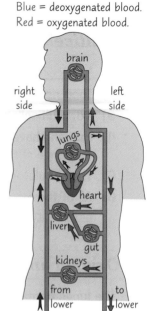

The Heart Pumps Blood Around The Body

1) The heart is an organ with four chambers. The walls of the chambers are made of cardiac muscle.

2) This muscle tissue is used to pump blood around the body. Here's how:

1) Blood flows into the two atria from the vena cava and the pulmonary vein.

2) The atria pump the blood into the ventricles.

3) The ventricles pump the blood out of the heart:

• Blood from the right ventricle goes through the pulmonary artery to the lungs.

• Blood from the left ventricle goes through the aorta to the rest of the body.

4) The blood then flows to the organs through arteries, and returns through veins (see next page).

5) The atria fill again — the whole cycle starts over.

Atrium is when there is just one. Atria is plural.

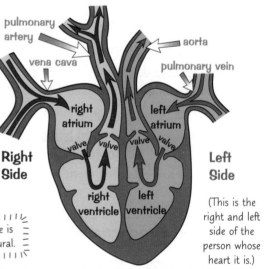

Right Side

Left Side

(This is the right and left side of the person whose heart it is.)

Features of the heart

• The left ventricle has a much thicker wall than the right ventricle. It needs more muscle because it has to pump blood around the whole body, not just to the lungs.

• The heart has valves. These prevent the backflow of blood in the heart.

• Cardiac muscle cells contain loads of mitochondria to provide them with ATP. This releases the energy needed for the muscle to pump blood.

• Coronary arteries supply the heart muscle itself with blood. They branch from the base of the aorta.

Okay — let's get to the heart of the matter...

Make sure you learn the names of the different parts of the heart and all the blood vessels that are attached to it.

Q1   Which chamber of the heart pumps deoxygenated blood to the lungs?   [1 mark]

Chapter B5 — The Human Body — Staying Alive

Blood Vessels

If you want to know more about the circulatory system you're in luck. Because here's a whole extra page.

Blood Vessels are Designed for Their Function

There are three main types of blood vessel:

1) ARTERIES — these carry the blood away from the heart.
2) CAPILLARIES — these are involved in the exchange of materials at the tissues.
3) VEINS — these carry the blood to the heart.

Arteries Carry Blood Under Pressure

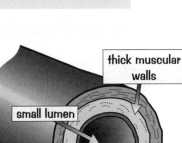

1) This is an artery.
2) The walls are thick. The hole in the middle (the lumen) is small.
3) Arteries carry blood away from the heart.
4) The heart pumps blood out at high pressure.
5) So artery walls are strong and elastic.
6) The walls have thick layers of muscle to make them strong. They also have elastic fibres to allow them to stretch.

thick muscular walls

small lumen

Capillaries are Really Small

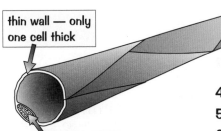

thin wall — only one cell thick

nucleus of cell

1) Arteries branch into capillaries.
2) Capillaries are really tiny — too small to see.
3) They fit into the gaps between cells and carry blood really close to every cell in the body.
4) They supply food and oxygen, and take away waste like CO_2.
5) They have permeable walls, so substances can diffuse in and out.
6) Their walls are usually only one cell thick, so substances can diffuse in and out quickly (because they only have a small distance to cross).

Veins Take Blood Back to the Heart

1) Capillaries join up to form veins.
2) The walls of veins are thinner than artery walls.
3) This is because veins carry blood at low pressure.
4) Veins have a bigger lumen than arteries.
5) This helps the blood to flow, even though the pressure is low.
6) Veins also have valves.
7) These help to stop the blood flowing backwards.

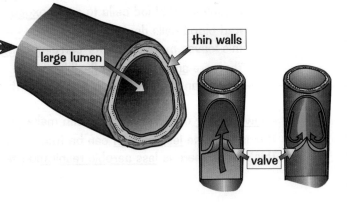

large lumen

thin walls

valve

Learn this page — don't struggle in vein...

Here's an interesting fact for you — your body contains about 60 000 miles of blood vessels.
That's about six times the distance from London to Sydney in Australia. It's hard to imagine all of that inside you.

Q1   Describe how veins are adapted to carry blood back to the heart.   [2 marks]

Q2   Explain how capillaries are adapted to their function.   [2 marks]

Blood

This page is all about the bits of the <u>blood</u> that <u>transport substances</u> around the body.

Blood Acts as a Transport System

There's more on platelets and white blood cells in Chapter B2 — see pages 11-12.

1) Blood is a <u>tissue</u>. It is made of many similar cells working together.

2) These cells are <u>red blood cells</u>, <u>white blood cells</u> and <u>platelets</u>. They are carried in a liquid called <u>plasma</u>.

Plasma is the Liquid Bit of Blood

1) <u>Plasma</u> is a pale yellow liquid.

2) It <u>carries just about everything</u> that needs transporting around your body:

- <u>Red blood cells</u> (see below), <u>white blood cells</u>, and <u>platelets</u>.
- <u>Water</u>.
- Digested <u>food products</u> like <u>glucose</u> and <u>amino acids</u> from the small intestine to all the body cells.
- <u>Carbon dioxide</u> from the body cells to the lungs.
- <u>Urea</u> from the liver to the kidneys (where it's removed in the urine).
- <u>Hormones</u> — these act like chemical messengers (see page 65).
- <u>Antibodies</u> — these are proteins involved in the body's immune response (see page 12).

Red Blood Cells Have the Job of Carrying Oxygen

1) Red blood cells carry <u>oxygen</u> from the <u>lungs</u> to <u>all</u> the cells in the body.

2) The <u>structure</u> of a red blood cell is adapted to its <u>function</u>:

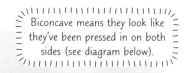

Biconcave means they look like they've been pressed in on both sides (see diagram below).

- Red blood cells have a <u>biconcave disc</u> shape.
  Their shape gives them a <u>large surface area</u> for <u>absorbing oxygen</u>.
- They contain a red substance called <u>haemoglobin</u>.
  It allows red blood cells to <u>carry oxygen</u>.
- Red blood cells <u>don't</u> have a <u>nucleus</u> —
  this leaves more space for carrying oxygen.
- They are <u>small</u> and very <u>flexible</u>.
  This means that they can easily pass through the <u>tiny capillaries</u>.

3) A <u>low number</u> of red blood cells can make you feel <u>tired</u>.

4) This is because <u>less oxygen</u> can be transported around the body.
   This means there is <u>less aerobic respiration</u> taking place to produce <u>ATP</u> (see page 50).

Blood's other function is to let you know you're bleeding...

Every single drop of blood contains millions of red blood cells — all of them perfectly designed for carrying plenty of oxygen to where it's needed. Right now, that's your brain, so you can get on with learning this page.

Q1   Name the red substance in red blood cells that allows them to carry oxygen.   [1 mark]

Q2   Explain three ways in which red blood cells are adapted to carry oxygen.   [3 marks]

The Nervous System

The <u>nervous system</u> lets you <u>react</u> to what goes on around you.

The Central Nervous System (CNS) Coordinates a Response

1) The nervous system is made up of <u>neurones</u> (nerve cells), which go to <u>all parts</u> of the body.

2) The body has lots of <u>sensory receptors</u>. These can detect a <u>change in your environment</u> (a <u>stimulus</u>). Different receptors detect <u>different stimuli</u>. For example, receptors in your <u>eyes</u> detect <u>light</u>.

3) When a <u>stimulus</u> is detected by <u>receptors</u>, the information is sent as <u>nervous (electrical) impulses</u>.

4) These impulses are sent along <u>sensory neurones</u> to the <u>CNS</u> (the <u>brain</u> and <u>spinal cord</u>).

5) The CNS <u>coordinates</u> the response (it <u>decides what to do</u> about the stimulus and tells something to do it).

6) The CNS sends impulses along a <u>motor neurone</u> to an <u>effector</u> (<u>muscle</u> or <u>gland</u>).

7) The effector then <u>responds</u> — e.g. a <u>muscle</u> may <u>contract</u> or a <u>gland</u> may <u>secrete a hormone</u>.

8) Nervous communication is very <u>fast</u>, but the responses <u>don't last long</u>.

You might also see "neurone" spelt as "neuron". Don't panic — they mean the same thing.

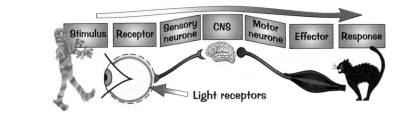

Stimulus → Receptor → Sensory neurone → CNS → Motor neurone → Effector → Response

Light receptors

Neurones Transmit Information Rapidly as Electrical Impulses

1) <u>Electrical impulses</u> are passed along the <u>axon</u> of a neurone.

2) Neurones have <u>branched endings</u> (<u>dendrites</u>) so they can <u>connect</u> with lots of other neurones.

3) Some axons are also surrounded by a <u>fatty (myelin) sheath</u>. This <u>speeds up</u> the electrical impulse.

4) Neurones are <u>long</u>. This <u>speeds up</u> the impulse because it reduces the number of <u>gaps</u> (see below).

Transmission of the impulse is slower at the gaps between neurones.

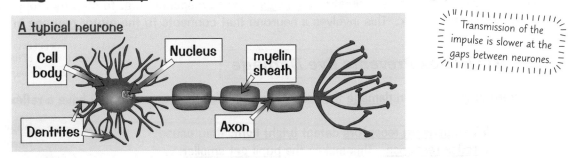

A typical neurone — Cell body, Nucleus, myelin sheath, Dentrites, Axon

5) A <u>synapse</u> is where <u>two neurones</u> join together. It is a very tiny <u>gap</u>.

• When an impulse reaches a synapse, <u>transmitter chemicals</u> are released. They <u>diffuse</u> across the gap.

• These chemicals bind to <u>receptors</u> in the membrane of the <u>next neurone</u>. This sets off a <u>new electrical impulse</u>.

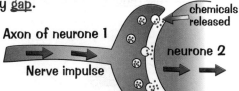

Axon of neurone 1 — Nerve impulse — chemicals released — neurone 2

Don't let the thought of exams play on your nerves...

Make sure you understand how the different parts of the nervous system (including receptors and effectors) work together to coordinate a response. There's more of the same coming up on the next page...

Q1 Name the two main parts of the central nervous system (CNS). [2 marks]

Reflexes

Information is passed between neurones really <u>quickly</u>, especially when there's a <u>reflex</u> involved.

Reflex Actions Stop You Injuring Yourself

1) <u>Reflexes</u> are <u>involuntary</u> (they happen without you <u>thinking</u>).
   This makes them <u>quicker</u> than normal responses.

2) Reflexes help to stop you <u>injuring yourself</u>, e.g. you <u>quickly</u> move your hand if you touch something <u>hot</u>.

3) The passage of information in a reflex (from receptor to effector) is called a <u>reflex arc</u>.

4) The neurones in reflex arcs go through the <u>spinal cord</u> or through an <u>unconscious part of the brain</u>
   (part of the brain not involved in thinking).

5) Here's an example of how a reflex arc would work if you were <u>stung by a bee</u>:

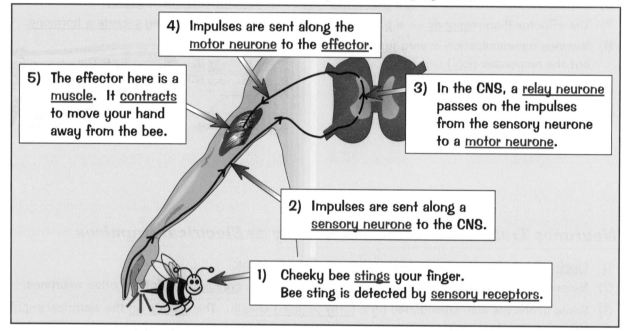

4) Impulses are sent along the <u>motor neurone</u> to the <u>effector</u>.

5) The effector here is a <u>muscle</u>. It <u>contracts</u> to move your hand away from the bee.

3) In the CNS, a <u>relay neurone</u> passes on the impulses from the sensory neurone to a <u>motor neurone</u>.

2) Impulses are sent along a <u>sensory neurone</u> to the CNS.

1) Cheeky bee <u>stings</u> your finger. Bee sting is detected by <u>sensory receptors</u>.

6) The conscious brain can sometimes <u>change</u> a reflex response, e.g. to stop us dropping a hot plate we
   don't want to break. This involves a neurone that connects to the <u>motor neurone</u> in the reflex arc.

The Iris Reflex Prevents Eye Damage

> The iris is the part of the eye with the muscles that cause the pupil to change size.

1) <u>Very bright</u> light can <u>damage</u> the cells at the back of the eye — so you have a reflex to protect them:

- When <u>sensory receptors</u> detect <u>bright light</u>, they cause a <u>reflex response</u>. This makes the <u>pupil get smaller</u>.
- This <u>reduces</u> the amount of light that enters the eye.

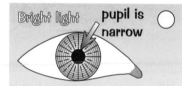

Bright light — pupil is narrow

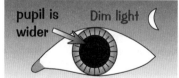

pupil is wider — Dim light

The opposite happens in dim light.
This time, the <u>reflex</u> causes the pupils to get <u>wider</u>.

2) You can <u>investigate</u> these reflex actions by <u>dimming the lights</u> and
   timing how long it takes for your pupils (or a friend's) to <u>widen</u>.

The iris reflex — watch out, flowers are getting their own back...

Reflexes allow organisms to respond rapidly to a stimulus — they're important for survival.

Q1   A chef touches a hot tray. A reflex causes him to immediately move his hand away.
     Describe the pathway of the reflex from stimulus to effector.

[4 marks]

Hormones in Reproduction

You need to know about sex hormones and how each one helps to control the menstrual cycle.

Hormones are Chemical Messengers Sent in the Blood

1) Hormones are chemicals produced in glands called endocrine glands. These glands make up your endocrine system. The endocrine system allows you to respond to internal and external stimuli.

2) Hormones are released into the blood. The blood then carries them to other parts of the body.

3) Hormones only produce a response from certain effectors. These effectors have receptors that the hormones bind to. When hormones bind to receptors, they cause a response.

Hormones are slow compared to nervous impulses but they have longer-lasting effects.

Hormones are Needed for Sexual Reproduction

1) Human sexual reproduction would be impossible without hormones.

2) Hormones regulate the female menstrual cycle.

3) The cycle has four stages:

Stage 1 Day 1 is when menstruation (bleeding) starts. The lining of the uterus breaks down.

Stage 2 The uterus lining builds up again, from day 4 to day 14. It builds into a thick spongy layer full of blood vessels. It's now ready to receive a fertilised egg.

Stage 3 An egg develops and is released from the ovary at day 14. This is called ovulation.

Stage 4 The lining is then maintained for about 14 days, until day 28. If no fertilised egg has landed on the uterus wall by day 28, the spongy lining starts to break down. The whole cycle starts over.

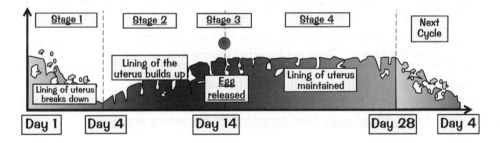

The Menstrual Cycle is Controlled by Four Hormones

These four hormones control each stage of the menstrual cycle:

1) FSH (follicle-stimulating hormone) — Causes an egg to mature in one of the ovaries.

2) Oestrogen — Causes the lining of the uterus to thicken and grow.

3) LH (luteinising hormone) — Causes the release of an egg (ovulation).

4) Progesterone — Maintains the lining of the uterus for a fertilised egg to be implanted.

What do you call a fish with no eye — FSH...

Try scribbling down everything here on some paper. Keep doing it until you can get it all without peeking.

Q1   Name the hormone that causes an egg to mature in one of the ovaries.   [1 mark]

Contraception

Pregnancy can happen if sperm reaches an egg. Contraception tries to stop this happening.

Contraceptives are Things That Prevent Pregnancy

Hormones can be Used to Prevent Pregnancy

1) The hormones that control the menstrual cycle (previous page) can be used in contraceptives. E.g:

   - If oestrogen levels are kept high for a long time, egg development stops.
   - So oestrogen can be used to stop an egg being released.

   - Progesterone makes the mucus in the cervix very thick.
   - This stops sperm swimming through the cervix and reaching the egg.

   The cervix is the opening to the uterus.

2) Some hormonal contraceptives contain both oestrogen and progesterone — e.g. the combined pill and the contraceptive patch (which is worn on the skin).

3) The mini-pill and the contraceptive injection only contain progesterone.

   The combined pill and the mini-pill are both oral contraceptives — that means that they're taken through the mouth.

Non-Hormonal Methods Can Also Prevent Pregnancy

1) Barrier methods are non-hormonal contraceptives (they don't involve hormones). They put a barrier between the sperm and egg so they don't meet. For example:

   - Condoms — male condoms are worn over the penis during sexual intercourse. Female condoms are worn inside the vagina.
   - Diaphragms — these are flexible, dome-shaped devices that cover the cervix. They are inserted before sex.

   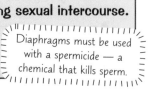

   Diaphragms must be used with a spermicide — a chemical that kills sperm.

   I've got this barrier thing sorted...

2) An intrauterine device (IUD) is another non-hormonal method. It is a T-shaped device that contains copper. It is inserted into the uterus to kill sperm. It can also stop fertilised eggs from attaching to the uterus lining.

Hormonal and Non-Hormonal Contraceptive Methods Have Pros and Cons

1) When they're used correctly, hormonal methods are usually better at preventing pregnancy than non-hormonal methods.

2) Also, when using hormonal methods, a couple don't have to think about contraception each time they have sex (as they would if they relied on barrier methods).

3) However, hormonal methods can have unpleasant side-effects, like headaches, acne and mood changes.

4) They have to be used correctly — e.g. if a woman doesn't take her pills regularly they won't work.

5) Hormonal methods don't protect against sexually transmitted infections (STIs) — condoms are the only form of contraception that do this.

The winner of best contraceptive ever — just not doing it...

By now you should be pretty clued up on the different methods of contraception. But whether hormonal or non-hormonal, no method is guaranteed to be 100% effective and each method has its own pros and cons.

Q1   Give one reason why a woman may prefer to use a diaphragm rather than an oral contraceptive.   [1 mark]

Homeostasis and Blood Sugar Level

Homeostasis means keeping the right conditions inside your body, so that everything works properly. Ace.

Homeostasis is Maintaining a Constant Internal Environment

1) Conditions in your internal environment (inside your body) need to be kept steady.

2) This is because your cells need the right conditions to work properly.

3) For example, they need the right conditions for enzyme activity (p.26) and processes in the body.

4) To keep conditions steady, your body needs to respond to changes that happen outside it (external changes) and changes that happen inside it (internal changes).

5) It does this using receptors, nerves, hormones and effectors (muscles and glands).

6) One condition that's kept steady is the level of glucose (sugar) in the blood.

7) Blood sugar level is controlled by the hormone insulin:

- If the blood glucose level gets too high, the pancreas releases insulin.
- Insulin causes glucose to move into cells (so it removes glucose from the blood).
- Glucose is converted to glycogen in liver and muscle cells.
- Glucose can be stored as glycogen.

> There is a narrow range of conditions in which your cells and enzymes will work best.

Blood glucose reduced

Insulin makes liver turn glucose into glycogen

Blood with too much glucose

Glucose moves from blood into liver and muscle cells

Insulin

Insulin released by pancreas

Having Diabetes Means You Can't Control Your Blood Sugar Level

There are two types of diabetes:

TYPE 1

1) Type 1 diabetes is where the pancreas stops making insulin.

2) This means that a person's blood glucose level can rise to a level that can kill them.

3) People with type 1 diabetes need insulin therapy. This usually involves injecting insulin into the blood several times a day (often at mealtimes).

4) This makes sure that glucose is removed from the blood quickly after food is digested.

TYPE 2

1) Type 2 diabetes is where a person's cells don't respond properly to insulin or their pancreas doesn't produce enough insulin.

2) Type 2 diabetes can be controlled by eating a healthy diet (one that contains complex carbohydrates, e.g. wholegrains).

3) Type 2 diabetes can also be controlled by taking regular exercise and by losing weight if needed.

4) Some people with type 2 diabetes also have insulin injections.

My sister never goes out — she's got homeostasis...

Make sure you learn that homeostasis is keeping a constant internal environment and that you know why it matters.

Q1   Describe how the body responds when the blood glucose level gets too high.   [3 marks]

Natural Selection and Evolution

Evolution is the <u>slow and continuous change</u> of organisms from one generation to the next.
<u>Natural selection</u> is used to explain how <u>evolution</u> happens.

Natural Selection Increases the Most Useful Characteristics

1) Populations of species usually show a lot of <u>genetic variation</u>.
This means that there's a big <u>mix</u> of genetic <u>variants</u> (alleles) in the population.

2) Genetic variants are caused by <u>mutations</u> (changes) in DNA (see page 3).
<u>Most</u> genetic variants have <u>no effect</u> on an organism's characteristics. <u>Some</u> genetic variants
have a <u>small effect</u>. A <u>very small number</u> have a <u>big effect</u> on an organism's characteristics.

3) Some genetic <u>variants</u> give individuals characteristics that make them <u>better suited</u> to
a particular environment (e.g. long legs so they can run away from predators faster).

4) These organisms have an <u>advantage</u>. They may be better able to <u>compete</u> for <u>resources</u>,
such as food and shelter. Or they may be better at coping with <u>environmental conditions</u>.

5) Individuals with these useful characteristics are <u>more likely to</u>
<u>survive</u> and <u>reproduce</u> than other individuals in the population.

6) This means that the genetic variants for the useful characteristics
are more likely to be <u>passed on</u> to the <u>next generation</u>.

Remember, the characteristics an organism has can also be called its 'phenotype'.

7) The <u>useful characteristics</u> become more <u>common</u> in the population over time.

8) Here's an example of <u>natural selection</u> in a population:

---

1) Once upon a time maybe all rabbits had <u>small ears</u>.

2) Then one day a <u>mutation</u> meant that one rabbit was born with <u>big ears</u>.

3) This rabbit could <u>hear better</u> — it was always the first to <u>hide</u> at the sound of a predator.

4) The big-eared rabbit <u>survived</u> and pretty soon it had lots of <u>baby rabbits</u> with <u>big ears</u>.

5) The <u>big-eared rabbits</u> were <u>more likely to survive</u> than small-eared rabbits.

6) The <u>big-eared rabbits</u> continued to <u>have babies</u>
with big ears and <u>small-eared rabbits</u> became
<u>less and less common</u>. FOX!

7) Eventually, the <u>whole population</u> had <u>big ears</u>.

Evolution is a Change in Inherited Characteristics

1) Natural selection leads to the <u>evolution</u> of species (<u>speciation</u>).

2) <u>Evolution</u> is the change in <u>inherited characteristics</u> of a population over
<u>several generations</u>, through the process of <u>natural selection</u>.

3) This means that as species evolve, the <u>characteristics</u> in the population <u>gradually change</u>.

4) Evolution can mean that a species' <u>phenotype</u> changes so much that a completely <u>new species</u> is formed.
The <u>new</u> species will be <u>unable</u> to reproduce with the <u>original</u> species to give <u>offspring that can reproduce</u>.

5) If <u>two populations</u> of an organism are <u>isolated</u> (<u>separated</u> from each other),
they are more likely to develop into <u>two different species</u>.

6) This is because <u>natural selection</u> will act on both populations <u>slightly differently</u>.

'Natural selection' — sounds like vegan chocolates...

Natural selection is a really important process in biology — make sure you've got your head around
what happens and how it leads to evolution. There's more about evolution coming up on the next page.

Q1   Musk oxen have thick fur, which helps them to survive in the cold climate in which they live.
Explain how the musk oxen may have developed this characteristic over many years.   [4 marks]

Evidence for Evolution

If you're sitting there thinking evolution is a load of <u>old nonsense</u>, here's a bit of <u>evidence</u> to help sway you...

There is Lots of Evidence for Evolution

1) The theory of evolution by natural selection was developed by <u>Charles Darwin</u>. It explained observations made by himself, <u>Alfred Russel Wallace</u> and other scientists — e.g. they had:
   * <u>compared fossils</u> with <u>living organisms</u>.
   * <u>looked at differences</u> between populations of a species living in <u>different environments</u>.

2) Evidence for the theory is <u>still being collected</u>. This makes support for the theory <u>even stronger</u>. It is now <u>widely accepted</u> by the scientific community.

3) <u>Fossils</u> and <u>antibiotic-resistant bacteria</u> both provide <u>evidence</u> for the theory:

Fossils Can Show How Organisms Changed Over Time

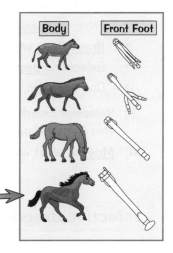

Body   Front Foot

1) A fossil is <u>any trace</u> of an animal or plant that lived <u>long</u> ago. They are most commonly found in <u>rocks</u>.

2) They can tell us a lot about what the organisms <u>looked like</u> and <u>how long ago</u> they lived.

3) By arranging fossils in date order, <u>gradual changes</u> in organisms can be seen.

4) This provides <u>evidence</u> for <u>evolution</u>. It shows how species have <u>changed</u> and <u>developed</u> over many years. For example, if you look at the <u>fossilised bones</u> of a <u>horse</u>, you can put together a family tree to suggest how the modern horse might have <u>evolved</u>.

Antibiotic-Resistant Bacteria Also Provide Evidence for Evolution

<u>Antibiotics</u> are drugs that kill <u>bacteria</u>. Bacteria can become <u>resistant</u> to antibiotics — this means that they're <u>not killed</u> by them. They become resistant by <u>natural selection</u>:

1) <u>Most</u> bacteria in a population <u>won't be resistant</u> to an antibiotic. However, <u>some</u> bacteria will have <u>genetic variants</u> which make them <u>resistant</u> to an antibiotic.

2) A person who is being <u>treated with antibiotics</u> might have <u>resistant bacteria</u> inside them.

3) The resistant bacteria are more likely to <u>survive</u> and <u>reproduce</u> than the non-resistant bacteria.

4) This leads to the genetic variants for antibiotic resistance being <u>passed on</u> to lots of <u>offspring</u>.

5) So, antibiotic resistance <u>spreads</u> and becomes <u>more common</u> in a population of bacteria <u>over time</u>.

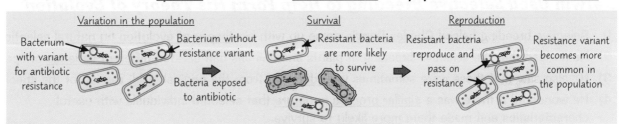

Variation in the population — Bacterium with variant for antibiotic resistance — Bacterium without resistance variant — Bacteria exposed to antibiotic — Survival — Resistant bacteria are more likely to survive — Reproduction — Resistant bacteria reproduce and pass on resistance — Resistance variant becomes more common in the population

6) Antibiotic-resistant bacteria provide <u>evidence for evolution</u>. There is a <u>change</u> in the <u>inherited characteristics</u> of a population <u>over time</u>. It happens by <u>natural selection</u>.

Fossils — they rock...

Life on Earth is still evolving — the evidence is right under our feet and under our microscopes.

Q1   Describe how fossils provide evidence for evolution.   [2 marks]

Selective Breeding

'Selective breeding' sounds like it could be a tricky topic, but it's actually dead simple.

Selective Breeding is Mating the Best Organisms to Get Good Offspring

1) Selective breeding is when humans choose which plants or animals are going to breed.
2) Organisms are selectively bred to develop features that are useful or attractive.
   For example:

   - Animals that produce more meat or milk.
   - Crops with disease resistance.
   - Plants that produce bigger fruit.

This is the basic process involved in selective breeding:
- From your existing stock, select the ones which have the feature you're after.
- Breed them with each other.
- Select the best of the offspring, and breed them together.
- Continue this process over several generations. Eventually, all offspring will have the feature you want.

3) Selective breeding means that food production is as high as possible.
   This is important because the human population is growing.
4) Most of what we eat nowadays comes from organisms which have been selectively bred.

Selective Breeding Has Disadvantages

There's more on alleles on page 3.

1) The main problem with selective breeding is that it reduces the number of different alleles in a population.
2) This is because the "best" animals or plants are always used for breeding, and they are all closely related.
3) This means there's more chance of selectively bred organisms having health problems caused by their genes.
4) There can also be serious problems if a new disease appears.
5) This is because it's less likely that organisms in the population will have resistance alleles for the disease.
6) So, if one individual is affected by the disease, the rest are also likely to be affected.

Darwin Used Selective Breeding to Help Form His Theory of Evolution

1) Selective breeding helped Charles Darwin come up with his theory of evolution by natural selection.
2) He noticed that the selective breeding of plants and animals had created different varieties of species.
3) He also saw that these were sometimes very different from the original 'wild' version of the species.
4) He wondered if there was a similar process in nature that selected individuals with useful characteristics and made them more likely to survive.
5) He thought that this could be the reason for the evolution of new species on Earth.

I use the same genes all the time too — they flatter my hips...

The basic process of selective breeding has stayed the same over many years — select the best individuals, let them reproduce, repeat over many generations, and there you go...

Q1 A farmer who grows green beans lives in an area that experiences a lot of drought. Explain how he could use selective breeding to improve the chances of his bean plants surviving the droughts. [3 marks]

Classification

People seem to really like putting things into groups — <u>biologists</u> certainly do anyway...

Classification is Organising Living Organisms into Groups

1) In the past, organisms were <u>classified</u> according to <u>characteristics</u> you can see (like number of legs).

2) As <u>technology got better</u>, this included things you can see with a <u>microscope</u>, e.g. <u>cell structure</u>.

3) These characteristics were used to classify organisms in the <u>five kingdom classification system</u>. In this system, living things are first divided into <u>five groups</u> called <u>kingdoms</u> (e.g. the plant kingdom, the animal kingdom).

4) The <u>kingdoms</u> are then split into smaller and smaller groups. These groups are <u>phylum</u>, <u>class</u>, <u>order</u>, <u>family</u>, <u>genus</u>, <u>species</u>.

Classification Systems Change Over Time

1) Because of developments in <u>technology</u>, our understanding of things like <u>genetics</u> has improved.

2) <u>New discoveries</u> have been made and the <u>relationships</u> between organisms have got <u>clearer</u>.

3) For example, two organisms may <u>look very similar</u>, but actually have very different <u>DNA sequences</u>. Scientists can use <u>DNA analysis</u> to find out the differences between organisms.

- Scientists can use DNA sequencing to compare <u>particular genes</u> or <u>entire genomes</u> of <u>different organisms</u>.

An organism's genome is all of its genetic material.

- The <u>more similar</u> the <u>DNA sequences</u> between species, or the more <u>genetic variants</u> they share, the <u>more closely related</u> they are.

- This means that they are <u>more likely</u> to be classified in the same group. E.g. the base sequence for human and chimpanzee DNA is about 94% the same, so humans and chimpanzees are <u>closely related</u> to each other.

4) Scientists can <u>also</u> use DNA sequences to estimate how <u>long ago</u> two species separated from each other.

Evolutionary Trees Show How Species are Related to Each Other

1) Scientists can <u>join</u> species together in <u>evolutionary trees</u>.

2) In an evolutionary tree, species are <u>connected to each other</u> by lines.

3) The lines between two species link them to their <u>most recent common ancestor</u>. This helps to show their <u>relationship</u> to each other.

The most recent common ancestor of two species is the most recent ancestor that they <u>both share</u>.

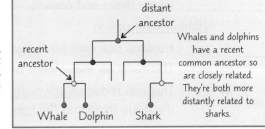

Whales and dolphins have a recent common ancestor so are closely related. They're both more distantly related to sharks.

4) The more <u>closely related</u> two species are to each other, the <u>fewer</u> the <u>number of steps</u> between them on the tree.

My brother's been reclassified — he's back with the apes...

As new techniques enable us to study organisms at the level of their genes, our classification systems get better.

Q1   Suggest one problem with classifying organisms based only on their visible characteristics.   [1 mark]

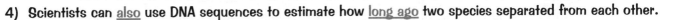

Chapter B6 — Life on Earth — Past, Present and Future

Biodiversity

Time for something less joyous. We <u>humans</u> can cause a lot of damage to ecosystems...

Biodiversity is all About the Variety of Life in an Area

<u>Biodiversity</u> is a combination of <u>three different things</u>. These are:

- the diversity (variety) of <u>living organisms</u> in a particular area.
- the diversity of different <u>genes</u> and <u>alleles</u> these organisms have.
- the diversity of different <u>ecosystems</u> in a particular area.

A <u>high level</u> of biodiversity means that if the environment <u>changes</u>, there's a good chance that at least <u>some species and ecosystems</u> will be able to <u>survive</u>.

Human Actions Can Reduce Biodiversity

1) The effect that humans have on ecosystems has <u>changed a lot</u> in the last 200 years. This is mostly because of:

- An <u>increasing human population</u> — the <u>population</u> of the world is <u>increasing</u> very quickly. A <u>larger population</u> means that humans use <u>more land</u> and <u>more resources</u> in order to survive.
- <u>Industrialisation</u> — there is more <u>industry</u> on Earth now than 200 years ago. This means that we are using <u>more resources</u> (e.g. oil, wood) and <u>more energy</u> to make things. We are also making <u>more waste</u>, which can lead to <u>pollution</u>.
- <u>Globalisation</u> — different countries have become more <u>connected</u> with each other. This is because of <u>better communication</u>, e.g. the internet. This means that what one country does can affect biodiversity in <u>another country</u>.

An industry is something that makes things that can be sold.

2) These changes can <u>damage</u> or <u>destroy</u> ecosystems. They can also <u>reduce</u> biodiversity:

<u>Sharing resources</u>
- <u>Globalisation</u> (see above) means that resources can be <u>shared</u> between countries.
- This can lead to a loss of <u>biodiversity</u>. For example, large companies can sell the <u>same types</u> of seeds to farmers in <u>many different countries</u>. This reduces the <u>number</u> of different seeds used for crops around the world. This reduces the world's <u>biodiversity</u>.

<u>Waste</u>
- Humans are producing more waste which can <u>damage ecosystems</u>.
- For example, <u>sewage</u> and <u>toxic chemicals</u> from <u>industry</u> and <u>farming</u> can pollute lakes, rivers and oceans. This affects the plants and animals that <u>live in the water</u>.

<u>Habitat destruction</u>
- Humans use land for things like <u>building</u>, <u>farming</u> and <u>quarrying</u>.
- This reduces the amount of <u>land</u> and <u>resources</u> available to <u>other</u> animals and plants.
- This can reduce <u>biodiversity</u> in an area. For example, clearing <u>woodland</u> for farmland destroys trees and the <u>habitats</u> of other organisms — this can <u>reduce biodiversity</u>.

3) Populations can often <u>adapt</u> to changes in the environment through <u>evolution</u> by <u>natural selection</u>.

4) However, many <u>human impacts</u> on ecosystems happen so <u>fast</u> that there is not <u>enough time</u> for organisms to adapt.

5) This could lead to the <u>loss of populations</u> of species or even the complete <u>extinction</u> of species.

I'm sorry but I'd prefer it if biodiversity was low inside my house...

Industrialisation and globalisation may be useful for us, but unfortunately it tends to be bad news for biodiversity.

Q1   Explain one way in which chemicals used in farming may lead to a loss in biodiversity.   [2 marks]

More on Biodiversity

As well as harming biodiversity, humans can also do things to protect it. This page gives you a few examples...

Humans Can Use Resources Sustainably

1) Using resources sustainably means that we don't use resources faster than they can be replaced.

2) We need to use resources sustainably so that people in the future will have enough resources to survive and so that the environment is not harmed.

> For example, sustainable harvesting of timber (wood) may involve replanting trees after harvesting. The new trees replace the ones that are cut down.

3) Sustainability means humans will have less of a negative impact on ecosystems and biodiversity.

Conservation Schemes Can Protect Biodiversity

Conservation schemes can help to protect biodiversity by conserving (protecting) species or their habitats. This can be done on different levels. For example:

Protecting certain species

1) Certain species can be protected in their natural habitat, e.g. by banning the hunting of some species.
2) Species can also be kept in safe areas, away from hunting or habitat destruction.
3) For animals, safe areas include zoos. For plants, they include botanical gardens and seed banks.
4) Animals can be bred in zoos to increase the number of individuals of a species. They can then be released back into the wild.

Protecting habitats and ecosystems

1) Certain areas can be protected, e.g. by banning farming or the building of houses.
2) This can help to protect habitats and ecosystems.
3) Protected areas include national parks and nature reserves.

Preventing damage on a global scale

1) Some human activities, such as burning fossil fuels, increase the amount of greenhouse gases in the air.
2) Greenhouse gases are causing global warming (the warming up of the planet).
3) Global warming is a type of climate change. It can cause other types of climate change, such as changing rainfall patterns.
4) Climate change could reduce biodiversity on Earth. For example, some species might not survive a change in the climate, and become extinct.
5) Controlling human activities that lead to climate change could help to protect global biodiversity.

My room is a protected area from the species Brother horribilis...

So, there you go — it's not all doom and gloom. There are lots of things that we can do to help biodiversity — we just have to hurry up if we want as many species as possible to survive in the future.

Q1 The Siberian tiger is an endangered species.
Explain how zoos could help to increase the number of Siberian tigers in the wild. [1 mark]

Maintaining Biodiversity

Trying to preserve biodiversity can be tricky but there are benefits for doing it...

Maintaining Biodiversity Benefits Wildlife and Humans

Humans depend on other organisms for their survival (e.g. for food).
This means that maintaining biodiversity often helps humans. For example:

All organisms depend on other organisms.

1) Protecting the human food supply — over-fishing has greatly reduced fish numbers in oceans. Schemes to control fishing aim to make sure that people will have fish to eat in the future.

2) Preventing damage to food chains — if one species becomes extinct, the organisms that feed on that species will also be affected. So, conserving one species may help others survive.

3) Providing future medicines — many of the medicines we use today come from plants. Undiscovered plant species may contain new chemicals that we can use in medicines. If these plants become extinct, we could miss out on new medicines.

4) Providing materials and fuels — plant and animal species are needed to make materials (e.g. wood, paper and oils) and some fuels. If these species become extinct these things may become more difficult to produce.

Maintaining Biodiversity can be Challenging

Maintaining biodiversity can be difficult to do.
Many things have to be considered before deciding to go ahead with conservation schemes.

Economic issues

1) Conservation schemes can be expensive.
2) The benefits of maintaining biodiversity have to be balanced against the cost.

Economic issues are to do with money.

Moral issues

1) The conservation of some species may have no benefit to humans. However, many people think it is wrong to let a species go extinct.
2) Protecting one species may mean killing individuals of another species. Some people think this is wrong.

Ecological issues

1) Conserving one species or habitat could have a negative effect on other parts of the ecosystem.
2) So the future effects of conservation schemes have to be considered before they are set up.

Political issues

1) Some conservation schemes need several different countries to work together. This can be difficult if some countries aren't willing to sign up to an agreement.
2) Local communities might also be against conservation schemes. E.g. people might not support a local scheme that reduces the money they make (e.g. fishing restrictions in a fishing village).

Locking your fridge also protects the human food supply...

Hmmm, I guess maintaining biodiversity can be a bit tricky. But if it keeps food on the table I'm keen...

Q1   Explain why maintaining biodiversity could be important for providing medicines in the future.   [2 marks]

Revision Questions for Chapters B5 & B6

Good work — now you should know a right old mix of stuff, from the circulatory system to the environment.
- Try these questions and tick off each one when you get it right.
- When you've done all the questions for a topic and are completely happy with it, tick off the topic.

Exchange of Materials and The Circulatory System (p.58-62) ☑

1) Name three substances that humans have to exchange with their environment. ☑
2) Give an example of a specialised exchange surface found in a human. ☑
3) Name the blood vessel that transports blood from the heart to the rest of the body. ☑
4) Which type of blood vessel carries blood at high pressure? ☑
5) Name four substances that are found in blood plasma. ☑

The Nervous System and Reflexes (p.63-64) ☑

6) State the purpose of: a) a sensory neurone, b) a motor neurone. ☑
7) Draw a diagram of a typical neurone and label all the parts. ☑
8) What is the purpose of a reflex action? ☑

Hormones in Reproduction and Contraception (p.65-66) ☑

9) What is a hormone? ☑
10) What does LH do in the menstrual cycle? ☑
11) Why can oestrogen be used as a form of contraception? ☑

Homeostasis and Blood Sugar Level (p.67) ☐

12) What is homeostasis? ☑
13) Where is glycogen stored in the body? ☑
14) Describe how type 2 diabetes can be treated. ☑

Natural Selection, Evolution and Selective Breeding (p.68-70) ☑

15) Describe how organisms evolve by the process of natural selection. ☑
16) Define 'evolution'. ☑
17) Give an example of evidence which shows that species evolve over time. ☑
18) What is selective breeding? ☑
19) Give one disadvantage of selective breeding. ☑

Classification (p.71) ☑

20) Before DNA analysis was developed, what was used to classify organisms into groups? ☑
21) Explain how DNA analysis helps scientists to classify organisms. ☑

Biodiversity (p.72-74) ☑

22) What is meant by biodiversity? ☑
23) What is meant by globalisation? ☑
24) Explain one way in which industrialisation can reduce biodiversity. ☑
25) What does using resources sustainably mean? Give an example. ☑
26) Describe one way in which humans can protect a certain species. ☑
27) Give one reason why climate change could reduce biodiversity. ☑
28) Give one advantage to humans of maintaining biodiversity. ☑
29) Describe one moral issue that might be considered before deciding to set up a conservation scheme. ☑

States of Matter

Substances are made up of <u>particles</u>, which could be atoms, ions or molecules. It's helpful to imagine the particles as little <u>golf balls</u> — sounds strange, but it's useful for explaining lots of stuff in chemistry.

The Three States of Matter — Solid, Liquid and Gas

1) Materials come in <u>three</u> different forms — <u>solid</u>, <u>liquid</u> and <u>gas</u>. These are the <u>three states of matter</u>.
2) Particles are <u>held together</u> by <u>forces</u> of <u>attraction</u>.
3) The <u>state</u> of a material at a <u>certain temperature</u> depends on how <u>strongly</u> the particles are held together.
4) You can use a <u>model</u> called <u>particle theory</u> to explain how the particles in a material behave. It works by imagining each particle as a <u>small, solid, inelastic (stiff) sphere</u> — just like a golf ball.

Solids

- In solids, there are <u>strong forces</u> of attraction between particles.
- They are held <u>close together</u> in <u>fixed positions</u>.
- All solids keep a <u>fixed shape</u> and <u>volume (size)</u>.
- The particles <u>vibrate</u> about their positions.
- The <u>hotter</u> the solid is, the <u>more</u> the particles vibrate.

Substances in different states of matter are all around us — in the earth, the oceans and the air.

Liquids

- In liquids, the forces of attraction between particles are <u>weaker</u> than in a solid.
- The particles are <u>randomly</u> arranged.
- They're <u>free</u> to <u>move</u> past each other. They tend to <u>stay close together</u>.
- Liquids have a fixed volume but <u>don't</u> keep a <u>fixed shape</u>.
- The particles are <u>always</u> moving <u>in random directions</u>.
- The <u>hotter</u> the liquid is, the <u>faster</u> the particles move.

Gases

- In gases, there's <u>no attraction</u> between the particles.
- This means that the particles are <u>far apart</u> from each other.
- They're always moving <u>in random directions</u> — but only in <u>straight</u> lines.
- Gases <u>don't</u> have a fixed <u>shape</u> or <u>volume</u>.
- The <u>hotter</u> the gas gets, the <u>faster</u> the particles move.

Atoms are Rearranged During Chemical Reactions

1) Substances can <u>change</u> from one state of matter to another (see next page).
2) This is known as a <u>physical change</u> — <u>no</u> new substances are made.
3) Physical changes are pretty <u>easy</u> to undo, e.g. by <u>heating</u> or <u>cooling</u>.
4) In a <u>chemical change</u>, <u>new</u> substances are <u>made</u>.
5) For example, a <u>chemical reaction</u> is a chemical change.
6) This is because, during a chemical reaction, bonds between atoms <u>break</u>.
7) Atoms can <u>change places</u> and make <u>new bonds</u> with <u>different</u> atoms.
8) Chemical changes are often <u>harder to undo</u> than physical changes.

I just feel as if a bond has broken between us...

I felt like changing state, so I moved from Florida to Texas...

After all this stuff about particle theory, let's have a go at putting theory into practice...

Q1 Describe the difference in the strength of attraction between particles in a solid, liquid and gas. [3 marks]

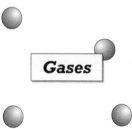

Changing State

This page is like a game show. To start, everyone seems nice and solid, but turn up the <u>heat</u> and it all changes.

Substances Can Change from One State to Another

Solid → Liquid → Gas

- When a solid is <u>heated</u>, its particles gain <u>energy</u> and <u>vibrate more</u>.
- Some of the forces between the particles <u>break</u>.
- At a <u>temperature</u> called the <u>melting point</u>, the particles have enough energy to <u>break free</u> from their positions. This is <u>MELTING</u>. The <u>solid</u> turns into a <u>liquid</u>.
- When a liquid is <u>heated</u>, the particles get even <u>more</u> energy.
- The forces holding the liquid together <u>weaken</u> and <u>break</u>.
- At a temperature called the <u>boiling point</u>, the particles have <u>enough</u> energy to <u>break</u> the forces. This is <u>BOILING</u>. The <u>liquid</u> becomes a <u>gas</u>.

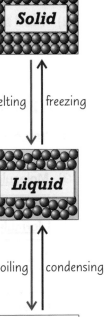

melting | freezing

boiling | condensing

Gas → Liquid → Solid

- As a gas <u>cools</u>, the particles have <u>less energy</u>.
- <u>Forces form</u> between the particles.
- At the <u>boiling point</u>, the forces between the particles are strong enough that the <u>gas</u> becomes a <u>liquid</u>. This is <u>CONDENSING</u>.
- When a <u>liquid cools</u>, the particles have <u>less energy</u>, so move around less.
- The <u>forces</u> between the particles become stronger.
- At the <u>melting point</u>, the forces between the particles are so strong that they're <u>held in place</u>. The <u>liquid</u> becomes a <u>solid</u>. This is <u>FREEZING</u>.

> The boiling point can also be called the condensing point. The melting point can also be called the freezing point.

1) The <u>amount</u> of energy needed for a substance to <u>change state</u> depends on <u>how strong</u> the forces of attraction between particles are.

2) The <u>stronger</u> the forces of attraction, the <u>more energy</u> is needed to break them, and so the <u>higher</u> the melting and boiling points of the substance.

> The changes of state that occur in the water cycle or that happened when the atmosphere and oceans formed, can be described using the particle model.

You Have to be Able to Predict the State of a Substance

1) You can predict <u>what state</u> a substance is in at a <u>certain temperature</u>.
2) If the temperature's <u>below</u> the <u>melting point</u> of substance, it'll be a <u>solid</u>.
3) If it's <u>above</u> the <u>boiling point</u>, it'll be a <u>gas</u>.
4) If it's <u>in between</u> the two points, then it's a <u>liquid</u>.

> The bulk properties such as the melting point of a material depend on how lots of particles interact together. A particle on its own doesn't have these properties.

EXAMPLE: Which of the substances in the table is a liquid at 25 °C?

	melting point	boiling point
oxygen	−219 °C	−183 °C
bromine	−7 °C	59 °C

Oxygen has a boiling point below 25 °C, so will be a gas at 25 °C.

The answer's bromine. It melts at −7 °C and boils at 59 °C. So, it'll be a liquid at 25 °C.

Some people are worth melting for...

You might be asked to predict the state of a substance at room temperature. You should assume that room temperature is between 20-25 °C. So, for example, something that boils at −100 °C is a gas at room temperature.

Q1 Ethanol melts at −114 °C and boils at 78 °C. Predict the state that ethanol is in at:
a) −150 °C   b) 0 °C   c) 25 °C   d) 100 °C   [4 marks]

Chemical Formulas

After this page, you won't need to write out <u>names</u> of compounds in <u>full</u> every time you mention them — great.

Atoms Can be Represented by Symbols

1) Atoms of each element can be represented by a <u>one, two or three letter symbol</u>.
2) You'll see these symbols on the <u>periodic table</u> (see p.93).
3) For example: | C = carbon   O = oxygen   H = hydrogen |

The Formula of a Molecule Shows the Numbers of Atoms

1) You can work out <u>how many atoms</u> of each type there are in a substance when you're given its <u>formula</u>.
2) There are <u>two</u> types of formula you need to know about — <u>molecular</u> and <u>displayed</u> formulas.
3) <u>Molecular formulas</u> show the <u>number</u> and <u>type</u> of <u>atoms</u> in a molecule as <u>symbols</u>.

> This is the <u>molecular</u> <u>formula</u> for <u>methane</u>. CH_4 It shows that methane contains <u>1 carbon</u> atom and <u>4 hydrogen</u> atoms.

4) If a formula has <u>brackets</u> in it then the number <u>after</u> the bracket tells you how many lots there are of what's <u>inside</u> the bracket.

> This is the <u>formula</u> for <u>butane</u>.
> The <u>2</u> after the bracket means that there are <u>2 lots of CH_2</u>.
> $CH_3(CH_2)_2CH_3$
> Altogether there are <u>4 carbon</u> atoms and <u>10 hydrogen</u> atoms.

5) <u>Displayed formulas</u> show the <u>atoms</u> and the <u>covalent bonds</u> in a molecule as a <u>picture</u>.

> This is the <u>displayed formula</u> for <u>methane</u>.
>
> $$\begin{array}{c} H \\ | \\ H-C-H \\ | \\ H \end{array}$$
>
> The little <u>lines</u> are <u>covalent bonds</u> between the atoms.

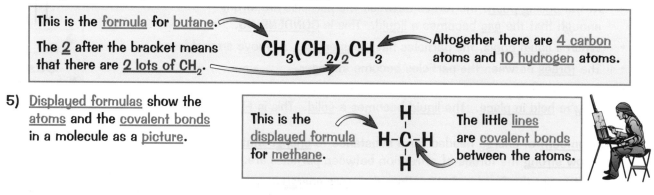

Prefixes Show How Many of a Certain Atom are in a Molecule

1) <u>Prefixes</u> are just the bits that come <u>before</u> a word. The main ones you'll need to know are:

| <u>mono-</u> = one, <u>di-</u> = two and <u>tri-</u> = three. |

E.g. each molecule of carbon dioxide contains two oxygen atoms.

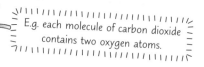

2) It's also a good idea to <u>learn</u> the chemical formulas of these common molecules.

| • Water — H_2O | • Ammonia — NH_3 | • Carbon dioxide — CO_2 |
| • Hydrogen — H_2 | • Chlorine — Cl_2 | • Oxygen — O_2 |

Formulas of Ionic Compounds Are More Like Ratios

1) The formula of an ionic compound tells you the <u>ratio</u> of the elements in the compound. E.g. sodium chloride, NaCl, has <u>one</u> chlorine atom for every <u>one</u> sodium atom.

> See p.104 for more about ionic compounds.

2) The <u>names</u> of ionic compounds don't include <u>prefixes</u> to help you work out the numbers in the formula — you have to figure them out from the <u>charges</u> on the ions (see p.104).

I can't tell you what's in compound X — it's a secret formula...

I expect some of this is pretty familiar, but that's no reason to just skip this page — make sure you know it all.

Q1   How many carbon atoms are in a molecule with the formula $CH_3(CH_2)_4OH$?   [1 mark]

Chemical Equations

<u>Chemical equations</u> are really important to chemistry. Pretty much like tomato ketchup is to a bacon butty.
Mmm... bacon butties... Sorry, I got distracted. Let's do this.

Chemical Reactions are Shown Using Chemical Equations

1) One way to show a chemical reaction is to write a <u>word equation</u>.

2) Word equations show the <u>names</u> of the chemicals that are reacting and being produced.

Here's an example — <u>methane</u> reacts with <u>oxygen</u> to make <u>carbon dioxide</u> and <u>water</u>:

The chemicals on the <u>left-hand side</u> of the equation are called the <u>reactants</u> (because they react with each other).

methane + oxygen → carbon dioxide + water

The chemicals on the <u>right-hand side</u> are called the <u>products</u> (because they've been produced from the reactants).

Symbol Equations Show the Atoms on Both Sides

1) Chemical <u>reactions</u> can be shown using symbol equations.

2) Symbol equations just show the <u>symbols</u> or formulas of the <u>reactants</u> and <u>products</u>.

magnesium + oxygen   magnesium oxide

$$2Mg + O_2 \rightarrow 2MgO$$

You'll have spotted that there's a '2' in front of the Mg and the MgO. The reason for this is explained below...

Symbol Equations Need to be Balanced

1) There must always be the <u>same</u> number of atoms of <u>each element</u> on <u>both sides</u> — they can't just <u>disappear</u>. This is called <u>conservation of mass</u> — there's more about it on pages 135-136.

2) You <u>balance</u> the equation by putting numbers <u>in front</u> of the formulas.
Take this equation for reacting sulfuric acid with sodium hydroxide:

$$H_2SO_4 + NaOH \rightarrow Na_2SO_4 + H_2O$$

<u>Left-hand side</u>
H = 3
S = 1
O = 5
Na = 1

<u>Right-hand side</u>
H = 2
S = 1
O = 5
Na = 2

3) The <u>formulas</u> are all correct but the numbers of some atoms <u>don't match up</u> on both sides.

4) The more you <u>practise</u>, the <u>quicker</u> you get, but all you do is this:

1) Find an element that <u>doesn't balance</u> and <u>pencil in a number</u> in front of one of the substances to try and sort it out.

2) <u>See where it gets you</u>. You might find a different element still isn't balanced. Don't worry, just pencil in <u>another number</u> to balance that element.

3) Keep doing this until the equation is <u>completely balanced</u>.

You can't change formulas like H_2SO_4 to H_2SO_5. You can only put numbers in front of them. You also can't add in new substances. E.g. you can't add in Na on the left hand side.

EXAMPLE: In the equation above you'll notice we're short of <u>Na atoms</u> on the LHS (Left-Hand Side).

1) The only thing you can do about that is make it <u>2NaOH</u> instead of just NaOH:

$$H_2SO_4 + 2NaOH \rightarrow Na_2SO_4 + H_2O$$

2) But that now gives <u>too many</u> H atoms and O atoms on the LHS. So to balance that up you could try putting <u>2H$_2$O</u> on the RHS (Right-Hand Side):

$$H_2SO_4 + 2NaOH \rightarrow Na_2SO_4 + 2H_2O$$

LHS	RHS
H = 4	H = 2
S = 1	S = 1
O = 6	O = 5
Na = 2	Na = 2

3) And suddenly there it is — <u>everything balances</u>. Woohoo.

Revision is all about getting the balance right...

It's important to practise balancing equations. Once you have a few goes you'll see it's less scary than it seemed.

Q1   Balance the equation: $Fe + Cl_2 \rightarrow FeCl_3$

[1 mark]

Endothermic and Exothermic Reactions

So, <u>endothermic</u> and <u>exothermic reactions</u> are all about taking in and giving out energy to the <u>surroundings</u>.

Reactions are Exothermic or Endothermic

1. An <u>EXOTHERMIC</u> reaction is one which <u>gives out energy</u> to the surroundings.
2. Exothermic reactions cause a <u>rise in temperature</u> of the surroundings.

Combustion reactions (where something burns in oxygen — see page 83) are always exothermic.

1. An <u>ENDOTHERMIC</u> reaction is one which <u>takes in energy</u> from the surroundings.
2. Endothermic reactions cause a <u>fall in temperature</u> of the surroundings.

'Surroundings' means the stuff that the reactants are in — like the water in a beaker.

You can calculate the <u>change in energy</u> in a reaction:

In an exothermic reaction, the reactants have an energy of 2000 J.
The products have an energy of 800 J. Calculate the energy change during the reaction.

1) Change in energy = energy of products − energy of reactants
2) So, change in energy = 800 J − 2000 J = −1200 J

Exothermic reactions have a negative energy change. Endothermic reactions have a positive energy change.

Reaction Profiles Show if a Reaction's Exothermic or Endothermic

1) <u>Reaction profiles</u> show the energy levels of the <u>reactants</u> and the <u>products</u> in a reaction.

2) You can use them to work out if energy is <u>released</u> (exothermic) or <u>taken in</u> (endothermic).

Exothermic Reaction

1) This reaction profile shows an <u>exothermic reaction</u>.

2) The products are at a <u>lower energy</u> than the reactants.

3) The <u>difference in height</u> represents the <u>energy given out</u> in the reaction.

The shape of reaction profiles is explained more on the next page.

Endothermic Reaction

1) This reaction profile shows an <u>endothermic reaction</u>.

2) The products are at a <u>higher energy</u> than the reactants.

3) The <u>difference in height</u> represents the <u>energy taken in</u> during the reaction.

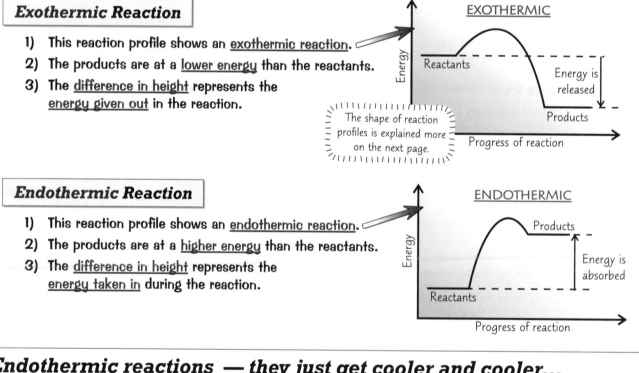

Endothermic reactions — they just get cooler and cooler...

There's a handy way to help remember whether energy is given out by a reaction.
<u>Ex</u>othermic reactions give out energy to the <u>ex</u>terior (outside). Neat eh?

Q1 The energy profile on the right shows how the energy changes during a reaction.
    a) State what type of energy change is shown. [1 mark]
    b) Predict how the temperature of the reaction mixture will change during this reaction. [1 mark]

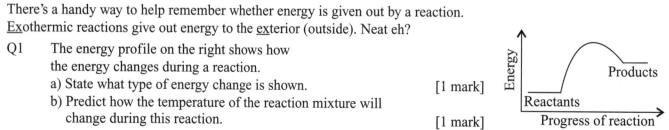

Bond Energies

Energy transfer in chemical reactions is all to do with <u>making and breaking bonds</u>.

Energy Must Always be Supplied to Break Bonds

There's more on energy transfer on page 80.

1) During a chemical reaction, <u>existing bonds are broken</u> and <u>new bonds are made</u>.

2) You need energy to break <u>bonds</u> — so bond breaking is an <u>endothermic</u> process.

3) Energy is <u>given out</u> when new bonds are <u>made</u> — so bond making is an <u>exothermic</u> process.

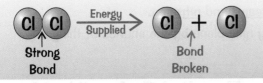

BOND BREAKING — ENDOTHERMIC

Cl Cl — Energy Supplied → Cl + Cl

Strong Bond   Bond Broken

BOND MAKING — EXOTHERMIC

C + O ⟶ C O + Energy Released

Strong Bond Formed

4) In <u>endothermic</u> reactions, the energy <u>used</u> to break bonds is <u>greater</u> than the energy <u>released</u> by forming new bonds.

5) In <u>exothermic</u> reactions, the energy <u>released</u> by forming bonds is <u>greater</u> than the energy used to <u>break</u> 'em.

Activation Energy is the Energy Needed to Start a Reaction

Energy has to be supplied before a fuel burns.

1) The <u>activation energy</u> is the <u>minimum</u> amount of energy needed for a reaction to <u>start</u>.

2) The activation energy is used to <u>break</u> the bonds between atoms.

3) If the energy you put in is <u>less</u> than the activation energy, the reaction <u>won't start</u>.

4) On a <u>reaction profile</u>, the <u>activation energy</u> is the <u>difference</u> between the <u>reactants</u> and the <u>highest point</u> on the curve.

(graph: Energy vs Progress of Reaction, showing Reactants, Products, Activation energy)

You Can Compare Reaction Profiles if They're Drawn on the Same Scale

1) Reactions with <u>high activation energies</u> have <u>bigger</u> differences between the energy of the <u>reactants</u> and the <u>top of the curve</u>.

2) Reactions with <u>high energy changes</u> have <u>bigger</u> differences between the energy of the <u>reactants</u> and the energy of the <u>products</u>.

3) For example, let's <u>compare</u> the two profiles drawn below using the <u>same scale</u>:

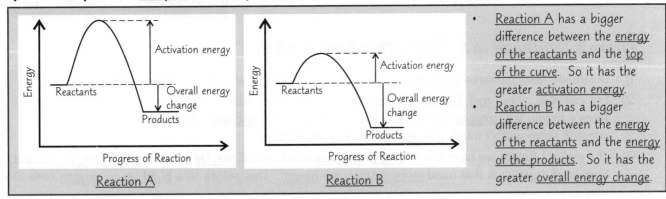

Reaction A *(graph: Energy vs Progress of Reaction — Reactants, Activation energy, Overall energy change, Products)*

Reaction B *(graph: Energy vs Progress of Reaction — Reactants, Activation energy, Overall energy change, Products)*

- <u>Reaction A</u> has a bigger difference between the <u>energy of the reactants</u> and the <u>top of the curve</u>. So it has the greater <u>activation energy</u>.

- <u>Reaction B</u> has a bigger difference between the <u>energy of the reactants</u> and the <u>energy of the products</u>. So it has the greater <u>overall energy change</u>.

Exothermic or endothermic, that is the question...

If you struggle to remember the energy changes when bonds are broken and made, don't panic. Bond breaking is like *ending* the bond — an *end*othermic process. Hmmm, that seems weird now I've written it down...

Q1   Is bond formation an endothermic or exothermic process? Explain your answer.   [2 marks]

The Evolution of the Atmosphere

Theories for how the Earth's atmosphere evolved have changed a lot over the years.
It's hard to gather evidence from so long ago (4.6 billion years). Here is one idea we've got:

Phase 1 — Volcanoes Gave Out Gases

1) For the first billion years of its life, Earth was very hot.
2) It was covered with volcanoes that were constantly erupting.
3) These eruptions released lots of gases.
4) The main gases in the atmosphere that formed because of these eruptions were carbon dioxide, water vapour (steam) and nitrogen.
5) There would have been nearly no oxygen — not a very nice place by the sounds of things...

Phase 2 — Oceans, Algae and Green Plants Absorbed Carbon Dioxide

1) As the Earth cooled down, the water vapour condensed (turned from gas to liquid) and formed the oceans.
2) Lots of carbon dioxide was removed from the air as it dissolved in the oceans.
3) Green plants and algae evolved and used some carbon dioxide for photosynthesis (see below).
4) When animals and plants in the sea died, they fell to the bottom of the sea and got buried.
5) Over millions of years, they were squashed and formed sedimentary rocks, oil and gas.
6) This trapped the carbon and kept the carbon dioxide levels in the atmosphere reduced.

Phase 3 — Green Plants and Algae Produced Oxygen

1) Green plants and algae use a reaction called photosynthesis. This reaction uses carbon dioxide and releases oxygen.
2) So when green plants and algae evolved, they helped to remove carbon dioxide and increase levels of oxygen in the air.
3) As oxygen levels built up in the atmosphere over time, more complex life (like animals) could evolve.
4) Eventually, the atmosphere reached a composition similar to what it is today:
   • 78% nitrogen
   • 21% oxygen
   • 1% other gases (like carbon dioxide and water vapour)

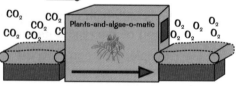

There's Evidence to Support This Explanation

1) Scientists have gathered evidence to back up this view of how the atmosphere evolved.
2) For example, some rock formations have been found which only form when there's hardly any oxygen about. The formations are very ancient, which suggest there wasn't much oxygen in the early atmosphere.
3) The earliest fossils we have are of tiny organisms which could survive without much oxygen around. Fossils of organisms that need more oxygen are newer. This points to a build up of oxygen over time.

The atmosphere's evolving — shut the window will you...

Try giving the page a good read, then cover it up and write down everything you can remember.
It'll be worth it when that question comes up asking you about the evolution of the atmosphere...

Q1   Give two reasons why carbon dioxide levels have decreased since the atmosphere was formed.   [2 marks]

Combustion and Greenhouse Gases

We burn lots of <u>fossil fuels</u> to supply the <u>energy</u> to sustain our <u>modern lifestyles</u> — but this comes at a <u>cost</u>...

Combustion Reactions are an Example of Oxidation

Combustion reactions happen when you burn substances in oxygen.

1) <u>Oxidation</u> is the <u>addition of oxygen</u> to a substance in a reaction.

2) For example, the <u>combustion</u> of <u>fossil fuels</u> is an <u>oxidation</u> reaction.

3) Fossil fuels contain compounds made of hydrogen and carbon only (<u>hydrocarbons</u>).

4) When you burn fossil fuels in <u>oxygen</u>, the <u>hydrogen</u> and <u>carbon</u> in the hydrocarbons bond to oxygen to form new compounds. They are <u>oxidised</u>.

5) <u>Complete combustion</u> happens when there is <u>plenty</u> of oxygen around. The only products are <u>carbon dioxide</u> and <u>water</u>.

> hydrocarbon + oxygen → carbon dioxide + water
> E.g. C_3H_8 + $5O_2$ → $3CO_2$ + $4H_2O$

6) <u>Incomplete combustion</u> happens if there's <u>not enough oxygen</u> around for complete combustion.

7) As well as carbon dioxide and water, incomplete combustion produces a mixture of <u>carbon monoxide</u> (CO) and <u>carbon</u> in the form of <u>soot</u>.

The bits of carbon that form soot are called particulates.

- <u>Carbon monoxide</u> can combine with red blood cells and stop your blood from <u>carrying oxygen</u>.
- Not enough oxygen in the blood supply to the brain can lead to <u>fainting</u>, a <u>coma</u> or even <u>death</u>.

- Soot makes buildings look <u>dirty</u>.
- It also <u>reduces air quality</u> which can cause <u>breathing problems</u>, or make them <u>worse</u> for people who already have them.

Carbon Dioxide is a Greenhouse Gas

1) <u>Greenhouse gases</u> in the atmosphere help to keep Earth <u>warm</u> enough for <u>life</u>.

2) <u>Carbon dioxide</u> and <u>methane</u> are both greenhouse gases.

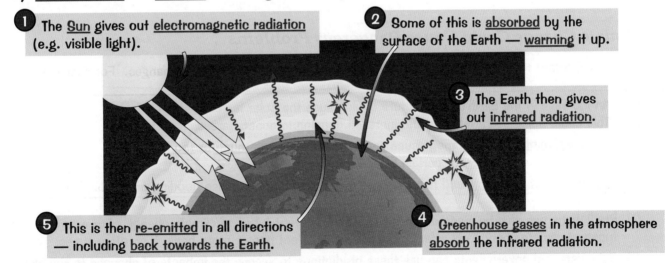

1 The <u>Sun</u> gives out <u>electromagnetic radiation</u> (e.g. visible light).

2 Some of this is <u>absorbed</u> by the surface of the Earth — <u>warming</u> it up.

3 The Earth then gives out <u>infrared radiation</u>.

4 <u>Greenhouse gases</u> in the atmosphere <u>absorb</u> the infrared radiation.

5 This is then <u>re-emitted</u> in all directions — including <u>back towards the Earth</u>.

3) By absorbing and re-emitting <u>infrared (thermal)</u> radiation, greenhouse gases keep the Earth <u>warmer</u> than it would otherwise be. This is called the <u>greenhouse effect</u>.

The greenhouse effect — good news for your tomatoes, I suppose...

Seriously, it's worth remembering the products of incomplete combustion — it could be really useful in the exams.

Q1   Give the names of four products which can be formed during incomplete combustion.   [4 marks]

Climate Change

Greenhouse gases are important but can also cause problems — it's all about keeping a delicate balance.

Increasing Carbon Dioxide is Linked to Climate Change

1) Human activity can increase the amount of greenhouse gases in the atmosphere. For example:

- Burning fossil fuels releases carbon dioxide.
- Farm animals (such as cows) produce methane when they digest their food.
- Deforestation (chopping down trees) means less carbon dioxide can be absorbed by forests.

2) Over the last 200 years, the amount of fossil fuels being burnt has gone up.

3) This links (correlates) with an increase in the level of carbon dioxide in the atmosphere and an increase in the temperature of the Earth.

4) Most scientists agree that extra carbon dioxide and other greenhouse gases from human activity are causing the increase in temperature.

5) They also agree that this temperature change will lead to other types of climate change.

6) Lots of different studies have shown there's a link between increasing carbon dioxide levels and climate change. This makes people more confident in the evidence.

7) Scientists can use data to build models and make predictions about the climate.

8) It's hard to predict how the climate will change in the future because we don't know how greenhouse gas emissions might change.

9) Also, the Earth's climate is very complex, so it's hard to make a model that isn't too simple. So, the models made can be complex and hard to use.

10) More data on climate change is being collected all the time. This means that uncertainties in data are getting smaller. So predictions and models are more likely to be realistic and accurate.

Global Temp. Change Compared to 1951-1980 average (°C) — Atmospheric CO_2 Concentration (ppm)

There's more about correlation on p.227.

Climate Change Could Cause Dangerous Problems

1) It's important to make predictions about what may happen if the climate changes. For example:

- An increase in the Earth's temperature could cause the polar ice caps to melt faster. This could make sea levels rise and increase flooding in coastal areas.
- Changing rainfall patterns may cause some areas to get too much or too little water. This may make it harder for certain places to produce food.
- Storms might get worse and happen more often, which could cause flooding on low land.

Rainfall patterns include the amount, timing and location of rain.

2) Predictions can also be made about the scale of different types of climate change. For example, some types of climate change will affect more people or affect people more badly than other types.

3) Scientists and governments can use these predictions to assess the impacts of changes to the climate.

4) This helps them to make decisions about how to reduce the impacts of climate change (see next page).

Think globally, act locally, panic internally...

Everyone's talking about climate change these days — it's pretty scary stuff, but make sure you get it.

Q1   Give three potential problems caused by climate change.   [3 marks]

Reducing Greenhouse Gas Emissions

To slow down global warming, we need to reduce the amount of carbon dioxide and methane we release to the air.

There are Ways of Reducing Greenhouse Gas Emissions

There are methods to try to reduce the amount of greenhouse gases we produce. For example:

1) Renewable energy sources or nuclear energy could be used instead of fossil fuels.
2) Using more efficient processes would use less energy, so less fossil fuels would need to be burnt.
3) Governments could tax companies or people based on how much greenhouse gas they emit. For example, taxing cars that use lots of fuel could mean that people choose to buy cars that use less fuel.

   > Arggh! I've been capped!

4) Governments can also put a cap on emissions of all greenhouse gases that companies make. The government could then sell licences for emissions up to that cap.

Greenhouse gas producers can also take steps to deal with the gases they do produce:

1) There are schemes that help to remove carbon dioxide from the atmosphere.
2) For example, for a certain amount of carbon dioxide emitted, trees can be planted (reforestation) to remove the same amount of carbon dioxide by photosynthesis.
3) There's also technology that captures the carbon dioxide before it's released into the atmosphere. It can then be stored deep underground in gaps in the rock such as old oil wells.

Not all methods reduce emissions by the same amount.

> Remember, it's not just carbon dioxide that's a problem — methane is a real pain too.

EXAMPLE: The table below shows how much carbon dioxide could be saved using two different methods. Which method would have a bigger impact on reducing carbon dioxide emissions?

1) A tax on cars that use lots of fuel would save 20 000 tons of carbon dioxide a year.
2) But using carbon capture would save 1 000 000 tons — that's 50 times as much as 20 000 tons.
3) The answer's **carbon capture**.

method	CO_2 saved in a year (thousands of tons)
tax on cars that use lots of fuel	20
carbon capture	1000

But Making Reductions is Still Difficult

1) It's easy enough saying that we should cut emissions, but actually doing it — that's a different story.
2) New technologies can have unexpected impacts.
3) For example, carbon capture schemes use lots of energy, so capturing the carbon dioxide produced by a power plant can make the plant much less efficient.
4) There could also be risks to people. For example, if the stored carbon dioxide leaks into water supplies.
5) New technologies could also impact the environment in ways that we haven't predicted.
6) The scale of emissions makes it hard to reduce them. It's not possible to store all the carbon dioxide we make underground, or to plant enough trees to cancel it out.

Cutting greenhouse gas production — emission possible...?

It's pretty hard to cut greenhouse gas emissions, especially in industry.
Thankfully, governments are starting to make it harder for businesses to just ignore their emissions.

Q1 State two things governments can do to try to reduce the greenhouse gas emissions of businesses. [2 marks]

Pollutants and Tests for Gases

We've already met some <u>pollutants</u> that can form when <u>fossil fuels</u> are burnt.
Hold on to your hats folks, because we're about to learn about some <u>more</u>.

Sulfur Dioxide and Oxides of Nitrogen Can Cause Air Pollution

1) Some fossil fuels, such as <u>coal</u>, contain <u>sulfur impurities</u>.

2) When these fuels are burnt, the sulfur can react with <u>oxygen</u> to form <u>sulfur dioxide</u> (SO_2).

3) <u>Nitrogen oxides</u> are created from a reaction between the <u>nitrogen</u> and <u>oxygen</u> in the <u>air</u>.

This can happen in the internal combustion engines of cars, due to the high temperatures of burning fuel.

4) When these gases mix with <u>clouds</u> they can cause <u>acid rain</u>.

5) Acid rain can <u>kill plants</u>. It also damages <u>buildings</u>, <u>statues</u> and <u>metals</u>.

6) Sulfur dioxide and nitrogen oxides can also cause ground-level air pollution called <u>smog</u> to form.

7) Smog can cause <u>breathing problems</u>.

8) Thankfully, there are a few ways to tackle these gases:

<u>Sulfur can be removed from fuels:</u>

1) Most of the sulfur can be <u>removed</u> from fuels <u>before</u> they're burnt. This makes <u>low sulfur</u> fuels (e.g. low sulfur petrol).

2) Removing sulfur from fuels takes <u>a lot of energy</u>.

3) This usually comes from burning fuel, which releases more <u>greenhouse gases</u>.

4) It can also be <u>expensive</u>.

<u>Emissions can be reduced:</u>

1) <u>Power stations</u> now have <u>acid gas scrubbers</u> to take the harmful gases <u>out</u> before they are released in to the air.

2) Most <u>cars</u> are now fitted with <u>catalytic converters</u>. These remove nitrogen oxides from <u>exhaust gases</u>.

3) We could also simply <u>reduce</u> our usage of <u>fossil fuels</u>.

Scientists monitor the levels of these pollutants in the air to make sure air quality standards are maintained.

There are Tests for 4 Common Gases
PRACTICAL

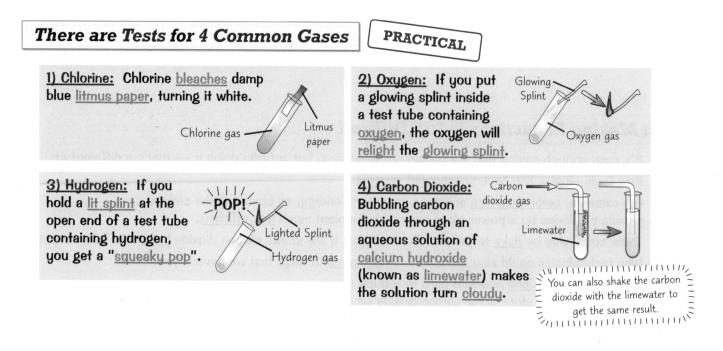

1) Chlorine: Chlorine <u>bleaches</u> damp blue <u>litmus paper</u>, turning it white.

Chlorine gas — Litmus paper

2) Oxygen: If you put a glowing splint inside a test tube containing <u>oxygen</u>, the oxygen will <u>relight</u> the <u>glowing splint</u>.

Glowing Splint
Oxygen gas

3) Hydrogen: If you hold a <u>lit splint</u> at the open end of a test tube containing hydrogen, you get a "<u>squeaky pop</u>".

POP!
Lighted Splint
Hydrogen gas

4) Carbon Dioxide: Bubbling carbon dioxide through an aqueous solution of <u>calcium hydroxide</u> (known as <u>limewater</u>) makes the solution turn <u>cloudy</u>.

Carbon dioxide gas
Limewater

You can also shake the carbon dioxide with the limewater to get the same result.

Struggling with revision? There's no need to sulfur in silence...

If you're wondering why the gas tests are on this page, it's not just because I had to fit them in *somewhere*. Honest...

Q1   Give two examples of how emissions of nitrogen oxides could be reduced.   [2 marks]

Water Treatment

Potable water is not to be confused with portable water, which is water you can fit in your pocket.

There are a Variety of Water Resources

1) The global population is increasing, so there's more need for <u>potable water</u> (water that's safe to <u>drink</u>).

2) There are a number of <u>sources of water</u> which can be treated to make potable water.

3) The three you need to know about are:

    1) <u>GROUND WATER</u>: from rocks that trap water underground.

    2) <u>WASTE WATER</u>: from water that's been <u>polluted</u> by a human process,
             e.g. waste water from sewage.

    3) <u>SALT WATER</u>: from the <u>sea</u>.

4) The way water is treated to make it safe to drink depends on the <u>source</u> that it comes from.

Ground Water is the Easiest Source of Water to Treat

1) The <u>first step</u> to treat ground water is often <u>aeration</u>.

2) During aeration, the water is <u>mixed</u> with <u>air</u> to increase the levels of dissolved <u>oxygen</u>.

3) This forces other <u>dissolved gases</u> that could be harmful out of the water.

4) Aeration also removes certain <u>ions</u>, which react with the oxygen to form solid oxides.

5) After aeration, the water is <u>filtered</u> to remove any <u>solid impurities</u>.

The Last Step is Chlorination

1) The final step in water treatment is usually <u>chlorination</u>.

2) <u>Chlorine gas</u> is bubbled through the water to kill <u>harmful bacteria</u> and other <u>microbes</u>.

3) However, chlorination can have <u>disadvantages</u>.

4) In <u>certain conditions</u>, chlorine can react with compounds found in the water to form <u>chemicals</u> that could be dangerous.

5) Levels of these chemicals have to be <u>carefully monitored</u>.

6) The <u>benefits</u> of chlorination are worth the <u>risks</u>, because it kills lots of pretty nasty bacteria.

7) So, in many countries, the <u>government</u> makes sure <u>water supplies</u> are <u>chlorinated</u>. In places where this <u>isn't</u> the case, there is a <u>greater risk</u> of water-borne <u>diseases</u>.

You can catch 'water-borne' diseases by coming in to contact with contaminated water (usually by drinking it).

If water from the ground is ground water, why isn't rain sky water?

Ahhh... Every glass of tap water I drink tastes all the sweeter for knowing all it had to go through to get to me...

Q1   Give two reasons why air is added to ground water during water treatment processes.   [2 marks]

More on Water Treatment

So we've already looked at how you can turn ground water into potable water.
Here's how you can do it for waste water and sea water. Yay!

Waste Water Treatment Happens in Several Stages

1) Waste water is normally a lot dirtier than ground water.

2) It usually needs many stages of treatment to make it potable.

3) It has to be filtered. This often involves multiple steps to remove different sizes of solid impurities.

4) Next, air is pumped through the water to encourage bacteria to grow.
These bacteria break down any organic matter.

5) For waste water containing nasty or harmful chemicals, extra stages of treatment
may be needed. This could include membrane filtration (see below).

6) The last stage is chlorination. This removes bacteria.

7) Waste water treatment uses less energy than treating salt water,
but more energy than treating ground water.

8) It could be used as a source of water in areas where there's not much ground water (e.g. hot countries).

You Can Get Potable Water by Distilling Sea Water

1) In some dry countries, sea water is distilled to produce drinking water.

2) On a small scale, sea water can be distilled using a solar still.
This is a bowl filled with salt water is covered with a clear, domed lid.

3) If it's left in the Sun, the water warms up and evaporates.

4) The water condenses on the lid, and can be collected. The salt is left behind in the bowl.

Evaporation means turning from liquid to gas. Condensation means turning from gas to liquid.

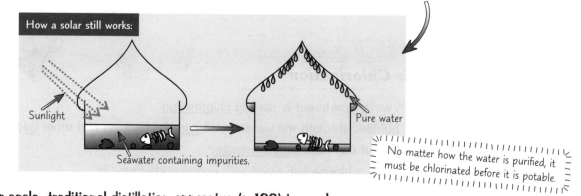

How a solar still works:

Sunlight

Seawater containing impurities.

Pure water

No matter how the water is purified, it must be chlorinated before it is potable.

5) On a larger scale, traditional distillation apparatus (p.132) is used.
This usually involves burning fossil fuels to heat the water. This is called thermal distillation.

7) Sea water can also be treated by filtering it through membranes.

8) The salt water is forced through a membrane that only allows water molecules to pass through.

9) Ions and larger molecules are trapped by the membrane and so separated from the water.

10) Treating salt water involves fewer stages than other purification methods.

11) But on a large scale, both thermal distillation and membrane
filtration need loads of energy. This makes them expensive.

Water couple of pages this has been...

That concludes our tour around the delightful world of air and water.
The fun doesn't stop there though, there's 24 amazing questions over the page — just for you...

Q1   Describe how sea water is made potable through the use of membranes.   [2 marks]

Revision Questions for Chapter C1

Hey, we made it to the end of <u>Chapter C1</u> — well done us. I'm proud of you, buddy.

• Try these questions and <u>tick off each one</u> when you <u>get it right</u>.

• When you've done <u>all the questions</u> for a topic and are <u>completely happy</u> with it, tick off the topic.

<u>States of Matter (p.76-77)</u> ☑

1) Name the three states of matter. ☑

2) When you heat a liquid, what happens to the speed of the particles? ☑

3) What name is given to the temperature at which a liquid becomes a gas? ☑

<u>Chemical Formulas and Equations (p.78-79)</u> ☑

4) Give the formula for: a) carbon dioxide b) ammonia ☑

5) What are the chemicals on the left-hand side of a chemical equation called? ☑

6) Balance these equations: a) $Mg + O_2 \rightarrow MgO$ b) $H_2SO_4 + NaOH \rightarrow Na_2SO_4 + H_2O$ ☑

<u>Temperature Changes and Bond Energies (p.80-81)</u> ☑

7) What effect will an endothermic reaction have on the temperature of the surroundings? ☑

8) Sketch a reaction profile for an exothermic reaction. ☑

9) Is energy released when bonds are broken or when they are made? ☑

10) What is meant by the term 'activation energy'? ☑

<u>The Atmosphere (p.82-86)</u> ☑

11) Name three gases given out by volcanoes billions of years ago. ☑

12) What change in the early atmosphere allowed complex organisms to evolve? ☑

13) Define the term 'oxidation'. ☑

14) Under what conditions does incomplete combustion occur? ☑

15) Give the name of the type of radiation that the Earth emits in the greenhouse effect. ☑

16) State three ways in which human activity is leading to an increase in carbon dioxide in the atmosphere. ☑

17) State one difficulty with reducing greenhouse gas emissions. ☑

18) Name a gas that can cause acid rain. ☑

19) Give two problems associated with acid rain. ☑

20) What is the chemical test for oxygen? ☑

<u>Water Treatment (p.87-88)</u> ☑

21) What is the difference between ground water and waste water? ☑

22) How does aerating water help to make it potable? ☑

23) Why is chlorine added to drinking water? ☑

24) Name two methods could you use for making salt water potable. ☑

The History of the Atom

Atoms are really, really <u>tiny</u> so we can't see them. Over time, <u>scientists</u> have carried out different <u>experiments</u> to figure out what they <u>look</u> like. Hold on to your hat, you're going on a journey through <u>time</u>...

Ideas About What Atoms Look Like Have Changed Over Time

1) In <u>Ancient Greece</u>, some people believed that everything was made from <u>four basic 'elements'</u> — earth, air, fire and water.

2) Over time, people began to think that everything was actually made up of tiny particles called <u>atoms</u>.

3) Over 2000 years later, a scientist, <u>Dalton</u>, thought that atoms were <u>solid spheres</u>.

4) Another scientist called <u>Thomson</u> then found that atoms contain even smaller, negatively charged particles — <u>electrons</u>.

5) This led to a model called the '<u>plum pudding model</u>' being created.

6) The plum pudding model showed the atom as a <u>ball</u> of <u>positive charge</u> with <u>electrons stuck</u> in this ball.

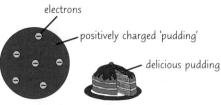

electrons

positively charged 'pudding'

delicious pudding

Experiments Showed that the Plum Pudding Model Was Wrong

1) Later, <u>Rutherford</u> carried out <u>alpha particle scattering experiments</u>. He fired very small, positively charged <u>alpha particles</u> at a very thin sheet of gold.

2) From the plum pudding model, he <u>expected</u> most of the particles to <u>go straight through</u> the sheet. He predicted that a few particles would <u>change direction</u> by a <u>small</u> amount.

3) But instead, some particles changed direction <u>more than expected</u>. A small number even went <u>backwards</u>.

     A few particles go backwards.

     Most of the particles pass through empty space, but a few change direction.

4) This meant the plum pudding model <u>couldn't</u> be right.

5) So, Rutherford came up with the <u>nuclear model</u> of the atom:

- There's a tiny, positively charged <u>nucleus</u> at the centre of the atom.
- Most of the <u>mass</u> is in the nucleus.
- The nucleus is surrounded by a 'cloud' of negative <u>electrons</u>.
- Most of the atom is <u>empty space</u>.

Bohr's Nuclear Model Explains a Lot

1) <u>Bohr</u> changed the nuclear model of the atom.

2) He suggested that the electrons <u>orbit</u> (go around) the nucleus in <u>shells</u> (levels).

3) Each shell is a <u>fixed distance</u> from the nucleus.

4) Bohr's theory was supported by many <u>experiments</u>. Experiments later showed that Bohr's theory was correct.

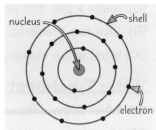

nucleus   shell

electron

Scientific Theories Have to be Backed Up by Evidence

1) Earlier ideas about atomic structure were <u>accepted</u> because they fitted the <u>evidence</u> available at the time.

2) The atomic model we use now looks a bit <u>different</u> to Bohr's model.

3) As scientists did more <u>experiments</u>, new evidence was found.

4) Our theory of the <u>structure</u> of the atom was then <u>changed</u> to fit this new evidence.

I wanted to be a model — but I ate too much plum pudding...

This is a great example of how science works. Scientists working together to find evidence. Lovely.

Q1   Describe the 'plum pudding' model of the atom.   [1 mark]

The Atom

If you thought atoms were small, wait till you learn about <u>protons</u>, <u>neutrons</u> and <u>electrons</u>. This won't be the last time you hear about these, so grab a biscuit and pay attention — you'll thank me later...

Atoms Contain Protons, Neutrons and Electrons

1) Atoms are tiny — about 10^{-10} m (0.0000000001 m) across. This is the atomic <u>diameter</u>.

2) The atom is made up of three types of <u>smaller particles</u> — protons, neutrons and electrons.

3) You need to know the <u>charges</u> of these particles and how <u>heavy</u> they are compared to each other (their <u>relative masses</u>).

- <u>Protons</u> are <u>heavy</u> (compared to electrons) and <u>positively</u> charged.
- <u>Neutrons</u> are <u>heavy</u> (compared to electrons) and <u>neutral</u>.
- <u>Electrons</u> have <u>hardly any mass</u> and are <u>negatively</u> charged.

Particle	Relative Mass	Relative Charge
Proton	1	+1
Neutron	1	0
Electron	0.0005	−1

Nucleus:
- It's in the <u>middle</u> of the atom.
- It contains <u>protons</u> and <u>neutrons</u>.
- The nucleus is really tiny — about a <u>hundred-thousandth</u> of the <u>diameter</u> of the atom.
- It has a <u>positive charge</u> because of the protons.
- Almost the <u>whole</u> mass of the atom is in the nucleus.

All of the objects that we come across in our day-to-day lives contain millions and millions of atoms.

If you magnified a nucleus to the size of a street rubbish bin in London, the electrons would be whizzing around the M25.

Electrons:
- Move <u>around</u> the nucleus in electron <u>shells</u> (levels).
- They're <u>negatively charged</u>.
- Electrons have almost <u>no</u> mass.

Molecules Form When Atoms Bond Together

1) <u>Molecules</u> are made up of <u>two or more</u> atoms.
2) These atoms are held together by <u>covalent bonds</u>.
3) The <u>bonds</u> tend to be about 10^{-10} m — about the same as the atomic diameter.
4) Molecules can be made of the <u>same element</u> (e.g. hydrogen), or <u>different elements</u> (e.g. ammonia).
5) <u>Simple molecules</u> (see page 113) are pretty tiny. They contain between <u>two</u> and a <u>few hundred</u> atoms. They're about 10^{-10} m to 10^{-9} m in size (they're a similar scale to atoms).
6) <u>Nanoparticles</u> (see page 126) are a bit bigger than simple molecules. They can contain between a few hundred and tens of thousands of atoms. They range from <u>1 nm</u> to <u>100 nm</u> in size.

hydrogen molecule   ammonia molecule

1 nanometre = 10^{-9} metres.

Let's be positive about this — unless you're an electron of course...

You need to learn what's in that table with the relative masses and charges of the different parts of the atom. Try remembering: **P**rotons are **P**ositive, **N**eutrons are **N**eutral and **E**lectrons are **E**... Never mind.

Q1   Where is most of the mass of an atom found? [1 mark]

Q2   Put the following things in order of size, starting with the smallest: atomic diameter, nucleus, nanoparticle, simple molecule (e.g. Cl_2). [2 marks]

Atoms and Isotopes

As if <u>atoms</u> weren't fiddly enough, time to meet pesky <u>isotopes</u>...

Atomic Number and Mass Number Describe an Atom

1) The <u>nuclear symbol</u> of an atom tells you its <u>atomic (proton) number</u> and <u>mass number</u>.

2) The <u>mass number</u> is always the <u>biggest</u> number.

3) You can use these two numbers to find <u>how many</u> protons, neutrons and electrons an atom has.

> <u>atomic number</u> = number of protons
> <u>mass number</u> = number of protons + number of neutrons

4) To get the <u>number of neutrons</u> just take away the atomic number (number of protons) from the mass number.

> <u>number of neutrons</u> = mass number – atomic number

5) Atoms have <u>no charge</u> overall (unlike ions, see page 102). They're <u>neutral</u>.

6) This is because they have the <u>same number</u> of <u>protons</u> as <u>electrons</u>. So, in an atom...

> <u>number of electrons</u> = atomic number

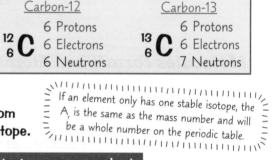

Nuclear symbol for sodium.

Mass number → ^{23} **Na** ← Element symbol (see page 78 for more on symbols).

Atomic number → $_{11}$

Number of <u>protons</u> = 11
Number of <u>neutrons</u> = 23 – 11 = 12
Number of <u>electrons</u> = 11

Isotopes are the Same Except for the Number of Neutrons

1) <u>Isotopes</u> are <u>different forms</u> of the <u>same element</u>. They have the <u>same</u> number of <u>protons</u> but a <u>different</u> number of <u>neutrons</u>.

2) This means they have the <u>same atomic number</u> but <u>different mass numbers</u>.

3) For example, carbon has two main isotopes — <u>carbon-12</u> and <u>carbon-13</u>.

4) If an element has a number of isotopes, you can describe it using <u>relative atomic mass</u> (A_r) instead of mass number. In fact, on a <u>periodic table</u> (see next page) the mass number is actually the <u>relative atomic mass</u>.

5) You can work out the relative atomic mass of an element from the <u>different masses</u> and <u>abundances</u> (amounts) of each isotope.

Carbon-12	Carbon-13
$^{12}_{6}$C 6 Protons 6 Electrons 6 Neutrons	$^{13}_{6}$C 6 Protons 6 Electrons 7 Neutrons

If an element only has one stable isotope, the A_r is the same as the mass number and will be a whole number on the periodic table.

$$\text{relative atomic mass } (A_r) = \frac{\text{sum of (isotope abundance} \times \text{isotope mass number)}}{\text{sum of abundances of all the isotopes}}$$

EXAMPLE: Copper has two stable isotopes. Cu-63 has an abundance of 69.2% and Cu-65 has an abundance of 30.8%. Calculate the relative atomic mass of copper to 1 decimal place.

abundance × mass number of Cu-63   abundance × mass number of Cu-65

$$\text{Relative atomic mass} = \frac{(69.2 \times 63) + (30.8 \times 65)}{69.2 + 30.8} = \frac{4359.6 + 2002}{100} = \frac{6361.6}{100} = 63.616 = \textbf{63.6}$$

abundance of Cu-63 + abundance of Cu-65

Don't trust atoms — they make up everything...

Urgh maths. But don't worry, if you learn the formulas above, you can plug in any numbers they give you.

Q1   Bromine has an atomic number of 35. It has 2 isotopes, bromine-79 and bromine-81.
       Work out how many neutrons, protons and electrons are in each isotope.   [2 marks]

The Periodic Table

We haven't always known as much about chemistry as we do now. Take the periodic table. Early chemists looked at patterns in the elements' properties to help them understand chemistry better.

Dmitri Mendeleev Made the First Proper Periodic Table

1) The first modern periodic table was made by a scientist called Mendeleev. He took the elements that had been discovered at the time and arranged them into a table.

2) He ordered them mainly by their atomic mass.

3) Sometimes he switched their positions or left gaps in the table.

4) This was so he could make sure that elements with similar properties stayed in the same groups.

5) Some of the gaps left space for elements that hadn't been found yet. Mendeleev used the position of the gaps to predict the properties of these elements.

6) New elements were later found which fitted into these gaps — they had the properties that Mendeleev had predicted. This showed that Mendeleev's ideas were right.

Mendeleev's Table of the Elements

```
H
Li  Be                                              B  C  N  O  F
Na  Mg                                             Al  Si  P  S  Cl
K   Ca  *  Ti  V   Cr  Mn  Fe  Co  Ni  Cu  Zn  *  *  As  Se  Br
Rb  Sr  Y  Zr  Nb  Mo  *   Ru  Rh  Pd  Ag  Cd  In  Sn  Sb  Te  I
Cs  Ba  *  *  Ta  W   *   Os  Ir  Pt  Au  Hg  Tl  Pb  Bi
```

This is How the Periodic Table Looks Today

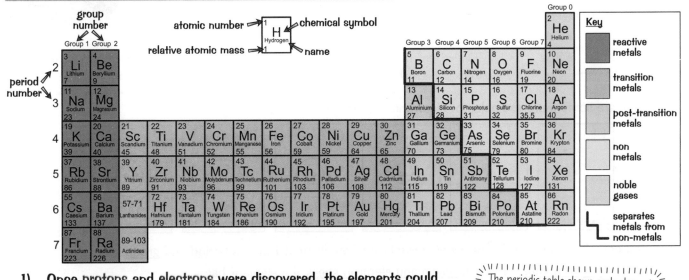

1) Once protons and electrons were discovered, the elements could be arranged in order of increasing atomic number (see p.92).

2) This arrangement in the periodic table means that there are repeated patterns in the properties of elements.

3) This order also fits the same pattern that Mendeleev worked out.

4) Elements with similar chemical properties are arranged to form columns. These columns are called groups.

5) The group number of an element is the same as the number of outer shell electrons it has. E.g. Group 1 elements have 1 outer shell electron, Group 7 elements have 7, etc. (Except for Group 0 — helium has two electrons in its outer shell and the rest have eight.)

6) The rows are called periods. The period number tells you how many shells contain electrons (see next page).

The periodic table shows each element using its chemical symbol. These can be used to write chemical formulas and equations (see pages 78-79).

I'm in a chemistry band — I play the symbols...

Because the periodic table is organised in groups and periods, you can see the patterns in the properties and reactivity of the elements. This means you can make predictions on how reactions will occur. How neat is that?

Q1   Using a periodic table, state how many electrons barium has in its outer shell.   [1 mark]

Electronic Structure

Like snails, <u>electrons</u> live in <u>shells</u>. Unlike snails, electrons won't nibble on your tulips...

Electron Shell Rules:

1) Electrons always move in <u>shells</u> (sometimes called <u>energy levels</u>).

2) The <u>inner</u> shells are <u>always filled first</u>. These are the ones closest to the nucleus.

3) Only <u>a certain number</u> of electrons are allowed in each shell:

1st shell	2nd shell	3rd shell
<u>2</u> electrons	<u>8</u> electrons	<u>8</u> electrons

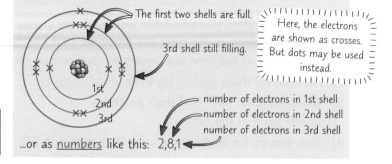

Electron structures can be shown as <u>diagrams</u> like this...

The first two shells are full.

Here, the electrons are shown as crosses. But dots may be used instead.

3rd shell still filling.

1st
2nd
3rd

number of electrons in 1st shell
number of electrons in 2nd shell
number of electrons in 3rd shell

...or as <u>numbers</u> like this: 2,8,1

Follow the Rules to Work Out Electronic Structures

You can easily work out the <u>electronic structures</u> for the first <u>20</u> elements of the periodic table.

EXAMPLE: What is the electronic structure of magnesium?

1) From the periodic table, you can see that magnesium's <u>atomic number</u> is 12. This means it has 12 protons. So it must have 12 electrons.

2) Follow the 'Electron Shell Rules' above. The first shell can only take <u>2 electrons</u>.

3) The second shell can take <u>up to 8 electrons</u>.

4) So far we have a total of 10 electrons (2 + 8). So the third shell must also be <u>partly filled</u> with 2 electrons. This makes 12 electrons in total (2 + 8 + 2).

Aren't you full?   Nope.

2...

2, 8...

So the electronic structure for magnesium must be 2,8,2.

Here are some more examples of electronic structures:

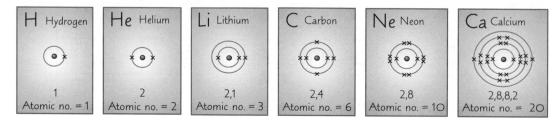

H Hydrogen	He Helium	Li Lithium	C Carbon	Ne Neon	Ca Calcium
1	2	2,1	2,4	2,8	2,8,8,2
Atomic no. = 1	Atomic no. = 2	Atomic no. = 3	Atomic no. = 6	Atomic no. = 10	Atomic no. = 20

You can also work out the electronic structure of an element from its <u>period</u> and <u>group</u>.

• The <u>period number</u> tells you <u>how many electron shells</u> the element has.

• The <u>group number</u> tells you <u>how many electrons</u> there are in the <u>outer shell</u> of the element.

<u>Example</u>: Sodium is in <u>period 3</u>, so it has <u>3</u> shells occupied. The first two shells must be full (2,8). It's in <u>Group 1</u>, so it has <u>1</u> electron in its outer shell. So its electronic structure is <u>2, 8, 1</u>.

Position in the Periodic Table Can Help You Predict Reactivity of Elements

1) The <u>way</u> that an element reacts depends on the <u>number of electrons</u> in its <u>outer shell</u>.

2) Elements with the <u>same number</u> of electrons in their outer shell (in the same group) react in <u>similar ways</u>.

3) The <u>number of shells</u> that an element has (the period it's in) affects <u>how reactive</u> it is.

4) So the reactivity of an element depends on <u>how many</u> electrons it has. This is the same as its <u>atomic number</u>.

The electronic structure of the fifth element — it's a bit boron...

Electronic structures may seem a bit complicated at first but once you learn the rules, it's not so bad.

Q1 Give the electronic structure of potassium (atomic number = 19). [1 mark]

Metals and Non-Metals

I am almost certain that you'll touch something <u>metallic</u> today, that's how important metals are to modern life.

Most Elements are Metals

1) <u>Metals</u> are elements which can <u>form positive ions</u> when they react.
2) They're on the <u>left-hand side</u> and towards the <u>bottom</u> of the periodic table.
3) <u>Most elements</u> in the periodic table are metals.
4) <u>Non-metals</u> are at the far <u>right</u> of the periodic table.
5) Non-metals <u>don't</u> usually <u>form positive ions</u> when they react.

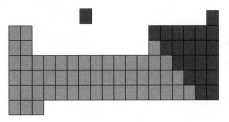

The blue elements are metals.
The red elements are non-metals.

The Electronic Structure of Atoms Affects How They Will React

1) Atoms are more <u>stable</u> with a full outer shell. So, they react by <u>losing</u>, <u>gaining</u> or <u>sharing</u> electrons until they have a <u>full outer shell</u>.
2) <u>Metal</u> elements <u>lose electrons</u> quite easily.
   When this happens, they <u>form positive ions</u>, with a full outer shell.
3) <u>Non-metals</u> don't lose electrons that easily.
   Instead, they <u>share</u> or <u>gain</u> electrons to get a full outer shell.

Metals and Non-Metals Have Different Physical Properties

1) All metals have <u>metallic bonding</u>, which causes them to have <u>similar</u> basic physical properties.
2) Non-metals <u>don't</u> have metallic bonding, so they have different properties to metals.

Metals	Non-metals
Tend to look <u>shiny</u>.	Tend to look <u>dull</u>.
<u>Great conductors</u> of heat and electricity.	<u>Poor conductors</u> of heat and electricity.
Tend to have <u>higher</u> densities.	Often have <u>lower</u> densities.
<u>High</u> melting and boiling points.	<u>Lower</u> melting and boiling points.
Usually <u>solid</u> at room temperature.	Usually <u>gases</u> or <u>liquids</u> at room temperature.
Get <u>more reactive</u> as you go <u>down</u> the periodic table.	Get <u>less reactive</u> as you go <u>down</u> the periodic table.
Form compounds with <u>ionic</u> or <u>metallic</u> bonds.	Form compounds with <u>ionic</u> or <u>covalent</u> bonds.

You can 'rock out' to metal, you can sway gently to non-metal...

When it comes to properties, metals and non-metals couldn't be much more opposite. Much like me and my sister...

Q1   Where are non-metals found in the periodic table?   [1 mark]

Q2   State three properties of metals.   [3 marks]

Group 1 Elements

Group 1 elements are metals found on the far left of the periodic table. As metals go, they're pretty reactive.

The Group 1 Elements are Reactive Metals

1) The Group 1 metals are lithium, sodium, potassium, rubidium, caesium and francium.

2) They all have one electron in their outer shell so they're very reactive and share similar properties.

3) As you go down Group 1, the elements get bigger as they each gain an extra shell of electrons. For example:

Lithium   Sodium   Potassium

electron shells

single outer electron

Group 1	Group 2
3 Li Lithium 6.9	
11 Na Sodium 23.0	
19 K Potassium 39.1	
37 Rb Rubidium 85.5	
55 Cs Caesium 132.9	
87 Fr Francium	

4) As you go down Group 1, the properties of the elements change. For example:
- reactivity increases.
- melting and boiling points get lower.

In the exam, you could be given the property of one Group 1 metal and asked to predict the property of another from given trends (see page 101).

5) These patterns in the properties down the group are called trends.

Melting and Boiling Points Decrease Down Group 1

1) Group 1 metals are held together with metallic bonds (see page 106).

2) In metallic bonds, the outer electron of each atom is free to move around.

3) There are strong attractions between these electrons and nuclei of the metal atoms.

4) As you go down Group 1, the atoms get bigger.
This means that the nucleus is further away from the free electrons. So the attractions get weaker.

5) This means less energy is needed to break the metallic bonds and turn the solid metal into a liquid and then to a gas. So melting and boiling points decrease down the group.

Group 1 Metals are Very Reactive

1) Group 1 metals easily lose their single outer electron to form a 1+ ion.
This gives them a full outer shell.

2) The more easily a metal loses its outer electrons, the more reactive it is — so the Group 1 metals are very reactive.

3) As you go down Group 1, the elements get bigger and so more reactive.

4) The outer electron is less strongly attracted to the nucleus because it's further away.
This means that the electron is more easily lost, as less energy is needed to remove it.

$$Li \rightarrow Li^+ + e^-$$

Wanna know more about Group 1 metals? K. Really? Na...

As you go down Group 1, the elements gain extra electron shells, causing the patterns in properties and reactivity.

Q1   Explain the increase in reactivity as you go down Group 1.   [3 marks]

Reactions of Group 1 Elements

You've just seen how Group 1 elements get <u>more reactive</u> as you go down the group. But different Group 1 elements react with the same substance to form the same <u>type</u> of product. Let's take a look at this in action.

Group 1 Elements React in Similar Ways

1) <u>Group 1</u> elements can take part in different reactions.
2) All Group 1 elements have <u>one electron</u> in their <u>outer shell</u>. So they will all react in <u>similar</u> ways.
3) Different Group 1 metals will react with a particular reactant to produce the <u>same type of product</u>.

> • The reactions of Group 1 metals with <u>chlorine gas</u> produce <u>metal chlorides</u>.
> • The reactions of Group 1 metals with <u>oxygen in moist air</u> produce <u>metal oxides</u>.
> • The reactions of Group 1 metals with <u>water</u> produce <u>metal hydroxides and hydrogen gas</u>.

4) This means that the <u>balanced symbol equations</u> (see p.79) will follow the <u>same pattern</u> — make sure you know how to write these for Group 1 reactions.
5) Although the <u>reactions are similar</u>, the reactions become <u>faster</u> as you go <u>down</u> the group. This is because the elements become <u>more reactive</u> (see previous page).
6) So, if you know how one Group 1 metal reacts, you can use the <u>pattern</u> of reactivity to <u>predict</u> how other Group 1 metals will react and the <u>products</u> that will form.

Group 1 Metals React in Moist Air

1) The Group 1 metals are <u>shiny</u> when <u>freshly cut</u> but they quickly react with <u>oxygen</u> in <u>moist air</u>.
2) This makes them turn a <u>dull grey</u>.
3) This is because a layer of <u>metal oxide</u> is formed on the surface.
4) Different types of <u>oxide</u> will form depending on the Group 1 metal.
5) As you go down Group 1, the elements react much more <u>quickly</u>.

Moist air is a mixture of air and water vapour.

Reaction with Chlorine Produces a Salt

1) The Group 1 metals react <u>violently</u> when heated in <u>chlorine gas</u> (a Group 7 element — see page 99).
2) The reaction produces <u>white salts</u> called '<u>metal chlorides</u>'.
3) As you go down the group, the reaction with chlorine gets <u>faster</u>.
4) This is because reactivity <u>increases</u> down the group.

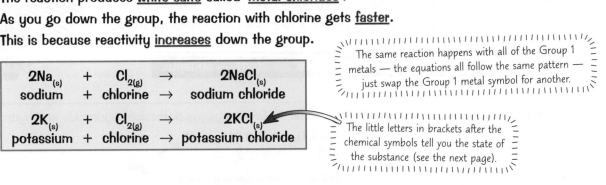

$$2Na_{(s)} + Cl_{2(g)} \rightarrow 2NaCl_{(s)}$$
sodium + chlorine → sodium chloride

$$2K_{(s)} + Cl_{2(g)} \rightarrow 2KCl_{(s)}$$
potassium + chlorine → potassium chloride

The same reaction happens with all of the Group 1 metals — the equations all follow the same pattern — just swap the Group 1 metal symbol for another.

The little letters in brackets after the chemical symbols tell you the state of the substance (see the next page).

I left some lithium in moist air — still not as dull as revision...

It might seem like there are loads of different reactions to learn, but if you remember that the reactions for the different Group 1 metals follow similar patterns, it will make your revision a whole lot easier.

Q1   Which Group 1 element will have the slowest reaction with chlorine gas?   [1 mark]

More Reactions of Group 1 Elements

That's right, we have even <u>more</u> reactions to learn on this page. But some of these cause <u>explosions</u>. Boom.

Reaction with Cold Water Produces a Hydroxide and Hydrogen Gas

1) When the <u>Group 1 metals</u> are put in <u>water</u>, they react to produce <u>hydrogen gas</u> and a metal <u>hydroxide</u>. For example, here's the overall equation for the reaction of <u>lithium</u> with <u>water</u>:

$$2Li_{(s)} + 2H_2O_{(l)} \rightarrow 2LiOH_{(aq)} + H_{2(g)}$$
lithium + water → lithium hydroxide + hydrogen

The symbol equations for the reactions of the other Group 1 metals follow the same pattern.

2) As you go <u>down</u> Group 1, the elements become <u>more reactive</u> (rubidium and caesium actually <u>explode</u>).

3) You can see this in the <u>rate of reaction</u> with water. You add a <u>small piece</u> of a Group 1 metal to a container of <u>water</u> and measure <u>how long</u> it takes for the metal to completely <u>disappear</u>. Then <u>repeat</u> with pieces of other Group 1 metals that are the <u>same size</u>.

4) The more reactive the element is, the quicker it will <u>react completely</u> with the water and disappear.

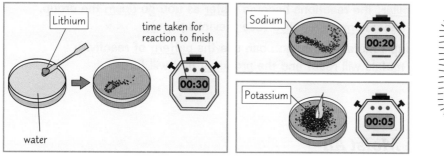

Make sure you know the formulas for the substances involved in Group 1 reactions, e.g. water and hydroxides, and that you can work out the formulas of Group 1 ionic compounds (see p.104).

- <u>Lithium</u> takes longer than sodium or potassium to react, so it's the <u>least reactive</u>. It <u>moves slowly</u> around the surface, <u>fizzing</u>, until it <u>disappears</u>.
- Sodium <u>fizzes rapidly</u> and <u>moves slowly</u> around the surface, and may <u>catch fire</u>.
- <u>Potassium</u> takes the shortest time to react of these three elements, so it's the <u>most reactive</u>. It reacts <u>violently</u>, burns with a <u>lilac flame</u> — and sometimes <u>explodes</u>.

State Symbols Tell You the State of a Substance in an Equation

1) Chemical reactions can be shown using <u>symbol equations</u>.
2) Symbol equations can also include <u>state symbols</u> next to each substance.
3) State symbols tell you what <u>physical state</u> the reactants and products are in:

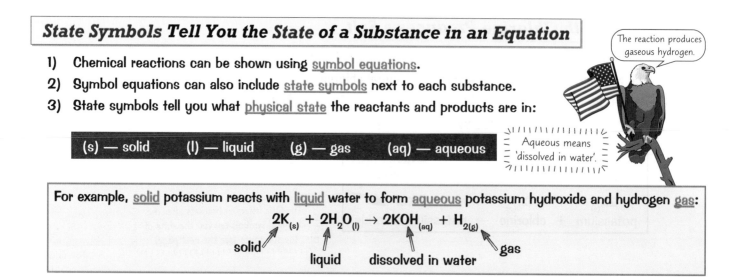

The reaction produces gaseous hydrogen.

| (s) — solid | (l) — liquid | (g) — gas | (aq) — aqueous |

Aqueous means 'dissolved in water'.

For example, <u>solid</u> potassium reacts with <u>liquid</u> water to form <u>aqueous</u> potassium hydroxide and hydrogen <u>gas</u>:

$$2K_{(s)} + 2H_2O_{(l)} \rightarrow 2KOH_{(aq)} + H_{2(g)}$$

solid   liquid   dissolved in water   gas

Back to the drawing board with my lithium swim shorts design...

You need to be careful when reacting Group 1 metals with water, as they fizz in water and might explode. Cool.

Q1   Give the balanced symbol equation for the reaction between rubidium and water.   [2 marks]

Group 7 Elements

Here's a page on another periodic table group that you need to be familiar with — the halogens.

Group 7 Elements are Known as the Halogens

Group 7 is made up of the non-metal elements fluorine, chlorine, bromine, iodine and astatine.

1) All Group 7 elements have 7 electrons in their outer shell.
This means they all have similar chemical properties (they react in similar ways).

2) As elements, the halogens form molecules that contain
two atoms joined together by a covalent bond (e.g. Cl_2).

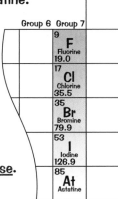

There are Patterns in the Properties of the Group 7 Elements

1) As you go down Group 7, the melting points and boiling points of the halogens increase.

2) This is because, as you go down the group, the number of electrons in each
atom increases. More electrons means there are greater forces between the molecules.
So more energy is needed to break the forces (see p.113 for more).

3) This means that at room temperature and pressure:

- Fluorine (F_2) is a pale yellow gas.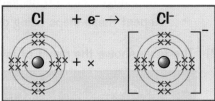
- Chlorine (Cl_2) is a green gas.
- Bromine (Br_2) is a red-brown liquid, which gives off an orange vapour at room temperature.
- Iodine (I_2) is a dark grey crystalline solid which gives off a purple vapour when heated.

Reactivity Decreases Going Down Group 7

1) Atoms with a full outer electron shell have a stable electronic structure.

2) A halogen atom only needs to gain one electron
to form a 1– ion with a full outer shell.

3) As you go down Group 7, the halogens become less reactive.

4) This is because the atoms have more shells of electrons.
So the outer shell gets further from the nucleus.

5) This makes it harder to attract the extra electron to fill the outer shell.

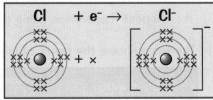

$$Cl + e^- \rightarrow Cl^-$$

The Halogens React With Group 1 Metals to Form Salts

1) The halogens will react vigorously with Group 1 metals (see page 97)
to form salts called 'metal halides'. For example:

$2Na_{(s)} + Cl_{2(g)} \rightarrow 2NaCl_{(s)}$ sodium + chlorine → sodium chloride	$2K_{(s)} + Br_{2(l)} \rightarrow 2KBr_{(s)}$ potassium + bromine → potassium bromide

All the reactions between Group 1
and Group 7 elements follow this
pattern — make sure you can write
equations for any of them.

2) Halogens higher up in Group 7 react more vigorously
with the alkali metals because they're more reactive.

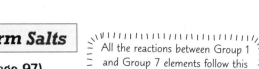

To know what type of salt is formed by a halogen,
just replace '-ine' with '-ide'. So, fluorine forms
fluoride salts and iodine forms iodide salts.

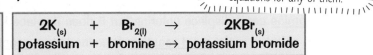

Halogens — one electron short of a full shell...

Don't get your trends mixed up with Group 1. Down Group 7, reactivity decreases and boiling point increases.

Q1   The melting point of chlorine (Cl_2) is –101 °C. Predict whether bromine (Br_2)
would be a solid, a liquid or a gas at –101 °C. Explain your answer.   [2 marks]

Displacement Reactions of Group 7

The halogens are a pretty competitive lot really. In fact the <u>more reactive</u> ones will push the <u>less reactive</u> ones out of a compound. Has nobody ever taught them that it's bad manners to push?

A More Reactive Halogen Will Displace a Less Reactive One

1) The elements in Group 7 take part in <u>displacement reactions</u>.

2) A <u>displacement reaction</u> is where a <u>more reactive</u> element 'pushes out' (<u>displaces</u>) a <u>less reactive</u> element from a compound.

3) For example, <u>chlorine</u> is more reactive than <u>bromine</u> (it's higher up Group 7). If you add <u>chlorine water</u> (a <u>solution</u> of <u>Cl_2</u> dissolved in water) to <u>potassium bromide</u> solution, the chlorine will <u>displace</u> the <u>bromine</u> from the salt solution.

chlorine water

colourless solution

potassium bromide

orange solution

bromine forming in solution

4) The <u>equation</u> for this reaction is shown below:

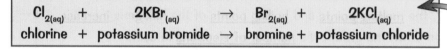

$$Cl_{2(aq)} + 2KBr_{(aq)} \rightarrow Br_{2(aq)} + 2KCl_{(aq)}$$

chlorine + potassium bromide $\rightarrow$ bromine + potassium chloride

If you ever need to write an equation for a different halogen displacement reaction, they all follow this pattern.

Displacement Reactions Show Reactivity Trends

1) You can use <u>displacement reactions</u> to show that halogens get <u>less reactive</u> down the group.

- Measure out a small amount of a <u>halide salt solution</u> in a test tube.
- Add a few drops of a <u>halogen solution</u>. Shake the tube gently.
- If you see an obvious <u>colour change</u>, then a reaction has happened. In this reaction, the halogen has <u>displaced</u> the halide ions from the salt. So the halogen is <u>more reactive</u> than the halide in the salt.
- If you <u>don't</u> see a colour change, then a reaction has <u>not</u> taken place. The halogen has not displaced the halide so it must be <u>less reactive</u>.
- Repeat these steps using <u>different combinations</u> of halide salt and halogen.

Get out of here, Bro!

2) The table shows the result of mixing different <u>halogen waters</u> with different <u>potassium halide solutions</u>.

Start with:	Potassium chloride solution $KCl_{(aq)}$ — colourless	Potassium bromide solution $KBr_{(aq)}$ — colourless	Potassium iodide solution $KI_{(aq)}$ — colourless
Add chlorine water $Cl_{2\,(aq)}$ — colourless	no reaction	orange solution (Br_2) formed	brown solution (I_2) formed
Add bromine water $Br_{2\,(aq)}$ — orange	no reaction	no reaction	brown solution (I_2) formed
Add iodine water $I_{2\,(aq)}$ — brown	no reaction	no reaction	no reaction

3) <u>Chlorine</u> displaces both bromine and iodine from salt solutions. <u>Bromine</u> can't displace chlorine but it does displace iodine. <u>Iodine</u> can't displace chlorine or bromine.

4) So chlorine is the <u>most reactive</u>, bromine is <u>less reactive</u> than chlorine but <u>more reactive</u> than iodine and iodine is the <u>least reactive</u>.

5) This shows the <u>reactivity trend</u> — the halogens get <u>less reactive</u> as you go <u>down</u> the group.

New information displaces old information from my brain...

If you remember that the halogens get less reactive as you go down the group, you can work out what will happen when you mix any halogen with any halide salt. You need to know the colour changes that go with the reactions too.

Q1 A student added a few drops of chlorine water to some potassium iodide solution. The solution turned brown. Explain why the solution changed colour.

[1 mark]

Group 0 Elements

The <u>Group 0 elements</u> are the last group in the periodic table.
They don't react with very much and you can't even see them — making them, well, a bit dull really.

Group 0 Elements are All Inert, Colourless Gases

1) Group 0 elements include the elements
<u>helium</u>, <u>neon</u> and <u>argon</u> (plus a few others).

2) They all have <u>eight electrons</u> in their outer electron shell,
apart from helium which has two. This gives them a <u>full outer shell</u>.

3) Since their outer shell is <u>full</u>, they're very stable.

4) This stability makes them very <u>unreactive</u> (<u>inert</u>). This means they
don't form molecules easily. So the elements are <u>single atoms</u>.

5) Group 0 elements have <u>low melting</u> and <u>boiling points</u>.
This means that they're all <u>colourless gases</u> at room temperature.

6) As the Group 0 gases are unreactive, they're <u>non-flammable</u> — they won't set on fire.

Helium only has electrons in the first shell, which only needs 2 to be filled.

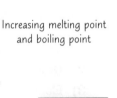

Group 0		
Group 6	Group 7	2 **He** Helium 4.0
		10 **Ne** Neon 20.2
		18 **Ar** Argon 39.9
		36 **Kr** Krypton 83.8
		54 **Xe** Xenon 131.3
		86 **Rn** Radon

There are Patterns in the Properties of the Group 0 Elements

1) As you go down the group, there is an <u>increase</u>
in the <u>number of electrons</u> in each <u>atom</u>.

2) This means that there are <u>stronger forces</u> between the atoms.

3) <u>More energy</u> is needed to break these stronger forces.

4) So melting and boiling points <u>increase</u> down the group.

5) In the exam you may be given the melting point or boiling
point of one noble gas and asked to <u>estimate</u> the value for
<u>another one</u>. So make sure you know the <u>pattern</u>.

The melting points and boiling points are still all low, even though they increase down the group.

Group 0 Element
helium
neon
argon
krypton
xenon
radon

Increasing melting point
and boiling point

EXAMPLE: Neon is a gas at 25 °C. Predict what state helium is at this temperature.

Helium has a lower boiling point than neon as it is further up the group.

So, helium must also be a gas at 25 °C.

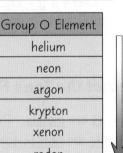

Here's another pattern. You don't have to learn this one...

EXAMPLE: Radon has a boiling point of −62 °C and krypton has a
boiling point of −153 °C. Predict the boiling point of xenon.

Xenon comes in between radon and krypton in the group.
So, you can predict that its boiling point would be between their boiling points.
E.g. xenon has a boiling point of −100 °C.

The actual boiling point of xenon is −108 °C — which is between −62 °C and −153 °C. Just as predicted.

...or this one.

Arrrgon — the pirate element...

As Group 0 elements don't really react there isn't too much to learn about them. If you understand why they are
unreactive and the trend in melting and boiling points as you go down the group, you're sorted.

Q1   Which has a higher boiling point, xenon or neon? [1 mark]

Q2   Explain why argon is very unreactive. [2 marks]

Ions

You've got to know quite a bit about <u>ions</u>. Thankfully, you've come to the right place...

Simple Ions Form When Atoms Lose or Gain Electrons

1) <u>Ions</u> are <u>charged</u> particles — they can be <u>single atoms</u> (e.g. Na^+) or <u>groups of atoms</u> (e.g. NO_3^-).

2) Ions are formed when atoms <u>gain</u> or <u>lose</u> electrons.

3) They do this to get a <u>full outer shell</u>. This is because a full outer shell is very <u>stable</u>.

Ions have Different Numbers of Protons and Electrons

1) <u>Negative ions</u> form when atoms <u>gain electrons</u> — they have more electrons than protons.
   <u>Positive ions</u> form when atoms <u>lose electrons</u> — they have more protons than electrons.

2) The <u>number</u> of electrons lost or gained is the same as the <u>charge</u> on the ion.
   E.g. if 2 electrons are <u>lost</u> the charge is <u>2+</u>. If 3 electrons are <u>gained</u> the charge is <u>3−</u>.

3) You can calculate the number of <u>protons</u> and <u>neutrons</u> in an ion the same way as for
   an atom (see page 92). Working out the number of <u>electrons</u> in an ion is a bit different.

   - F^- — there's a <u>single negative charge</u>, so there must be one more electron than protons.
     F has an atomic number of 9, so has 9 protons. So F^- must have 9 + 1 = <u>10 electrons</u>.
   - Fe^{2+} — there's a <u>2+ charge</u>, so there must be two more protons than electrons.
     Fe has an atomic number of 26, so has 26 protons. So Fe^{2+} must have 26 − 2 = <u>24 electrons</u>.

You Can Predict the Ions Formed by Elements in Groups 1 and 7

1) <u>Group 1 elements</u> are <u>metals</u>. They <u>lose</u> electrons to form <u>positive ions</u>.

2) <u>Group 7 elements</u> are <u>non-metals</u>. They <u>gain</u> electrons to form <u>negative ions</u>.

3) Elements in the same <u>group</u> all have the same number of <u>outer electrons</u>. So they have to <u>lose or gain</u>
   the same number to get a full outer shell. And this means that they form ions with the <u>same charge</u>.

4) You <u>don't</u> have to <u>remember</u> what ions <u>most elements</u> form. You can just look at the periodic table.

- <u>Group 1</u> elements have <u>one electron</u> in their outer shell.
- They form ions by <u>losing one</u> electron.
- They form <u>1+</u> ions with a full outer shell.

- <u>Group 7</u> elements have <u>seven electrons</u> in their outer shell.
- They form ions by <u>gaining one</u> electron.
- They form <u>1−</u> ions with a full outer shell.

H																	He
Li	Be											B	C	N	O	F	Ne
Na	Mg											Al	Si	P	S	Cl	Ar
K	Ca	Sc	Ti	V	Cr	Mn	Fe	Co	Ni	Cu	Zn	Ga	Ge	As	Se	Br	Kr
Rb	Sr	Y	Zr	Nb	Mo	Tc	Ru	Rh	Pd	Ag	Cd	In	Sn	Sb	Te	I	Xe
Cs	Ba	La	Hf	Ta	W	Re	Os	Ir	Pt	Au	Hg	Tl	Pb	Bi	Po	At	Rn
Fr	Ra	Ac	Rf	Db	Sg	Bh	Hs	Mt	Ds	Rg	Cn	Uut	Fl	Uup	Lv	Uus	Uuo

I've got my ion you...

You need to be able to predict the ions the atoms in Groups 1 and 7 will form. So have a look at the periodic table above to make sure you know what charged ion each group forms. Keep looking till you've got it sorted.

Q1   Calcium (Ca) has an atomic number of 20. How many electrons will a calcium ion (Ca^{2+}) have?   [1 mark]

Ionic Bonding

You need to be able to draw <u>dot and cross diagrams</u> to show how ions form. Not quite noughts and crosses...

Forming Ionic Compounds — Transfer of Electrons

1) When a <u>metal</u> and a <u>non-metal</u> react together:
   - the <u>metal atoms lose</u> electrons to form <u>positive ions</u>.
   - the <u>non-metal atoms gain electrons</u> to form <u>negative ions</u>.

2) These oppositely charged ions are <u>strongly attracted</u> to one another by <u>electrostatic forces</u>.
   E.g. the <u>1+ ions</u> formed by Group 1 elements are strongly attracted to the
   <u>1– ions</u> formed by Group 7 elements. These attractions are called <u>ionic bonds</u>.

A 2D model shows that the particles in an ionic compound are positive and negative ions.

Dot and Cross Diagrams can Show the Formation of Ionic Compounds

1) Dot and cross diagrams show the <u>arrangement</u> of electrons in an atom or ion.

2) They can also be used to model what happens to the electrons when atoms <u>react</u> with each other.

3) Each electron is represented by a <u>dot</u> or a <u>cross</u>.

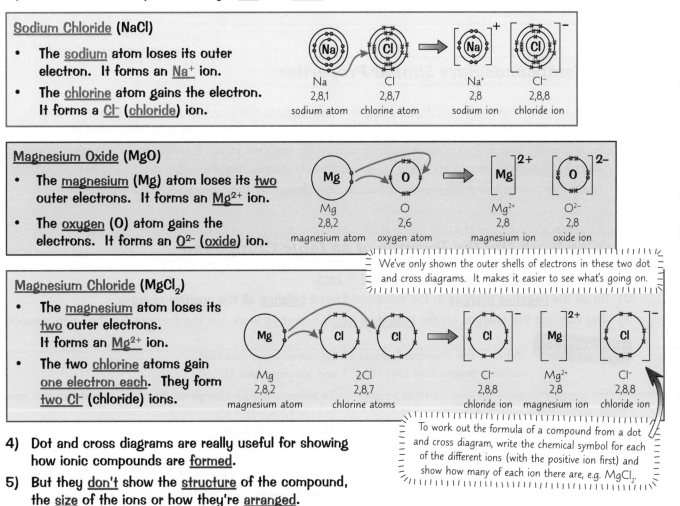

<u>Sodium Chloride</u> (NaCl)
- The <u>sodium</u> atom loses its outer electron. It forms an <u>Na$^+$</u> ion.
- The <u>chlorine</u> atom gains the electron. It forms a <u>Cl$^-$</u> (<u>chloride</u>) ion.

Na 2,8,1 sodium atom — Cl 2,8,7 chlorine atom — Na$^+$ 2,8 sodium ion — Cl$^-$ 2,8,8 chloride ion

<u>Magnesium Oxide</u> (MgO)
- The <u>magnesium</u> (Mg) atom loses its <u>two</u> outer electrons. It forms an <u>Mg^{2+}</u> ion.
- The <u>oxygen</u> (O) atom gains the electrons. It forms an <u>O^{2-}</u> (<u>oxide</u>) ion.

Mg 2,8,2 magnesium atom — O 2,6 oxygen atom — Mg^{2+} 2,8 magnesium ion — O^{2-} 2,8 oxide ion

We've only shown the outer shells of electrons in these two dot and cross diagrams. It makes it easier to see what's going on.

<u>Magnesium Chloride</u> (MgCl$_2$)
- The <u>magnesium</u> atom loses its <u>two</u> outer electrons. It forms an <u>Mg^{2+}</u> ion.
- The two <u>chlorine</u> atoms gain <u>one electron each</u>. They form two <u>Cl$^-$</u> (<u>chloride</u>) ions.

Mg 2,8,2 magnesium atom — 2Cl 2,8,7 chlorine atoms — Cl$^-$ 2,8,8 chloride ion — Mg^{2+} 2,8 magnesium ion — Cl$^-$ 2,8,8 chloride ion

To work out the formula of a compound from a dot and cross diagram, write the chemical symbol for each of the different ions (with the positive ion first) and show how many of each ion there are, e.g. MgCl$_2$.

4) Dot and cross diagrams are really useful for showing how ionic compounds are <u>formed</u>.

5) But they <u>don't</u> show the <u>structure</u> of the compound, the <u>size</u> of the ions or how they're <u>arranged</u>.

Any old ion, any old ion — any, any, any old ion...

When drawing dot and cross diagrams, don't worry about showing the inner shells of electrons.
The important thing to show is the arrangement of electrons in the outer shell.

Q1 Draw a dot and cross diagram to show how a potassium atom (electronic structure 2,8,8,1) and a chlorine atom (electronic structure 2,8,7) react to form potassium chloride (KCl). [3 marks]

Ionic Compounds

Here's a bit more about how <u>ionic compounds</u> form and the <u>properties</u> that make them special...

Ionic Compounds Have a Giant Ionic Lattice Structure

1) Ionic compounds are made up of lots of <u>positive</u> and <u>negative</u> ions held together by ionic bonds.

2) <u>Ionic compounds</u> always have <u>giant ionic lattice</u> structures.
    This means they contain <u>lots of ions</u> arranged in a <u>pattern</u>.

3) There are very strong <u>electrostatic forces of attraction</u> between <u>oppositely charged</u> ions, in <u>all directions</u>.

<u>Sodium chloride</u> (NaCl) has a giant ionic lattice structure. It can be drawn in different ways:

- This is a ball and stick model. It shows how the ions are arranged.
- But it doesn't show how big the ions are compared to each other.
- It also doesn't show how the electrons moved to form the compound.
- And it makes it look like there are gaps between the ions. But there aren't really.

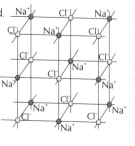

- This is a 3D model. It shows how big the ions are compared to each other.
- It also shows that the ions are ordered in a pattern.
- But it only lets you see the outer layer of the piece of the compound.
- And it doesn't show how the electrons moved to form the compound.

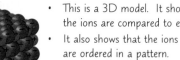 ● = Cl⁻ ● = Na⁺

If you know the distance between the ions, you can work out the length of the sides of a cube-shaped section of a crystal and then calculate its volume using the formula: volume = (side length)³.

Ionic Compounds Have Similar Properties

- Ionic compounds generally have <u>high melting</u> and <u>boiling points</u> due to <u>strong attractions</u> between oppositely charged ions. It takes lots of <u>energy</u> to overcome these attractions compared to some other types of bonding.
- Solid ionic compounds <u>don't</u> conduct electricity because the ions can't move. But when an ionic compound <u>melts</u> or is <u>dissolved</u> in solution, the ions are <u>free to move</u>. So ionic compounds that are <u>molten</u> or <u>dissolved</u> can <u>conduct electricity</u>.
- Many ionic compounds <u>dissolve</u> in water because their <u>charges</u> let them <u>interact</u> with the <u>water</u> molecules.

You Can Work Out the Formula of an Ionic Compound

1) The <u>overall charge</u> of <u>any ionic compound</u> is <u>zero</u>.

2) So all the <u>negative charges</u> in the compound must <u>balance</u> all the <u>positive charges</u>.

3) You can use the charges on the <u>individual ions</u> present to work out the formula for the ionic compound.

EXAMPLE: What is the chemical formula of the ionic compound that contains magnesium ions (Mg^{2+}) and bromine ions (Br^-)?

The <u>overall charge</u> on the formula must be <u>zero</u>, so work out the ratio of Mg : Br that gives an overall neutral charge.

To balance the 2+ charge on Mg^{2+}, you need two Br^- ions: $(+2) + (2 \times -1) = 0$.
The formula is $MgBr_2$

- To <u>name</u> the compound you always name the <u>positive</u> metal ion <u>first</u> (this has the same name as the element). You then name the <u>negative</u> non-metal ion. E.g. lithium bromide (Li^+ = positive ion, Br^- = negative ion).
- A <u>negative ion's</u> name will end in <u>-ate</u> if the ion contains <u>oxygen</u> and at least one <u>other</u> element (e.g. nitrate, NO_3^-). Negative ions end in <u>-ide</u> (e.g. iodide, I^-) if the ion contains <u>just one element</u> (apart from hydroxide ions, OH^-).

What's a chemist's favourite vegetable? A giant ionic lettuce...

Make sure you remember that even though individual ions are charged, ionic compounds are neutral overall.

Q1   Give the formula of the ionic compound, lithium oxide, which contains the ions Li^+ and O^{2-}.   [1 mark]

Revision Questions for Chapter C2

Well, that's <u>Chapter C2</u> almost done and dusted — just a few more questions to go...

- Try these questions and <u>tick off each one</u> when you <u>get it right</u>.
- When you've done <u>all the questions</u> for a topic and are <u>completely happy</u> with it, tick off the topic.

Atoms and Isotopes (p.90-92) ☑

1) Name the four basic elements that the Ancient Greeks believed made up everything. ☑

2) Describe the experiment that Rutherford carried out that showed the plum pudding model of the atom was wrong. ☑

3) Which subatomic particle has a relative mass of 1 and a relative charge of 0? ☑

4) How big is the nucleus of an atom compared to the diameter of the atom? ☑

5) What does the mass number tell you about an atom? ☑

6) How can you calculate the number of neutrons in an atom? ☑

7) True or false? Isotopes have the same number of neutrons but a different number of protons. ☑

The Periodic Table and Electronic Structure (p.93-94) ☑

8) Which scientist's periodic table led directly to the one that we use today? ☑

9) What does the period number tell you about the electronic structure of an element? ☑

10) How many electrons can the first electron shell of an atom contain? ☑

11) A magnesium atom contains 12 electrons. What is the electronic structure of magnesium? ☑

Groups of the Periodic Table (p.95-101) ☑

12) True or false? Metals form positive ions when they react. ☑

13) How do metals get a full outer shell of electrons? ☑

14) Give two properties of non-metals. ☑

15) How many electrons do Group 1 metals have in their outer shell? ☑

16) How does the boiling point of the elements change as you go down Group 1? ☑

17) Why do Group 1 metals turn a dull grey when left in moist air? ☑

18) Name the type of salt that is formed when a Group 1 metal reacts with chlorine gas. ☑

19) What would you expect to see when a piece of lithium is added to water? ☑

20) What is the state symbol for an aqueous substance? ☑

21) Describe fluorine's state and appearance at room temperature. ☑

22) Describe how the reactivity of the Group 7 elements changes as you go down the group. ☑

23) Give a balanced symbol equation of the reaction between potassium (K) and bromine (Br_2). ☑

24) A student mixes a halogen solution with a halide salt solution.
She observes a colour change. What does this show? ☑

25) Name two Group 0 elements. ☑

26) Which Group 0 element has the lowest boiling point? ☑

Ionic Compounds (p.102-104) ☑

27) Does a positive ion have more protons or more electrons? ☑

28) Draw a dot and cross diagram to show how a sodium atom (electronic structure 2,8,1) and a chlorine atom (electronic structure 2,8,7) form sodium chloride (NaCl). ☑

29) Why can ionic compounds conduct electricity when molten but not when solid? ☑

30) What is the overall charge of an ionic compound? ☑

Metallic Bonding

Ever wondered what makes <u>metals</u> tick? Well, either way, this is the page for you.

Metallic Bonding Involves Free Electrons

1) <u>Metals</u> are held together in a <u>giant structure</u>.
This means that <u>lots of atoms</u> are all <u>bonded together</u> to make the metal.

2) The <u>bonding</u> in metals can be described by a model.

3) This model says that the electrons in the <u>outer shell</u> of the metal atoms are <u>free</u> to <u>move around</u>.

4) The <u>positive metal ions</u> sit in a 'sea' of shared <u>negative electrons</u>.

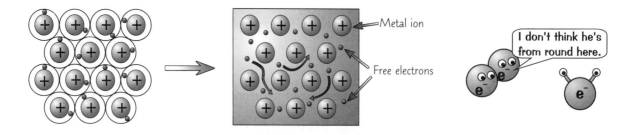

5) There are strong <u>electrostatic forces</u> of <u>attraction</u> between the <u>metal ions</u> and the free <u>electrons</u>.

6) The forces of attraction are known as <u>metallic bonding</u>.

7) These forces <u>hold</u> the <u>ions</u> close together.

8) Metallic bonding is very <u>strong</u>.

Metallic Bonding is Responsible for the Properties of Metals

1) The <u>bulk properties</u> of metals are related to their <u>metallic bonding</u>.

2) The forces between the metal ions and the sea of free electrons are very <u>strong</u>. This means that they need <u>lots of energy</u> to be broken.

> Bulk properties of a material come from how all the particles in a material behave together.

3) Because of this, most substances with metallic bonds have very <u>high</u> melting and boiling points.

4) The <u>free electrons</u> can move around, so they can carry electrical current and heat through the material. This makes metals good <u>conductors</u> of <u>electricity</u> and <u>heat</u>.

5) The layers of atoms in a metal can <u>slide</u> over each other <u>without</u> the metallic bonds <u>breaking</u>.

6) This means metals can be <u>stretched</u> into wires (they're <u>ductile</u>).

7) It also means metals can be easily <u>hammered</u>, <u>bent</u> or <u>rolled</u> into a shape without breaking (they're <u>malleable</u>).

> The properties of metals make them useful (see p.123).

I saw a metal on the bus once — he was the conductor...

Remember, most of the properties of metals come from their metallic bonding.

Q1   a) Copper is a metal that can be used in electrical circuits.
           Explain why copper can conduct electricity.   [1 mark]
      b) Explain why it is easy to shape metals.   [1 mark]

Reactivity and Reactions of Metals

Not all metals are made equal. Some are more <u>reactive</u> than others...

The Reactivity Series — How Well a Metal Reacts

1) The <u>reactivity series</u> puts metals in <u>order</u> of how reactive they are.

2) Metals at the <u>top</u> of the reactivity series are the <u>most</u> reactive, and metals at the <u>bottom</u> are the <u>least</u> reactive.

3) When <u>metal atoms</u> react, they form <u>positive ions</u> by losing one or more electrons.

4) The <u>higher</u> up in the reactivity series a metal is, the more easily it loses electrons and forms <u>positive ions</u>.

5) You can use the reactivity series to <u>predict</u> how a metal will react.

6) You can work out the <u>order of reactivity</u> of different metals by looking at their <u>reactions</u> with other compounds (see below and next page).

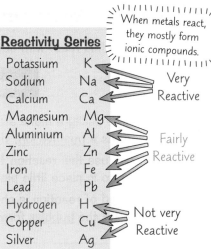

Hydrogen is a non-metal but is often included in the reactivity series.

When metals react, they mostly form ionic compounds.

Reactivity Series

Potassium	K	Very Reactive
Sodium	Na	
Calcium	Ca	
Magnesium	Mg	Fairly Reactive
Aluminium	Al	
Zinc	Zn	
Iron	Fe	
Lead	Pb	
Hydrogen	H	Not very Reactive
Copper	Cu	
Silver	Ag	

More Reactive Metals Displace Less Reactive Ones

1) If you put a <u>more reactive metal</u> into a solution of a <u>less reactive metal salt</u>, the reactive metal will <u>replace</u> the <u>less reactive metal</u> in the salt.

2) This is known as a <u>displacement reaction</u>.

> <u>Example</u>: Iron is more reactive than copper. So, if you put <u>iron</u> in a solution of <u>copper sulfate</u>, the iron will "<u>kick out</u>" the copper from the salt. You end up with <u>iron sulfate solution</u> and <u>copper metal</u>.
>
> Word equation: copper sulfate   +   iron $\rightarrow$ iron sulfate   +   copper
>
> Symbol equation: $CuSO_{4(aq)}$ + $Fe_{(s)}$ $\rightarrow$ $FeSO_{4(aq)}$ + $Cu_{(s)}$

3) If you put a <u>less reactive metal</u> into a solution of a <u>more reactive metal salt</u>, <u>no</u> displacement reaction will occur.

4) You can use displacement reactions to work out <u>where</u> in the reactivity series a metal should go.

EXAMPLE: A student heats some metals with oxides of other metals and records whether any reactions happen. Use her table of results, below, to work out an order of reactivity for the metals.

- Zinc displaces both copper and iron, so it must be more reactive than both.

- Copper is displaced by both iron and zinc, so it must be less reactive than both.

- Iron can displace copper, but not zinc, so it must go between them.

	copper oxide	iron oxide	zinc oxide
copper	no reaction	no reaction	no reaction
iron	iron oxide and copper formed	no reaction	no reaction
zinc	zinc oxide and copper formed	zinc oxide and iron formed	no reaction

The order of reactivity, from most to least, is: zinc, iron, copper.

And that's why Iron Man never goes swimming in copper sulfate...

If you're asked whether you think a particular displacement reaction will take place, remember the reactivity series. A metal will only displace another metal if it's higher in the reactivity series.

Q1   Using the reactivity series, state whether lead would displace zinc from zinc chloride solution. Explain your answer.
[2 marks]

More Reactions of Metals

Reactive metals tend to do exciting, fizzy things when you drop them into acid or water. If you do the same with an unreactive metal, it'll just sit there. How boring. Here's a bit more detail on reactivity experiments...

How Metals React With Acids Tells You About Their Reactivity

1) Some metals react with acids to make a salt and hydrogen gas.

$$\text{acid} + \text{metal} \rightarrow \text{salt} + \text{hydrogen}$$

2) The more easily a metal atom loses its outer electrons and forms a positive ion, the more reactive it will be.

3) You can use this reaction to put different metals in order of reactivity. All you do is place little pieces of metals into dilute acid.

4) The speed of reaction is shown by how fast the bubbles of hydrogen are given off. The faster the bubbles form, the faster the reaction and the more reactive the metal.

You could monitor the rate of these reactions using a gas syringe (p.145).

The top line shows the equations for the reaction with sulfuric acid.

Magnesium reacts very strongly with cold dilute acids and produces loads of bubbles.

Zinc reacts slowly with dilute acids but will react more quickly if you heat it up.

Copper doesn't react with dilute acids.

Magnesium
$$Mg_{(s)} + H_2SO_{4(aq)} \rightarrow MgSO_{4(aq)} + H_{2(g)}$$
$$Mg_{(s)} + 2HCl_{(aq)} \rightarrow MgCl_{2(aq)} + H_{2(g)}$$

Zinc
$$Zn_{(s)} + H_2SO_{4(aq)} \rightarrow ZnSO_{4(aq)} + H_{2(g)}$$
$$Zn_{(s)} + 2HCl_{(aq)} \rightarrow ZnCl_{2(aq)} + H_{2(g)}$$

Copper
no reaction

The bottom line shows the equations for the reaction with hydrochloric acid.

5) Very reactive metals (like potassium) will react violently with acids.

6) Fairly reactive metals (e.g. aluminium) will fizz a lot.

7) Less reactive metals (e.g. lead) will bubble a bit.

8) Unreactive metals (e.g. copper and silver) will not react with dilute acids at all.

Metals Also React With Water

1) The reactions of metals with water also show the reactivity of metals. This is the basic reaction:

$$\text{metal} + \text{water} \rightarrow \text{metal hydroxide} + \text{hydrogen}$$

2) Very reactive metals like potassium and sodium will react very strongly with water to form metal hydroxides.

E.g. $2Na_{(s)} + 2H_2O_{(l)} \rightarrow 2NaOH_{(aq)} + H_{2(g)}$

3) Metals further down the reactivity series won't react much with cold water.

4) The metals right at the bottom of the reactivity series (e.g. lead, copper and silver) don't react with water at all.

I AM NOT HIGHLY REACTIVE — OK...

This stuff isn't too bad — who knows, you might even get to have a go at these experiments in class...

Q1   A student adds a piece of unknown metal, **X**, to a test tube containing dilute hydrochloric acid. She does not see any bubbles. Suggest what metal **X** might be.

[1 mark]

Chapter C3 — Chemicals of the Natural Environment

Extracting Metals

Metals come from the ground, but we can't just dig 'em up to use straight away — they need to be extracted...

Some Metals can be Extracted by Reduction with Carbon

1) Ores are rocks that have enough metal in them to make it worthwhile extracting the metal from them.

2) Ores often contain compounds of the metal (e.g. metal oxides).

3) Before metals can be used, they need to be extracted from their ores.

4) The position of a metal in the reactivity series (see p.107) tells you how it can be extracted.

5) Metals below carbon in the series are extracted using carbon.

6) Carbon (a non-metal) displaces (kicks out) the metal from the ore.

7) Carbon can only displace metals which are less reactive than carbon itself.

There's more about oxidation and reduction on p.122.

8) During the process, carbon gains oxygen — it's oxidised.

9) The metal has its oxygen removed by carbon — it's reduced.

10) For example, zinc can be extracted from its ore using carbon:

The Reactivity Series	
Potassium	K
Sodium	Na
Calcium	Ca
Magnesium	Mg
Aluminium	Al
CARBON	C
Zinc	Zn
Iron	Fe
Lead	Pb
Copper	Cu
Silver	Ag

Extracted using electrolysis

Extracted by reduction using carbon

---

1) First, the compounds in the zinc ore are reacted to form zinc oxide (ZnO).

2) To extract the zinc, you need to heat the zinc oxide with carbon at a high temperature. The carbon reduces the zinc oxide by removing the oxygen.

3) This forms a mixture of zinc vapour and either carbon monoxide or carbon dioxide.

$$ZnO_{(s)} + C_{(s)} \rightarrow Zn_{(g)} + CO_{(g)}$$
$$2ZnO_{(s)} + C_{(s)} \rightarrow 2Zn_{(g)} + CO_{2(g)}$$

4) The impure zinc vapour is condensed (turned into a liquid).

5) The zinc is then separated from the mixture and purified.

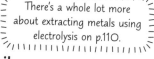

Reduction of metal

Some Metals have to be Extracted by Electrolysis

There's a whole lot more about extracting metals using electrolysis on p.110.

1) Metals more reactive than carbon are extracted from ores using electrolysis.

2) First the metal compound is melted. Then an electric current is passed through it. This causes the metal ore to decompose — the metal is split from the rest of the ore.

3) Lots of energy is needed to melt the ore and produce the electric current.

4) Electricity is expensive so this process is much more expensive than reduction with carbon.

[Please insert ore-ful pun here]...

Make sure you've got that reactivity series sorted in your head. If a metal's below carbon in the reactivity series, then it's less reactive than carbon. That means that it can be extracted from its ore by reduction using carbon.

Q1   How would you extract iron from its metal ore? Explain your answer.   [2 marks]

Chapter C3 — Chemicals of the Natural Environment

Electrolysis

Electrolysis uses <u>electricity</u> to cause a reaction. It's actually pretty cool. No, really...

Electrolysis Means 'Splitting Up with Electricity'

1) An <u>electrolyte</u> is just a <u>liquid or solution</u> that can <u>conduct electricity</u>.
   For example, an ionic compound that's either <u>dissolved</u> in water, or <u>melted</u> so it's a liquid.
2) An <u>electrode</u> is a <u>solid</u> that is put in the electrolyte and <u>conducts electricity</u>.
3) In <u>electrolysis</u>, two electrodes are placed in an electrolyte.
   An <u>electric current</u> is passed through the electrolyte.
4) The <u>ions</u> in the electrolyte move to the <u>electrodes</u>, where they <u>react</u>. The compound then <u>breaks down</u>.
5) <u>Positive metal or hydrogen ions</u> move to the <u>cathode</u> (negative electrode). Here, they <u>gain</u> electrons.
6) <u>Negative non-metal ions</u> move towards the <u>anode</u> (positive electrode). Here, they <u>lose</u> electrons.
7) As ions gain or lose electrons they form the <u>uncharged element</u>. They're <u>removed</u> from the electrolyte.
8) A <u>flow of charge</u> is created through the <u>electrolyte</u> as the ions travel to the electrodes.

Elect Toad!

He's the best!
Froget the rest!

Electrolysis of Molten Ionic Solids Forms Elements

1) <u>Molten ionic compounds can</u> be electrolysed because
   the ions can <u>move freely</u> and conduct electricity.
2) Molten ionic liquids are always broken up into their <u>elements</u>.
3) The <u>metal</u> (or hydrogen) forms at the <u>cathode</u>. The <u>non-metal</u> is formed at the <u>anode</u>.

> The electrodes should be inert (unreactive) so they don't react with the electrolyte.

> When molten <u>lead bromide</u> is electrolysed, <u>lead</u> forms at the cathode and <u>bromine</u> forms at the anode.

Metals can be Extracted From Their Ores Using Electrolysis

1) <u>Electrolysis</u> can be used to <u>extract</u> metals from their <u>ores</u> that can't be reduced by <u>carbon</u> (p.109).
2) Aluminium is extracted from an ore that contains <u>aluminium oxide</u>, Al_2O_3.
3) Aluminium oxide is <u>melted</u> at a <u>high temperature</u> and an <u>electric current</u> is passed through it.
4) The <u>positive Al^{3+} ions</u> are attracted to the <u>negative electrode</u> where they form <u>aluminium atoms</u>.
5) The <u>negative O^{2-} ions</u> are attracted to the <u>positive electrode</u> where they react to form <u>oxygen</u> (O_2).

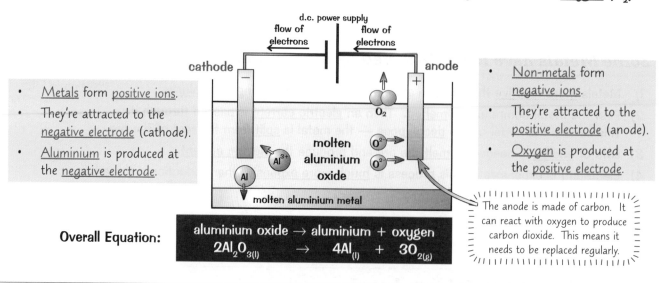

- <u>Metals</u> form <u>positive ions</u>.
- They're attracted to the <u>negative electrode</u> (cathode).
- <u>Aluminium</u> is produced at the <u>negative electrode</u>.

- <u>Non-metals</u> form <u>negative ions</u>.
- They're attracted to the <u>positive electrode</u> (anode).
- <u>Oxygen</u> is produced at the <u>positive electrode</u>.

> The anode is made of carbon. It can react with oxygen to produce carbon dioxide. This means it needs to be replaced regularly.

Overall Equation:
aluminium oxide → aluminium + oxygen
$$2Al_2O_{3(l)} \rightarrow 4Al_{(l)} + 3O_{2(g)}$$

Faster shopping at the supermarket — use Electrolleys...

When you electrolyse a molten salt, the <u>non</u>-metal is formed at the a<u>no</u>de. So the metal is formed at the cathode.

Q1   In electrolysis of molten sodium chloride, what is produced at: a) the anode?   b) the cathode?   [2 marks]

Electrolysis of Aqueous Solutions

You can do electrolysis on <u>solutions</u> containing <u>salts</u> dissolved in <u>water</u> too — that means more ions...

Electrolysis of Aqueous Solutions is a Bit More Complicated

1) <u>Water</u> can break down into <u>hydrogen ions</u> (H^+) and <u>hydroxide ions</u> (OH^-): $H_2O \rightleftharpoons H^+ + OH^-$.

2) In a solution containing a <u>salt</u> dissolved in <u>water</u>, there will be ions from the <u>salt</u> and also H^+ and OH^- ions from the <u>water</u>.

3) So <u>water</u> can be <u>electrolysed</u> depending on what other <u>ions</u> (e.g. sodium ions) are in the solution.

4) If the metal in the salt is <u>more reactive</u> than hydrogen, <u>hydrogen gas</u> will form at the <u>cathode</u>. If the metal is <u>less reactive</u> than hydrogen, then a solid layer of <u>pure metal</u> will form at the cathode.

5) At the <u>anode</u>, if there's a <u>concentrated</u> solution of <u>chloride ions</u>, <u>chlorine</u> molecules will form. If there aren't any <u>chloride ions</u>, then OH^- ions lose electrons and <u>oxygen</u> will be formed.

> '$\rightleftharpoons$' means that the reaction is reversible (p.148).

A solution of <u>copper sulfate</u> ($CuSO_4$) contains <u>four different ions</u>: Cu^{2+}, SO_4^{2-}, H^+ and OH^-.
- <u>Copper</u> metal is less reactive than hydrogen. So at the <u>cathode</u>, <u>copper metal</u> is produced.
- There aren't any <u>chloride ions</u> present. So at the <u>anode</u>, <u>oxygen</u> and <u>water</u> are formed.

> A solution that contains water is called an 'aqueous solution'.

Here's How to Carry Out Electrolysis of an Aqueous Solution

PRACTICAL

You need to know how to <u>set up</u> the equipment for electrolysis of an aqueous solution. Here's how you'd set it up for <u>sodium chloride solution</u>:

1) Get <u>two electrodes</u> made out of an <u>unreactive</u> material (e.g. <u>platinum</u>). Clean the surfaces of the electrodes using a piece of <u>sandpaper</u>.

2) Be careful not to touch the surfaces of the electrodes so that <u>oils</u> from your <u>skin</u> don't get on the electrodes.

3) Place both electrodes into a <u>beaker</u> filled with your <u>electrolyte</u> — here it's sodium chloride solution.

4) Connect the electrodes to a power supply using <u>crocodile clips</u> and <u>wires</u>.

5) You can <u>collect</u> any gases that form using the set up on p.239.

6) You can <u>work out</u> what the gases are by using the <u>tests</u> on p.86.

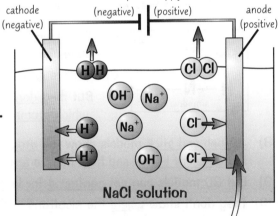

> The electrode that's attached to the positive end of the power supply becomes the anode. The one that's attached to the negative end is the cathode.

A solution of <u>sodium chloride</u> (NaCl) contains <u>four different ions</u>: Na^+, Cl^-, H^+ and OH^-.
- <u>Sodium</u> metal is more reactive than hydrogen. So at the cathode, <u>hydrogen gas</u> is produced.
- <u>Chloride ions</u> are present in the solution. So at the anode, <u>chlorine gas</u> is produced.

A Chemists Book of Poetry, page 34 — An Ode to Electrolysis...

Some reactivity series (see p.107) include hydrogen in the list. You can use these to find out which metals are more or less reactive than hydrogen.

Q1 An aqueous solution of concentrated potassium chloride, KCl, is electrolysed using unreactive electrodes. Name the product formed at the anode. [1 mark]

Covalent Bonding

Some elements bond ionically (see page 103) but others <u>share</u> electrons to form strong <u>covalent</u> bonds.

Covalent Bonds — Sharing Electrons

1) When <u>non-metal</u> atoms bond together, they <u>share</u> pairs of electrons to make <u>covalent bonds</u>.

2) Covalent bond are very <u>strong</u> because the nuclei of the bonded atoms are attracted to the shared pair of electrons by <u>electrostatic forces</u>.

3) Atoms only share electrons from their <u>outer shell</u>.

4) Generally, each <u>single</u> covalent bond means an atom has one <u>extra electron</u> in its <u>outer shell</u>.

5) Each atom involved generally makes <u>enough</u> covalent bonds to <u>fill up</u> its outer shell. This makes it very <u>stable</u>.

6) Covalent bonds try to get as <u>far away</u> from each other as possible. This creates the <u>shape</u> of the molecule.

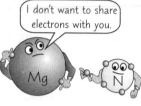

I don't want to share electrons with you.

There are Different Ways of Showing Covalent Bonding

1) <u>Dot and cross diagrams</u> show the bonding in covalent compounds.

2) Electrons drawn in the <u>overlap</u> between the outer shells of two atoms are <u>shared</u> between those atoms.

3) Dot and cross diagrams show <u>which atoms</u> the electrons in a covalent bond come from.

4) But they <u>don't</u> show how big the atoms are compared to each other, or how the atoms are <u>arranged</u>.

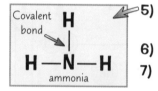

Covalent bond

H | H—N—H

ammonia

5) <u>Displayed formulas</u> show the covalent bonds as single lines between atoms.

6) They're great for showing <u>how</u> atoms are connected in <u>large</u> molecules.

7) But they <u>don't</u> show the molecule's <u>3D structure</u>. They also don't show <u>which atoms</u> the electrons in the covalent bonds have come from.

The dots show the H electrons and the crosses show the N electrons.

Nitrogen has <u>five</u> outer electrons...

Strong covalent bond.

ammonia

...so it forms <u>three covalent bonds</u> to <u>fill</u> it's outer shell.

8) <u>3D ball and stick</u> models show the <u>atoms</u>, the <u>covalent bonds</u> and how they're <u>arranged</u>.

9) But 3D models can get <u>confusing</u> for large molecules.

10) They don't show <u>where</u> the electrons in the bonds have <u>come from</u>.

11) 3D models also suggest that there are <u>gaps</u> between the atoms. Actually, this space is where the <u>shared electrons</u> are.

12) A <u>molecular formula</u> shows you how many <u>atoms</u> of each element are in a molecule. You can find the <u>molecular formula</u> from <u>any</u> of these diagrams by <u>counting up</u> how many atoms of each element there are.

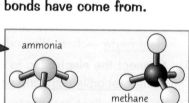

ammonia

methane

EXAMPLE: A diagram of the molecule ethane is shown on the right. Use the diagram to find the molecular formula of ethane.

In the diagram, there are two carbon atoms and six hydrogen atoms. So the molecular formula is C_2H_6.

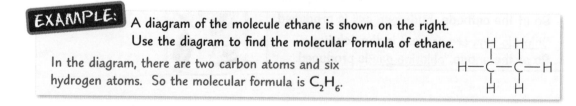

Sharing is caring...

There are a few different ways to show the covalent bonding in molecules. But they each have some flaws. Make sure you can describe the problems of each type.

Q1   Using the diagrams above, give the molecular formula of ammonia.   [1 mark]

Chapter C3 — Chemicals of the Natural Environment

Simple Covalent Substances

These molecules might be <u>simple</u>, but you've still gotta know about them. I know, the world is a cruel place.

Simple Covalent Substances Contain Just a Few Atoms

1) Substances that have <u>simple covalent structures</u> are made from molecules which contain only <u>few atoms</u>.
2) The atoms in these molecules are joined together by <u>covalent bonds</u>.
3) Here are some <u>common examples</u>...

<u>Water, H$_2$O</u>
- You can work out dot and cross diagrams by looking at <u>how many electrons</u> each atom needs to <u>fill</u> its outer shell.
- Oxygen has <u>six</u> outer electrons. It needs <u>two more</u> to fill its outer shell.
- <u>Each</u> hydrogen atom already has <u>one</u> electron. They each need <u>one more electron</u> to fill their outer shell.
- So, in <u>water molecules</u>, the oxygen atom shares electrons with two hydrogen atoms.
- This forms two <u>single covalent bonds</u>.

<u>Methane, CH$_4$</u>
- Carbon has <u>four outer electrons</u>.
- It can form <u>four covalent bonds</u> with <u>hydrogen</u> atoms to fill up its outer shell.

Dot and cross diagrams can also be drawn showing the inner shells of electrons.

<u>Oxygen, O$_2$</u>
- Each oxygen atom needs <u>two more electrons</u> to complete its outer shell.
- In <u>oxygen gas</u>, two oxygen atoms share <u>two pairs</u> of electrons with each other.
- This makes a <u>double covalent bond</u>.
- The double bond means each oxygen atom gains <u>two</u> electrons.

For almost all the elements you'll come across, a full shell is made up of 8 electrons. The common exception is hydrogen — its outer shell can only hold up to 2 electrons.

Properties of Simple Covalent Substances

'Intermolecular' means between molecules — intermolecular forces are what attract molecules towards each other.

1) Substances containing <u>covalent bonds</u> usually have <u>simple molecular structures</u>.
2) The covalent bonds between atoms <u>within</u> the molecules are <u>very strong</u>.
3) The forces of attraction <u>between</u> these molecules (intermolecular forces) are <u>very weak</u>.
4) To melt or boil a simple molecular compound, you only need to break these <u>weak intermolecular forces</u>. The covalent bonds aren't broken.
5) <u>Not much</u> energy is needed to break the intermolecular forces between the molecules. So, the melting and boiling points are <u>very low</u>.
6) <u>Bigger</u> molecules have <u>stronger</u> intermolecular forces than smaller molecules. So, <u>bigger</u> molecules generally have <u>higher melting</u> and <u>boiling</u> points than <u>smaller</u> molecules. This is because <u>more energy</u> is needed to break the intermolecular forces (see p.77).
7) Molecular compounds <u>don't conduct electricity</u>. This is because they <u>aren't charged</u>, so there are <u>no free electrons</u> or ions to carry an electric current.

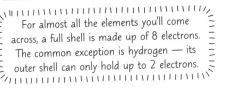
Weak intermolecular forces
<u>Oxygen</u>

May the intermolecular force be with you...

Never forget that it's the weak intermolecular forces <u>between</u> molecules that get broken when a simple molecular substance melts. Nothing happens to the covalent bonds within the molecules.

Q1   Explain why oxygen (O$_2$) is a gas at room temperature.   [2 marks]

Empirical Formulas

Molecular formulas (see p.78) can be simplified to empirical formulas.
Prepare yourself for some maths... Don't worry, it's not as bad as it sounds.

The Empirical Formula is the Simplest Ratio of Atoms

The empirical formula of a compound tells you the smallest whole number ratio of atoms in the compound.

> **EXAMPLE:** Find the empirical formula of ethane, C_2H_6.
>
> 1) The numbers in the molecular formula of ethane are 2 and 6.
> 2) To simplify the ratio, divide by the largest number that goes into 2 and 6 exactly — that's 2.
>
> C: $2 \div 2 = 1$
> H: $6 \div 2 = 3$
>
> The empirical formula of ethane is CH_3.

You can use the Empirical Formula to Find the Molecular Formula

You can use the empirical formula of a compound, together with its relative formula mass, M_r (see p.134), to find its molecular formula.

> **EXAMPLE:** Compound X has the empirical formula C_2H_6N. The relative molecular mass of compound X is 88.0. Find the molecular formula of compound X.
>
> 1) Start by finding the relative formula mass of the empirical formula.
>   To do this, add up all the relative atomic masses (A_r) of the atoms in the formula.
>   The A_r of carbon is 12.0, the A_r of hydrogen is 1.0 and the A_r of nitrogen is 14.0.
>
> Relative formula mass of C_2H_6N $= (2 \times C) + (6 \times H) + N$ ——— There are six hydrogen atoms and one nitrogen
>
> There are two carbon atoms in the empirical formula. So, the relative formula mass of the empirical formula will have two lots of the A_r of carbon (12.0).
>
> $= (2 \times 12.0) + (6 \times 1.0) + 14.0$ atom in the empirical formula. So there will
> $= 24.0 + 6.0 + 14.0$ be six lots of the A_r of hydrogen (1.0) and one
> $= 44.0$ lot of the A_r of nitrogen (14.0) in the relative
>   formula mass of the empirical formula.
>
> 2) Now divide the relative molecular mass of compound X by the relative formula mass of the empirical formula. This tells you how many lots of the empirical formula there are in the molecular formula. $88.0 \div 44.0 = 2$
>
> 3) The molecular formula of compound X contains two lots of the empirical formula. So to get the molecular formula just multiply everything in the empirical formula by 2.
>
> C: $2 \times 2 = 4$
> H: $6 \times 2 = 12$ The molecular formula of
> N: $1 \times 2 = 2$ compound X is $C_4H_{12}N_2$.

If only there was a special formula for passing science exams...

I know this page has been pretty maths-y, I'm sorry. Make sure you're comfortable with working out the empirical formulas of molecules — you'll feel daft if it comes up in the exam and you haven't revised it...

Q1   Define the term 'empirical formula'.   [1 mark]

Q2   What is the empirical formula of C_8H_{18}?   [1 mark]

Homologous Series and Alkanes

Compounds can belong to <u>families</u>. Compounds within a family share some <u>similar properties</u>.

Compounds in a Homologous Series Share Similar Chemical Properties

1) A <u>homologous series</u> is a <u>family</u> of molecules which share the same <u>general formula</u>. The general formula is a bit like a <u>template</u> for the molecular formulas of compounds in a homologous series.

2) Molecules in the same homologous series share similar <u>chemical properties</u>. This means they react in a similar way.

3) The molecular formulas of <u>neighbouring compounds</u> in a homologous series differ by a <u>CH_2</u> unit.

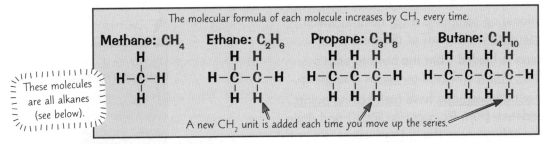

The molecular formula of each molecule increases by CH_2 every time.

Methane: CH_4 Ethane: C_2H_6 Propane: C_3H_8 Butane: C_4H_{10}

These molecules are all alkanes (see below).

A new CH_2 unit is added each time you move up the series.

4) You can see <u>trends</u> in the <u>physical properties</u> of compounds in a homologous series.

5) For example, the <u>bigger</u> a molecule is, the <u>higher</u> the <u>boiling point</u> will be.

Increasing size of molecule

Alkane	Molecular formula	Boiling point (°C)
Methane	CH_4	−162
Ethane	C_2H_6	−89
Propane	C_3H_8	-42
Butane	C_4H_{10}	-1

Properties Change as the Carbon Chain Gets Longer

As the <u>length</u> of the carbon chain changes in a homologous series, the <u>properties</u> of the molecules change.

1) <u>Viscosity</u> means how <u>thick</u> or <u>runny</u> a substance is. The <u>shorter</u> the chains, the <u>more runny</u> (less viscous) a substance will be.

2) Substances containing molecules with shorter chains have <u>lower</u> boiling points.

3) Also, the <u>shorter</u> the carbon chains, the easier to set on fire (the more flammable) the compounds will be.

The <u>properties</u> of alkanes affect how they're used for fuels. E.g. compounds with <u>short</u> chains and <u>low</u> boiling points are used as a fuel for things like camping stoves.

Alkanes Have All C–C Single Bonds

Alkane, Al saw, Al conquered.

Give it a rest, Alan!

The 'n' in the general formula is how many carbon atoms are in the molecule.

1) <u>Alkanes</u> are the <u>simplest</u> homologous series you can get.

2) The atoms in alkanes are held together by <u>single covalent bonds</u>.

3) All alkanes have the general formula C_nH_{2n+2}.

4) Alkanes are <u>hydrocarbons</u> — compounds containing only <u>hydrogen</u> and <u>carbon</u> atoms.

5) The first four alkanes are <u>methane</u>, <u>ethane</u>, <u>propane</u> and <u>butane</u> — see above.

Alkanes — full of bonds just looking for love...

So alkanes only contain two ingredients — carbon and hydrogen. Jamie Oliver would not be happy.

Q1   A scientist has two alkanes, C_5H_{12} and $C_{10}H_{22}$. Compare the following properties of the alkanes:
   a) viscosity,   b) boiling point,   c) how easy they are to set on fire.   [3 marks]

Fractional Distillation of Crude Oil

Don't panic — not those types of <u>fractions</u>, there's no maths on this page. Thank heavens...

Fractional Distillation can be Used to Separate Hydrocarbon Fractions

1) Crude oil is a <u>mixture</u> of <u>lots of different hydrocarbons</u>, most of which are <u>alkanes</u>.

2) The different compounds in crude oil are <u>separated</u> by <u>fractional distillation</u>.

3) Here's how it works:

• The oil is <u>heated</u> until most of it has turned into <u>gas</u>. The gases enter a <u>fractionating column</u>.

• The fractionating column is a <u>tall</u> column which has <u>condensers</u> coming off at different points.

• The column is heated from the bottom so it's <u>hot</u> at the <u>bottom</u> and gets <u>cooler</u> as you go up.

• The <u>longer hydrocarbons</u> have <u>high boiling points</u>. They condense (turn from gas to <u>liquid</u>) and <u>drain out</u> of the column near the <u>bottom</u> where it's <u>hot</u>.

• The <u>shorter</u> hydrocarbons have <u>lower boiling points</u>. They condense and drain out near to the <u>top</u> of the column where it's cooler.

Shorter chains leave the column up here.

COOL

Longer chains leave the column down here.

VERY HOT

LPG

Petrol

Kerosene

Diesel oil

Heavy fuel oil

Bitumen

4) You end up with the crude oil mixture separated out into <u>different fractions</u>.

5) Each fraction contains a mixture of mainly alkanes that have a <u>similar</u> number of <u>carbon atoms</u>, so have similar <u>boiling points</u>.

6) Fractional distillation can also be carried out in the <u>lab</u> (see p.132). It's used to separate <u>mixtures</u> of liquids with <u>similar boiling points</u>.

Intermolecular Forces are Much Weaker Between Smaller Molecules

1) There are <u>two</u> types of bonding in crude oil. <u>Strong covalent</u> bonds between atoms <u>within</u> hydrocarbon molecules, and <u>weaker intermolecular forces</u> of attraction <u>between</u> hydrocarbon molecules.

2) When the crude oil mixture is <u>heated</u>, the molecules are supplied with <u>extra energy</u>. This makes the molecules <u>move about</u> more.

3) Eventually, a molecule will have enough energy to <u>break</u> the <u>intermolecular forces</u> that keep it with the other molecules. It can then <u>whizz off</u> as a <u>gas</u>.

4) Intermolecular forces between <u>small</u> molecules need less energy to break than they do between big molecules. This is because the intermolecular forces between small molecules are much <u>weaker</u>.

5) That's why <u>small</u> molecules generally have <u>lower boiling points</u> than big molecules do.

6) It's thanks to this that we can do fractional distillation.

I'm free!!

How much petrol is there in crude oil? Just a fraction...

There's two key things to remember about fractional distillation. First, that it separates mixtures because molecules have different boiling points. Second, the boiling points of molecules depend on their size.

Q1   In fractional distillation, where is the hottest part of the column?   [1 mark]

Chapter C3 — Chemicals of the Natural Environment

Uses of Crude Oil

Crude oil really <u>improves</u> our lives in lots of ways, but we're using up our supplies way too <u>quickly</u>...

Crude Oil has Various Important Uses in Modern Life...

1) Most of the hydrocarbons that we use today have come from <u>crude oil</u>.

2) <u>Crude oil</u> provides the <u>fuel</u> for most modern <u>transport</u> — like the <u>diesel</u> and <u>petrol</u> fractions used in cars.

3) Some of the hydrocarbons from crude oil can be used as a <u>feedstock</u> (starting material) to make things like <u>polymers</u> (plastics).

4) Almost all of the <u>consumer products</u> we use, from cleaning products to smart phones, use crude oil. Crude oil is normally used to <u>make</u> them or <u>transport</u> them (or both).

The industry that uses crude oil to make new products is called the 'petrochemical industry'.

...But It Will Run Out Eventually... Eeek

1) Crude oil is a <u>finite</u> resource — if we keep using it at the current rate, it will eventually <u>run out</u>.

2) <u>New sources</u> of crude oil are sometimes found, but they are still not enough.

3) One way to use less crude oil is to develop <u>alternative energy sources</u>. These alternatives have their own <u>problems</u>, but we'll need them when the oil runs out.

4) By using <u>less</u> crude oil for <u>fuel</u>, there'll be more to use to make important products that modern life depends on.

5) We need to balance the <u>short-term</u> benefits of using crude oil with the need to save it for the future.

Cracking Means Splitting Up Long–Chain Hydrocarbons

1) Crude oil contains many <u>large</u> alkane molecules. We don't really have a lot of uses for these molecules.

2) <u>Cracking</u> is a process where long chain alkane molecules are <u>split</u> into <u>smaller</u>, <u>more useful</u> ones. These smaller alkanes are really useful as <u>fuels</u> (e.g. petrol).

3) During cracking, the hydrocarbons are <u>heated</u> to turn them into a gas. The gas is then passed over a <u>catalyst</u> or mixed with <u>steam</u>. This causes the hydrocarbons to <u>split apart</u>.

4) As well as alkanes, cracking also produces another type of hydrocarbon called <u>alkenes</u>.

5) <u>Alkenes</u> are more reactive than alkanes. They're used as a starting material for many other compounds such as <u>polymers</u>.

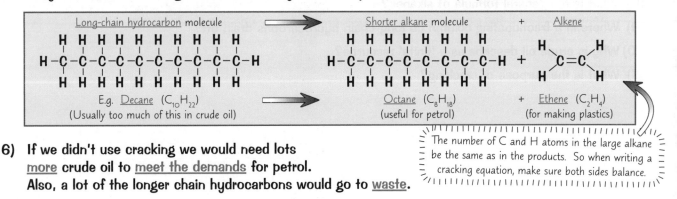

6) If we didn't use cracking we would need lots <u>more</u> crude oil to <u>meet the demands</u> for petrol. Also, a lot of the longer chain hydrocarbons would go to <u>waste</u>.

The number of C and H atoms in the large alkane be the same as in the products. So when writing a cracking equation, make sure both sides balance.

I'm not one to brag, but this really is a cracking page...

Alternative fuels are great but we still haven't developed them properly yet.
That's why cracking's important — we can use crude oil until we're ready to use alternative fuels.

Q1   Give one benefit of cracking long chain hydrocarbons.   [1 mark]

Revision Questions for Chapter C3

All good things must come to an end — <u>Chapter C3</u> included. So make the most of these questions...
*   Try these questions and <u>tick off each one</u> when you <u>get it right</u>.
*   When you've done <u>all the questions</u> for a topic and are <u>completely happy</u> with it, tick off the topic.

<u>The Reactions and Reactivity of Metals (p.106-108)</u> ☑

1) What makes metallic bonding strong? ☑
2) If a metal is very reactive, will it be difficult or easy for it to form positive ions? ☑
3) What will happen if you put a less reactive metal into a solution of a more reactive metal salt? ☑
4) A scientist adds some potassium to cold dilute acid. Will a reaction take place? ☑
5) A student has a piece of sodium and a piece of silver. Which metal will react with water? ☑

<u>Extracting Metals from their Ores (p.109-111)</u> ☑

6) Where do metals need to be in the reactivity series
    so they can be extracted by reduction by carbon? ☑
7) Some metals can be extracted from their ore using reduction by carbon.
    What happens to the metal ore when it is reduced? ☑
8) Define the term 'electrolyte'. ☑
9) During electrolysis, which electrode do the negative ions in the electrolyte move towards? ☑
10) In the electrolysis of aluminium oxide, is aluminium produced at the anode or the cathode? ☑
11) Which ions will be present in a solution of copper sulfate? ☑

<u>Covalent Bonds (p.112-114)</u> ☐

12) What is a covalent bond? ☑
13) Give a limitation of using dot and cross diagrams to display the covalent bonding in a molecule. ☑
14) What happens to the intermolecular forces when a simple covalent substance is boiled? ☑
15) Why don't simple covalent substances conduct electricity? ☑
16) What is the empirical formula of C_2H_6? ☑

<u>Alkanes and Crude Oil (p.115-117)</u> ☑

17) How does boiling point change as the size of the alkane increases in a homologous series? ☑
18) What is the general formula of alkanes? ☑
19) Where in a fractionating column do long-chain hydrocarbons drain off? ☑
20) Why is crude oil describe as a 'finite' resource? ☑
21) What is the purpose of cracking? ☑

Polymers

Polymers are made up of <u>lots</u> of the same molecule <u>joined together</u> in one long chain. They're what make up plastics. You can make them as hard or as soft as you like, which makes them darn useful to modern society.

Polymers Are Held Together by Covalent Bonds and Intermolecular Forces

1) <u>Polymers</u> are long molecules formed when lots of small molecules join together.

2) In polymers, all the atoms in a chain are joined by strong <u>covalent bonds</u>.

3) There are <u>weaker forces</u> between the chains called <u>intermolecular forces</u>.

4) In general, polymers are <u>larger</u> than simple molecules. So, the intermolecular forces between polymer chains are <u>stronger</u> than between simple molecules.

5) Because of this, <u>more energy</u> is needed to break the intermolecular forces between the <u>polymer molecules</u> than between <u>simple molecules</u>. This means most polymers are <u>solid</u> at room temperature.

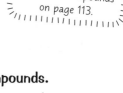
There's more on the bonding in simple molecular compounds on page 113.

6) The intermolecular forces in polymers are <u>weaker</u> than ionic or covalent bonds. So polymers generally have <u>lower</u> melting points than <u>ionic</u> or <u>giant covalent</u> compounds.

7) If you heat a polymer, it will turn <u>soft</u> before it melts. The weaker the forces between the chains, the lower the temperature at which it becomes soft (the <u>softening point</u>).

The Forces Between Chains Affect the Properties of a Polymer

1) Polymers have different properties depending on how the <u>chains</u> are <u>arranged</u>.

- If there's lots of <u>space</u> between the chains in a polymer, the forces between the chains will be <u>weak</u>. This makes the polymer <u>flexible</u>.
- If the chains are packed <u>closely</u> together, the forces between them will be <u>stronger</u>. This makes the polymer <u>stiff</u>.

2) The <u>type of forces</u> between the chains also affects the properties of polymers. As well as intermolecular forces, some <u>polymers</u> also form <u>covalent</u> or <u>ionic crosslinks</u> between the chains.

- Polymers that only have <u>intermolecular forces</u> between the chains can be <u>melted</u>.
- This is because the forces between the chains are <u>weak</u> enough to be broken without the <u>chains</u> breaking down.

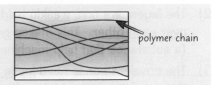
polymer chain

- Some polymers have <u>covalent</u> or <u>ionic bonds</u> between the chains known as <u>crosslinks</u>.
- The chains are held together very <u>strongly</u> in a <u>rigid</u> structure.
- This makes the polymers <u>strong</u>, <u>hard</u> and <u>stiff</u>.
- These polymers <u>don't soften</u> when they're heated.

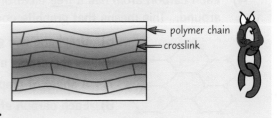
polymer chain
crosslink

Revision's like polymers — it's all about stringing facts together...

Make sure you understand that it's the forces between the chains in a polymer that decide what properties it has.

Q1   A polymer contains crosslinks. State four properties you would expect it to have.   [4 marks]

Giant Covalent Structures

If you thought <u>polymers</u> were large, just wait til you meet these beauties... And I'm not joking about them being beautiful — <u>sparkly diamonds</u> have giant covalent structures. Ooooh... Sparkles...

Giant Covalent Structures Contain Many Covalent Bonds

1) In a <u>giant covalent structure</u>, all the atoms are <u>bonded</u> to <u>each other</u> by <u>strong</u> covalent bonds.

2) This means that they have <u>very high</u> melting and boiling points.

3) They tend to be <u>insoluble</u> in water.

4) They <u>don't contain charged particles</u> so they <u>don't conduct electricity</u> (except for <u>graphite</u> and <u>graphene</u> — see below).

5) The examples of <u>giant covalent structures</u> that you need to know about are made from <u>carbon atoms</u>.

6) <u>Carbon</u> can form <u>lots</u> of different materials, both <u>natural</u> and <u>man-made</u>. This is because carbon atoms can form up to <u>four covalent bonds</u>. Carbon atoms can also bond <u>to each other</u> to make <u>chains</u> and <u>rings</u>.

Carbon compounds can be put into families of similar molecules called homologous series. For example, the alkanes (see p.115) are a homologous series of carbon compounds.

Diamond

1) In diamond, each carbon atom forms <u>four covalent bonds</u> in a <u>very rigid</u> giant covalent structure.

2) All those <u>strong covalent bonds</u> take a lot of energy to break and give diamond a <u>very high melting point</u>.

3) The covalent bonds also make diamond <u>really hard</u>. This means it can be used as a <u>cutting tool</u>.

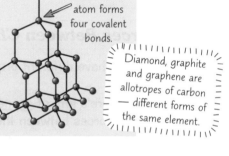

Each carbon atom forms four covalent bonds.

Diamond, graphite and graphene are allotropes of carbon — different forms of the same element.

Graphite and Graphene

1) In graphite, each carbon atom only forms <u>three covalent bonds</u>. This creates <u>sheets of carbon atoms</u>.

2) The layers are only <u>weakly</u> held together, so they can <u>slide over each other</u>. This makes graphite a good <u>lubricant</u> (a substance that help machine parts move smoothly).

3) The covalent bonds need <u>loads of energy</u> to break. So, graphite's got a <u>high melting point</u>.

4) Each carbon atom has a <u>free</u> electron that can <u>move</u> around. This means that graphite conducts <u>electricity</u>.

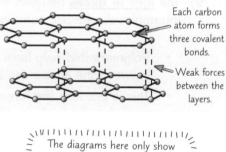

Each carbon atom forms three covalent bonds.

Weak forces between the layers.

The diagrams here only show part of the structures of diamond, graphite and graphene.

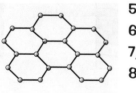

5) <u>Graphene</u> is a <u>single sheet</u> of graphite.

6) All the atoms are held together by <u>covalent bonds</u>. So graphene is very <u>strong</u>.

7) A sheet of graphene is so thin that it's <u>see-through</u> and very <u>light</u>.

8) Each carbon atom has one electron that's <u>completely free</u> to move about. This makes it very good at <u>conducting electricity</u> and <u>thermal energy</u>.

So that pencil I gave her was just the same as a diamond, really...

One of the weirdest things about carbon is that it can form chains and rings with itself. That's pretty rare, for an element. It's one of the main reasons why there are so many different types of carbon based compound.

Q1 Give two similarities between diamond and graphite, in terms of their structure and properties. [2 marks]

Bulk Properties of Materials

The way a material behaves is all to do with its <u>structure</u> and the type of <u>bonding</u> it contains.

Different Materials Have Different Structures

Chemists use information about bonding and structure to predict properties of materials.

1) The properties of materials depend on their <u>bonding</u> and <u>structure</u>. That's why some materials have <u>different properties</u> even though they're made of the <u>same elements</u>.

2) These are the <u>types of structure</u> you need to know about:

Structure	Ionic (p.103-104)	Simple Molecular (p.113)	Metallic (p.106)	Polymer (p.119)	Giant Covalent (p.120)
Type of bonding	Electrostatic attractions between oppositely charged ions in all directions.	Strong covalent bonds between atoms. Weak intermolecular forces between molecules.	Electrostatic attractions between positive metal ions and delocalised 'sea' of electrons.	Strong covalent bonds between atoms. Intermolecular forces between chains (stronger than between simple molecules). Can contain crosslinks.	Covalent bonds between atoms.

Different Materials Have Different Bulk Properties

Melting point

1) The <u>melting point</u> is the temperature at which the <u>solid</u> material turns to <u>liquid</u>.

2) The <u>stronger</u> the forces between particles, the <u>higher</u> the melting point.

Hardness

1) Hard materials are <u>difficult</u> to <u>cut</u> into.

2) The <u>stronger</u> the forces between particles, the <u>harder</u> a material tends to be.

Conductivity

1) To conduct <u>electricity</u>, a material must have <u>charged particles</u> (<u>ions</u> or <u>electrons</u>) which can <u>move</u>.

2) Materials with free electrons are often good <u>conductors of heat</u> as the electrons can transfer energy <u>quickly</u> through the material.

3) Materials without free electrons are often <u>thermal insulators</u>. This is because they can only <u>transfer energy</u> through their <u>bonds</u> which is <u>slow</u>.

Strength

A force could be a push (like hitting something with a hammer) or a pull (like stretching a rubber band).

1) <u>Strength</u> is how much <u>force</u> is needed to <u>break</u> a material or to permanently change its <u>shape</u>. The stronger something is, the <u>greater</u> the force that's needed for this to happen.

2) If the atoms are held <u>firmly</u> in place (e.g. ionic compounds) then the material will be <u>strong</u>. If they can <u>move around</u> a bit (e.g. metals) then the material will be <u>weak</u>.

3) There are <u>two</u> types of strength you need to know about:
   • <u>TENSILE STRENGTH</u> — how much a material can resist a <u>pulling</u> (stretching) <u>force</u>.
   • <u>COMPRESSIVE STRENGTH</u> — how much a material can resist a <u>pushing</u> (squashing) <u>force</u>.

Stiffness

1) <u>Stiff</u> materials don't bend easily. <u>Flexible</u> materials easily bend without breaking.

2) The stronger the forces between particles, the <u>stiffer</u> a material is.

Ease of reshaping

1) Some materials <u>change shape</u> but don't break when a force is applied to them. They can be <u>moulded</u>.

2) These materials have particles that can <u>move</u> without the bonds breaking permanently.

Brittleness

1) <u>Brittle</u> materials <u>break</u> if they're hit by a sudden <u>force</u>.

2) They tend to have structures where particles <u>can't move</u> without the <u>bonds</u> between them <u>breaking</u>.

3) <u>Diamond</u> is brittle because the covalent bonds <u>break</u> if the atoms move. <u>Metals</u> aren't brittle because the atoms can <u>slide</u> over each other without the metallic bonds breaking.

Hulk properties — green, strong, and able to reshape...

Bulk properties depend on lots of particles interacting. Individual particles in a material don't have these properties.

Q1   What characteristic of a material allows it to conduct electricity?   [1 mark]

Types of Materials

I can tell you now that this page is going to be <u>smashing</u>. At least the bit about <u>ceramics</u> will be...

Ceramics are Stiff but Brittle

<u>Ceramics</u> are made by baking substances like clay to produce a <u>brittle</u>, <u>stiff</u> material.

- <u>Clay</u> is <u>soft</u> when it's <u>wet</u>, so it's <u>easy to mould</u> into different shapes e.g. for pottery or bricks.
- It's made into a ceramic by <u>baking</u> at very <u>high temperatures</u>.
- It has a high <u>compressive strength</u> (it doesn't break or change shape if it's squashed). This means it can be used as a <u>building</u> material.

- <u>Glass</u> is generally <u>transparent</u> and <u>strong</u>.
- It can be <u>moulded</u> when hot and can be <u>brittle</u> when thin.

Composites are Made of Different Materials

For more about nanoparticles, see p.126-127.

1) Composites are made of one material <u>set into</u> in another.
2) The materials could be embedded on a <u>large (bulk) scale</u>, like when concrete is reinforced with steel.
3) Or, they could be on a <u>small scale</u>. E.g. <u>nanoparticles</u> can be set in another material to make a composite.
4) The <u>properties</u> of a composite depend on the properties of the materials it is <u>made from</u>.

<u>Carbon fibre</u> composites are made using carbon <u>nanotubes</u> (p.127) set in a polymer. These composites are <u>strong</u> and very <u>light</u> for their <u>size</u> so they're used to make <u>sports equipment</u>.

Some Materials are Damaged by Corrosion

1) Some materials, such as <u>metals</u>, can be <u>destroyed</u> by a process called <u>corrosion</u>.
2) If <u>iron</u> comes into contact with <u>oxygen</u> (e.g. from the air) and <u>water</u>, it will slowly <u>corrode</u> (rust). This means that things made out of <u>iron</u> only <u>last</u> for a certain amount of time before they <u>corrode</u> away. This is a big <u>problem</u>, because iron is used to make so <u>many</u> things.
3) Luckily, there are ways to help <u>stop metals corroding</u>. For example, you can create a <u>barrier</u> (e.g. with paint). This stops the metal coming into contact with water or oxygen.

If your name's not iron, you're not getting in.

Iron Gains Oxygen When it Corrodes

1) <u>Oxidation</u> is when an element or compound <u>gains</u> oxygen.
2) <u>Reduction</u> is when oxygen is <u>removed</u> from an element or compound. For example:

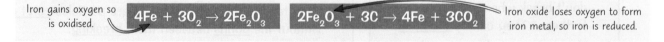

Iron gains oxygen so is oxidised. $4Fe + 3O_2 \rightarrow 2Fe_2O_3$ $2Fe_2O_3 + 3C \rightarrow 4Fe + 3CO_2$ Iron oxide loses oxygen to form iron metal, so iron is reduced.

3) When iron <u>corrodes</u>, it gains <u>oxygen</u>. So the <u>iron</u> is <u>oxidised</u>.

Porcelain jugs never cry — they've got a stiff upper lip...

So many materials, but my favourite type of material will always be the soft, fluffy kind...

Q1   Name one composite material.   [1 mark]

Materials and their Uses

It's all very well making a material, but it needs to be <u>fit for purpose</u>. You need to be able to understand <u>why</u> a certain material is used and <u>not</u> another material. For example, a teapot made of ceramic instead of chocolate.

Different Materials are Suited to Different Jobs

What purposes materials are used for depends on their <u>properties</u>.

1) <u>Polymers</u> are often <u>cheap</u>.
2) Some are <u>flexible</u>, so they can be bent without breaking.
3) Others can be <u>easily shaped</u>.
4) They tend to be <u>less dense</u> than metals or ceramics.
5) They're also <u>thermal (heat)</u> and <u>electrical insulators</u>.
6) But, polymers can <u>break down</u> over time.

1) <u>Ceramics</u> are <u>insulators</u> of heat and electricity.
2) They're usually <u>brittle</u> and <u>stiff</u>.
3) But they're also <u>strong</u>.
4) They don't <u>break down over time</u> like other materials, so they can last longer.

1) <u>Composites</u> have different properties depending on the materials used to make them.
2) The <u>materials</u> used can be changed. So, composites can be designed to have the right properties for a <u>specific purpose</u>. This means they can be used for <u>lots</u> of different things.
3) They're normally much more <u>expensive</u> than other materials.

1) <u>Metals</u> are <u>good conductors</u> of <u>heat</u> and <u>electricity</u>.
2) They generally have high <u>melting points</u>.
3) They are easy to make into <u>different shapes</u>.
4) Some metals corrode easily, but products made from <u>corrosion resistant</u> metals can last for a very long time.
5) They're usually <u>less brittle</u> than either ceramics or some polymers.

> You should know all about the bonding in metals (see page 106) and polymers (see page 119).

You Need to Be Able to Interpret Information about Materials

Chemists <u>can measure</u> the physical properties of materials. Then they can use this information to <u>work out</u> how <u>suitable</u> different materials would be for different uses.

EXAMPLE: A company is designing a camping cup. The cup needs to be lightweight. It also needs to withstand the temperature of hot drinks and shouldn't be brittle. Using the data in the table, suggest which material the company should use.

Material	Melting point (°C)	Density (g/cm³)	Brittleness
Aluminium	660	2.7	Low
Glass	700 (softens)	2.6	High
Poly(propene)	171	0.94	Medium

Aluminium can be ruled out — it has a high melting point and isn't brittle but it's the densest material.

Glass has a high softening point. It's less dense than aluminium, but it's brittle, so breaks easily.

A hot drink could be up to 100 °C. Poly(propene) melts above 100 °C, is lightweight and not too brittle. So **poly(propene)** is the best material for the job.

> Density is how much substance there is in a certain volume. A small amount of a dense substance will be quite heavy.

Compost-sites — piles of old vegetables embedded in muck...

So, you can't use any old material for any old job. My steel pillow and my glass duvet taught me that.

Q1 Look at the table in the example above. Glass and poly(propene) are fairly unreactive and aluminium is fairly reactive. Which of the three materials would you use to make a piece of equipment for heating chemicals to 300 °C? Explain your answer. [3 marks]

Reuse and Recycling

Recycling's a hot topic. It's really important to make sure we don't run out of lots of important raw materials.

We Can Reuse or Recycle Things Instead of Throwing Them Away

1) Reusing means using a product again in the same form.

2) Recycling means using the materials in a product to make new things.

3) Extracting raw materials can take large amounts of energy. Lots of this energy comes from burning fossil fuels. Fossil fuels are running out so we need to use less of them.

4) Recycling a product normally uses less energy than making it from scratch.
And reusing a product uses even less energy than recycling it.

5) So recycling or reusing a product saves fossil fuels and also saves money.

6) Recycling and reusing means we use less non-renewable (finite)
raw materials, e.g. metal ores and crude oil.

7) However, we can't get all the material we need from recycling and reusing.
To stop us from running out of finite resources, society also needs to use less.

- Plastic drinks bottles are usually made from a polymer called PET.
They can be recycled to make other packaging materials.
- First, PET objects are separated from other plastic materials in the waste.
- The PET objects are then shredded and cleaned.
- The PET is then melted down and made into new objects.
- Recycling PET is viable (worthwhile) because it uses fewer resources and less energy than making 'new' PET.
- PET can easily be reused because it lasts quite a long time without breaking down.
- If PET isn't recycled or reused, it's usually thrown away in landfill which takes up lots of space.

Sometimes Recycling isn't Straightforward

1) Not all materials are suitable for recycling. You have to think about whether the benefits of recycling a material would outweigh the drawbacks.

2) It takes time and energy to collect, sort and clean the material that you want to recycle.
Energy costs money, so sometimes a material won't be recycled because it's too expensive.

3) Sometimes, the processes used to recycle a material have bad effects on the environment.
So it may be better for the environment to just throw away the material and make it from 'new'.

4) Materials won't be recycled if there's not enough demand for products made from the recycled material.

5) In some cases, there might not be enough of the used material to make it worthwhile recycling it.

Compost-sites — piles of old vegetables embedded in muck...

Great jokes like this grow on trees you know. So to save trees, I've reused that hilarious pun from page 123.

Q1   Explain why recycling PET is viable.   [1 mark]

Life Cycle Assessments

If a company wants to manufacture a new product, it will carry out a <u>life cycle assessment</u> (LCA).

Life Cycle Assessments Look at the Impact of a Product on the Environment

1) A <u>life cycle assessment (LCA)</u> looks at each <u>stage</u> of the <u>life</u> of a product.

2) It works out how each stage might affect the <u>environment</u>.

3) The stages it looks at include making the <u>material</u> from natural raw materials, making the <u>product</u> from the material, <u>using</u> the product and <u>disposing</u> of the product.

Choice of material

1) <u>Metals</u> have to be <u>mined</u> and <u>extracted</u> from their ores (see p.109-110). These processes need a lot of <u>energy</u> and cause a lot of <u>pollution</u>.

2) <u>Materials</u> used to make chemicals often come from <u>crude oil</u>. Getting crude oil from the ground and making it into raw materials uses lots of <u>energy</u> and causes <u>pollution</u>.

3) Some raw materials are <u>non-renewable</u>. Using too much of these materials means they'll <u>run out</u>. It's often better to use <u>renewable materials</u>.

Manufacture

1) <u>Manufacturing</u> products uses a lot of <u>energy</u> and other resources such as <u>water</u>.

2) It can also cause a lot of <u>pollution</u>, e.g. <u>harmful gases</u> such as CO or greenhouse gases.

3) Manufacture produces <u>waste</u> which has to be <u>disposed</u> of. Some waste can be used for <u>other things</u>, which means it doesn't need to be sent to <u>landfill</u>.

4) Manufacture usually needs <u>water</u> which needs to be <u>treated</u> before it's put back into rivers.

Product Use

<u>Using</u> a product could damage the environment. For example:

1) <u>Paint</u> gives off <u>toxic fumes</u>.

2) <u>Burning fuels</u> releases <u>greenhouse gases</u> and other <u>pollutants</u>.

> Companies may have to make assumptions and estimations when making LCAs. For example, an object may be recyclable, but they don't know how many users will actually recycle it. Or there may not be enough data available about a material they want to use.

Disposal

1) Products are often <u>thrown away</u> in a <u>landfill</u> site. This takes space and can <u>pollute</u> land and water.

2) If the products are <u>biodegradeable</u>, they'll <u>break down</u> quite <u>quickly</u>. But, if they're <u>non-biodegradeable</u>, they'll hang around in landfill for <u>years</u>.

3) Products might be burnt (incinerated) to generate <u>electricity</u>. This <u>saves</u> fossil fuels. However, it causes air <u>pollution</u>.

4) Recycling or reusing a product <u>reduces</u> the impact of throwing it away, and saves raw materials.

4) <u>Transporting</u> the product at each stage also has an environmental <u>impact</u>. Things like trucks and trains are often powered by burning <u>fossil fuels</u>. This releases <u>greenhouse gases</u> and other nasty stuff into the air.

EXAMPLE: The life cycle assessments for two cars, A and B, are shown in the table. Using the data in the table, explain which car would have less impact on the environment.

Car	Expected lifespan of product (years)	CO_2 emissions (tonnes)	Waste solid produced (kg)	Water used (m³)
A	9	21	5900	6.0
B	12	34	15 010	9.5

Car A has a shorter lifespan than car B, but car A produces less CO_2 and waste solids and uses less water. So, on balance, **car A** looks like it will have the smallest environmental impact.

My cycle assessment — two wheels, a bell, an uncomfortable seat...

Don't get your bike-cycle and life cycle assessments confused. Life cycle assessments are the ones you'll need.

Q1 For the example above, suggest two further things (that aren't outlined in the table) that the company should consider when forming a life cycle assessment for the cars. [2 marks]

Nanoparticles

Just time to squeeze in something <u>really small</u> before the end of the chapter...

Nanoparticles Are Really Really Really Really Tiny... ...smaller than that.

1) The sizes of very small particles are often given in <u>nanometres</u> or '<u>nm</u>'.

2) 1 nm is the same as <u>0.000000001 m</u>.

3) Rather than writing lots of zeros, it can be easier to write very small numbers in <u>standard form</u>.

This number must always be greater or equal to 1 and less than 10. → $A \times 10^n$ ← This number is the number of places the decimal point moves.

4) If 'n' is <u>positive</u>, the number is <u>greater than 1</u>. More positive values of 'n' mean <u>larger</u> numbers. If 'n' is <u>negative</u> the number is <u>less than 1</u>. More negative values of 'n' mean <u>smaller</u> numbers.

5) So 1 nm = 1×10^{-9} m.

6) <u>Nanoparticles</u> have a diameter between 1 nm and 100 nm. They're <u>bigger</u> than <u>atoms</u> (0.1-0.5 nm) and <u>simple molecules</u> (e.g. methane is about 0.4 nm), but smaller than most other things.

Nanoparticles Have a Large Surface Area to Volume Ratio

1) The surface area to volume ratio <u>affects</u> the way that a particle <u>behaves</u>.

2) As particles <u>decrease</u> in size, the size of their surface area <u>increases</u> compared to their volume. This causes the surface area to volume ratio to <u>increase</u>.

3) You can see this happening by using two <u>cubes</u> as an example:

EXAMPLE: Find the surface area to volume ratio for each of the cubes below.

The surface area of one face of a cube is side length × side length.

This cube has sides of length 1 mm.

Each face has a surface area of 1 mm × 1 mm = 1 mm^2

The cube has six faces, so the total surface area is 6 × 1 mm^2 = 6 mm^2

The volume of the cube is 1 mm × 1 mm × 1 mm = 1 mm^3

The surface area to volume ratio = <u>6 : 1</u>
Surface area / Volume

The volume of a cube is side length × side length × side length.

These diagrams aren't to scale. Obviously.

This cube has sides of length 1×10^{-5} mm.

Each face has a surface area of (1×10^{-5}) mm × (1×10^{-5}) mm = 1×10^{-10} mm^2

The cube has six faces, so the total surface area is 6 × $(1 \times 10^{-10}$ mm$^2)$ = 6×10^{-10} mm^2

The volume of the cube is (1×10^{-5}) mm × (1×10^{-5}) mm × (1×10^{-5}) mm = 1×10^{-15} mm^3

1×10^{-5} mm

The surface area to volume ratio = 6×10^{-10} : 1×10^{-15} = **600 000 : 1**

These two ratios are the same, we've just simplified the first one so that it's easier to compare with the ratio for the 1 mm cube.

4) Nanoparticles have a very <u>high</u> surface area to volume ratio. This means the surface area is very <u>large</u> compared to the volume.

Nannyparticles

5) A material can have <u>different properties</u> when it's in the form of <u>nanoparticles</u> to when it's in <u>bulk</u>.

6) This is because, in a nanoparticle, a higher percentage of the atoms are <u>at the surface</u> compared to when it's in bulk. This means that more of the atoms are able to <u>interact</u> with other substances.

Nano nano nano nano nano nano nano nano — particles...

Nanoparticles are between ten and one thousand times larger than atoms and simple molecules. That's teeny tiny.

Q1   Would you expect the surface area to volume ratio to be greater for a nanoparticle with a diameter of 20 nm or for a molecule of a similar shape with a diameter of 0.2 nm?   [1 mark]

Uses of Nanoparticles

'What's the use of something so small that not even a flea can see it?' I hear you cry. Well, as you're about to find out, scientists have developed some pretty exciting uses for nanoparticles.

Fullerenes are Nanoparticles of Carbon

1) Fullerenes are a form of carbon.
   They're large molecules shaped like hollow balls or tubes.

2) The carbon atoms in fullerenes are arranged in rings, similar to those in graphite (see page 120).

3) Even though they are molecular substances, their melting and boiling points are pretty high. This is because they're big molecules. Bigger molecules have stronger intermolecular forces between the particles which take more energy to break (see p.113).

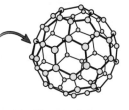

There's more about the other forms of carbon on p.120.

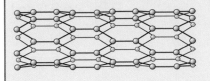

- Fullerenes can form tiny tubes called nanotubes.
- Nanotubes have free electrons so they conduct electricity and heat.
- They also have a high tensile strength.
  This means they don't break easily when they're stretched.

Nanoparticles Can Change the Properties of Materials

Using nanoparticles is known as nanotechnology. Many new uses of nanoparticles are being developed:

1) They have a huge surface area to volume ratio, so they can make good catalysts (see p.144).

2) The shape of fullerenes means they could be used to carry small drug molecules. They are absorbed very easily by the body. This means that they could deliver drugs right to the cells where they're needed.

3) Fullerenes can also be used as molecular sieves. Small molecules can pass through the material, but larger molecules get trapped on the other side.

Fullerenes and graphene are fairly recent discoveries. It took some pretty creative people to imagine new uses for them.

4) Nanoparticles are added to plastics to make composite materials (p.122). These are used to make sports equipment, e.g. golf balls. They make the plastic much stronger without making it much heavier.

The Effects of Nanoparticles on Health Aren't Fully Understood

1) Although nanoparticles are useful, they might have risks that we don't understand yet.

2) For example, there hasn't been time to see if they have any long-term impacts on health.

3) They're so small that they can get into cells deep within the body. Their high surface area means they could react in unknown ways with cells, which could cause harm.

4) The benefits of using nanoparticles need to be weighed up against the possible risks. For example, nanoparticles that are useful for drug delivery could also have unknown harmful effects. But the drug could save someone's life. So it may be used anyway as this benefit outweighs the risks.

Not to be confused with my Irish granny, Nan O'Brien...

It seems like small particles are big business — but as with any new technology there are good and bad sides.

Q1   Give two examples of uses of nanoparticles.   [2 marks]

Revision Questions for Chapter C4

Phew. That's almost it for Chapter C4. But before you run off, time to have a go at a few questions.
*   Try these questions and tick off each one when you get it right.
*   When you've done all the questions for a topic and are completely happy with it, tick off the topic.

Polymers (p.119) ☐

1) What type of bonds are there between the atoms in a polymer chain? ☑
2) Give one difference between the properties of a polymer that forms crosslinks and one that doesn't. ☑

Giant Covalent Structures (p.120) ☐

3) What is a giant covalent structure? ☑
4) Explain how the structure of graphite causes:
    a) its high melting point,   b) its electrical conductivity. ☑

Properties and Uses of Materials (p.121-123) ☐

5) Name three types of structure that particles can form. ☑
6) What factor determines the melting point of a substance? ☑
7) What is stiffness? ☑
8) Give two examples of properties of ceramics. ☑
9) What is a composite? ☑
10) Give one example of something you could do to stop iron from corroding. ☑
11) Define 'reduction'. ☑
12) Are metals thermal conductors or insulators? ☑

Reuse, Recycling and Life Cycle Assessments (p.124-125) ☐

13) What is reuse? ☑
14) Give two benefits of recycling. ☑
15) Give one reason why a material may not be recycled. ☑
16) What is a life cycle assessment? ☑

Nanoparticles (p.126-127) ☐

17) What is a nanoparticle? ☑
18) Give a brief description of the structure of fullerenes. ☑
19) Give one example of a problem related to using nanoparticles. ☑

Purity and Mixtures

Mixtures in <u>chemistry</u> are like mixtures in baking, lots of <u>separate</u> things all mixed together. Just don't eat them.

Purity Has a Specific Meaning in Chemistry

1) In <u>everyday life</u>, when you say a <u>substance</u> is <u>pure</u> you mean that <u>nothing</u> has been <u>added</u> to it — so it's in its <u>natural state</u>. For example, pure milk or pure orange juice.

2) In <u>chemistry</u>, a pure substance is something that only contains <u>one compound</u> or <u>element</u>. It's <u>not mixed</u> with anything else.

Having impure thoughts
again, Henry?

The Melting Point Tells You How Pure a Substance Is

1) A chemically pure substance will <u>melt</u> at a <u>specific temperature</u>, e.g. 126 °C.

2) <u>Impure</u> substances generally melt over a <u>range</u> of temperatures, e.g. 120-124 °C.

3) You can <u>test</u> how pure a sample of a substance is by measuring its <u>melting point</u>.
You can then compare this value with the melting or boiling point of the <u>pure substance</u>.

4) The <u>closer</u> your measured value is to the actual melting point, the <u>purer</u> your sample is.

5) Impurities in the sample will <u>lower</u> the <u>melting point</u> and <u>increase</u> the <u>melting range</u> of the substance.

A Substance that isn't Pure is a Mixture

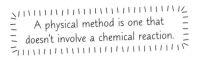

A physical method is one that
doesn't involve a chemical reaction.

1) A mixture contains <u>at least two</u> different <u>elements</u> or <u>compounds</u> that can be <u>separated</u> by <u>physical methods</u>.

2) <u>Physical methods</u> include chromatography (p.130), filtration (p.133), crystallisation (p.133), simple distillation (p.132) or fractional distillation (p.132).

3) For example, <u>crude oil</u> is a <u>mixture</u> of different hydrocarbon molecules.

4) The <u>properties</u> of a mixture are just a <u>mix</u> of the properties of the <u>separate parts</u>.
The chemical properties of a substance <u>aren't</u> affected by it being part of a mixture.

Formulations are Mixtures with Exact Amounts of Each Part

1) <u>Formulations</u> are useful mixtures that are made by following a <u>formula</u> (a recipe).

2) Each part in a formulation is <u>measured carefully</u> so that it's there in the <u>right amount</u>.
This is to make sure that the formulation has the right <u>properties</u>, so it will work as it's supposed to.

3) Lots of <u>everyday products</u> are formulations. For example, many medicines, paints, fuels and cosmetics.

4) It's important that the chemicals used to make formulations like medicines and cosmetics are <u>pure</u>.
If impurities get into the formulation, people could be <u>harmed</u> when they use them.

5) You can use a <u>ratio</u> to describe the recipe for a formulation:

> **EXAMPLE:** A formulation is made by mixing water and ethanol in the ratio 2 : 1 in a total volume of 15 cm³.
> $$\text{The proportion of ethanol} = \frac{\text{volume of ethanol}}{\text{total volume}}$$
> Calculate the volume of ethanol used to make the formulation.
>
> 1) Rearrange the equation to work out the volume: volume of ethanol = proportion of ethanol × total volume
>
> 2) Use the ratio to find the proportion of ethanol: $\text{proportion} = \frac{\text{parts of ethanol in the ratio}}{\text{total number of parts in the ratio}} = \frac{1}{2+1} = \frac{1}{3}$
>
> 3) Calculate the volume of ethanol: volume of ethanol $= \frac{1}{3} \times 15 \text{ cm}^3 = 5 \text{ cm}^3$

I was hoping for pure joy, but this page was a real mixture...

All formulations are mixtures, but not all mixtures are formulations. To be a formulation, a mixture has to have been made for a certain use and to be made up from a recipe using carefully measured amounts of each substance.

Q1   The melting point of pure aspirin is 136 °C. The melting point of a sample of aspirin is measured as over 128-132 °C. Give two reasons why this suggests that the sample is not pure aspirin.   [2 marks]

Chromatography

Chromatography sounds weird and complicated, but read on and you'll find that it's actually pretty nifty.

Chromatography uses Two Phases

1) Chromatography is a method used to separate and identify the substances in a mixture.

2) You need to know how to do paper chromatography. Like all types of chromatography it has two phases:

-   A mobile phase — where the molecules can move.
    In paper chromatography, this is a solvent (e.g. water or ethanol).
-   A stationary phase — where the molecules can't move.
    In paper chromatography, this is the paper.

3) During paper chromatography the solvent moves up the paper.
    As the solvent moves, it carries the substances in the mixture with it.

4) In a chromatography experiment, the amount of time a chemical spends dissolved in the solvent or stuck on the paper is called its 'distribution'.

5) The more soluble a chemical is, the more time it will spend dissolved in the solvent.
    This means that the chemical will move further up the paper.

6) Different chemicals will be dissolved in the solvent for different amounts of time. So the different chemicals will move different distances up the paper. This means they separate into different spots.

7) What solvent you use will depend on the mixture that you're testing. Some mixtures will dissolve in water. For mixtures that don't, you'll need to use a non-aqueous solvent (like ethanol) instead.

Here's How to Do Paper Chromatography:

PRACTICAL

-   Draw a line near the bottom of a sheet of filter paper using a pencil. ← Pencil marks won't dissolve in the solvent.
-   Add a spot of the test substance to the line. Place the sheet in a beaker of solvent so that the solvent is just below the spot but not touching it.
-   Place a lid on top of the container to stop the solvent from evaporating.
-   The solvent soaks up the paper, carrying the substances with it.
-   When the solvent has nearly reached the top of the paper, take the paper out.
-   Mark the point that the solvent reached with a pencil and leave the paper to dry. The point the solvent has reached is called the solvent front.

filter paper, spot of ink, pencil line, lid, solvent front, shallow solvent

1) If your test substance is a mixture (not a pure substance), you'll see more than one spot.

2) If you only see one spot, the substance may well be pure. (But to be sure, you'd have to check that the substance only produces one spot when you use other solvents too).

3) If there are colourless chemicals in the mixture, you can use locating agents to make them visible.

-   Spraying ninhydrin solution on the paper will turn any spots containing amino acids purple.
-   Or you could dip the paper into a jar containing a few iodine crystals. Iodine vapour will stick to the chemicals on the paper and they'll show up as purple spots.

Chromatography revision — it's a phase you have to get through...

You can't see the chemicals moving between the two phases, but it does happen. You'll just have to trust me.

Q1   What is the stationary phase in paper chromatography?   [1 mark]

Interpreting Chromatograms

So, what use is <u>chromatography</u>, apart from making a pretty pattern of spots? Prepare to find out...

You can Calculate the Rf Value for Each Chemical

1) In <u>paper chromatography</u>, the piece of paper that you end up with is called a <u>chromatogram</u>.

2) You need to know how to work out <u>Rf values</u> for <u>spots</u> on a chromatogram.

3) An Rf value is the <u>ratio</u> between the distance travelled by the <u>solute</u> (spot) and the distance travelled by the <u>solvent</u>.

4) You can calculate the Rf values of spots using this <u>formula</u>:

$$Rf = \frac{\text{distance travelled by solute}}{\text{distance travelled by solvent}}$$

EXAMPLE:

A chromatography experiment produced the chromatogram shown on the right. Calculate the Rf value for spot A.

$$Rf = \frac{\text{distance travelled by solute}}{\text{distance travelled by solvent}}$$

Rf value of spot A = 3 ÷ 10 = 0.3

To find the distance travelled by a substance, always measure from the baseline to the centre of the spot.

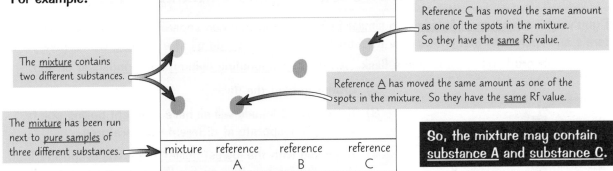

You can Identify Substances in Mixtures Using Chromatography

1) You can run <u>pure samples</u> of substances (called <u>references</u>) next to the mixture you're analysing.

2) If the Rf value of a reference <u>matches</u> a spot in the mixture, that substance <u>could</u> be in the mixture.
   For example:

The <u>mixture</u> contains two different substances.

The <u>mixture</u> has been run next to <u>pure samples</u> of three different substances.

mixture   reference   reference   reference
                A   B   C

Reference <u>C</u> has moved the same amount as one of the spots in the mixture. So they have the <u>same</u> Rf value.

Reference <u>A</u> has moved the same amount as one of the spots in the mixture. So they have the <u>same</u> Rf value.

So, the mixture may contain substance <u>A</u> and substance <u>C</u>.

3) If any of the Rf values <u>match</u>, you can <u>check</u> to see if the chemicals <u>are</u> the same by repeating the whole thing with a <u>different solvent</u>. If they match again, there's a <u>high chance</u> that they're the <u>same</u>.

Rf Values can Change if the Conditions are Different

The <u>Rf value</u> of a substance can <u>change</u> if you change the conditions used in a chromatography experiment. For example, if you use a different <u>solvent</u>, <u>temperature</u> or <u>stationary phase</u>.

- Sometimes you get spots on a chromatogram that don't <u>separate properly</u>. Repeating the experiment using <u>different conditions</u> can get them to separate.

- If the spots for two of your <u>reference compounds</u> end up at the same height, you might need to re-run your experiment using a different solvent.

And now, Sam and Abi will interpret a chromatogram through the medium of dance.

Leopard, cheetah, dalmatian — I love identifying spots...

Make sure you know the equation for calculating Rf values. It could save the day in the exam.

Q1   The solvent front on a chromatogram is at 6.0 cm. There is one visible spot at 4.8 cm.
       Calculate the Rf value of the visible spot.

[2 marks]

PRACTICAL

Distillation

Chemical reactions often make a <u>mixture</u> of products. Chemists need ways of <u>separating out</u> the products they <u>want</u> from the ones they don't. Distillation is a method used to <u>separate mixtures</u> which contain <u>liquids</u>.

Simple Distillation Can be Used to Separate Solutions

<u>Simple distillation</u> is used to separate a <u>liquid</u> from a <u>solution</u>, or to separate liquids that have <u>very different</u> boiling points.

For example, here's how you'd <u>distil seawater</u> (a <u>solution</u> of salt dissolved in water) to get pure water:

1) Set up the <u>apparatus</u> as shown in the diagram on the right.
2) Gradually <u>heat</u> the flask.
3) The part of the mixture with the <u>lowest</u> boiling point will <u>evaporate</u> (turn into a gas). In this case that's the water.
4) The water vapour moves into the condenser, where it <u>cools</u> and <u>condenses</u> (turns back into a liquid).
5) It drips out of the <u>condenser</u> and is collected in the beaker.
6) Eventually you'll end up with just the <u>salt</u> left in the flask.

Simple distillation can't be used to separate mixtures of liquids with <u>similar boiling points</u>. So, you need to use another method instead — like fractional distillation...

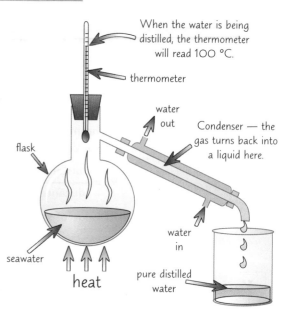

When the water is being distilled, the thermometer will read 100 °C.

thermometer

water out

Condenser — the gas turns back into a liquid here.

flask

water in

seawater

heat

pure distilled water

Fractional Distillation Can be Used to Separate Mixtures of Liquids

If you've got a <u>mixture of liquids</u> with <u>similar boiling points</u>, you can separate it using <u>fractional distillation</u>. Here's an experiment that shows how fractional distillation of <u>crude oil</u> at a <u>refinery</u> works (see p.116).

1) Put your <u>crude oil substitute</u> in a flask. Attach a <u>fractionating column</u> and <u>condenser</u> on top.

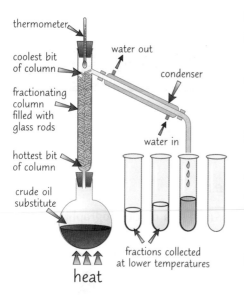

thermometer

coolest bit of column

water out

condenser

fractionating column filled with glass rods

hottest bit of column

water in

crude oil substitute

fractions collected at lower temperatures

heat

2) Gradually <u>heat</u> the flask.

3) The different liquids will all have <u>different boiling points</u>, so they'll evaporate at different temperatures.

4) The liquid with the <u>lowest boiling point</u> will evaporate first. When the temperature on the thermometer matches the boiling point of this substance, it has reached the <u>top</u> of the column.

5) The substance will then enter the condenser, where it will cool and <u>condense</u>.

6) You can <u>collect</u> the liquid as it drips out of the condenser.

7) Liquids with <u>higher boiling points</u> may also start to evaporate. But the column is cooler towards the top, so they'll only get part way up before <u>condensing</u> and running back down into the flask.

8) When the first liquid has been collected, <u>raise</u> the <u>temperature</u> until the <u>next one</u> reaches the top. <u>Collect</u> each liquid in a separate container.

Fractionating — *sounds a bit too much like maths to me...*

So if you're separating two liquids with different boiling points or a liquid from a solution, use simple distillation. If the boiling points are much closer together then grab yourself a fractionating column.

Q1   A mixture contains three liquids. Liquid A boils at 97 °C, liquid B boils at 65 °C and liquid C boils at 78 °C. A student uses fractional distillation to separate the mixture. State which liquid will be collected in the first fraction. Explain your answer.   [2 marks]

Separating Mixtures

PRACTICAL

Filtration and crystallisation are ways of separating mixtures. Chemists use these methods to separate out solids from liquids — and you need to know how to do them too.

Filtration is Used to Separate an Insoluble Solid from a Liquid

1) To separate out an insoluble solid from a liquid, you can use filtration.

2) All you do is pop some filter paper into a funnel and pour your mixture into it.

3) The liquid part of the mixture runs through the paper. The solid bits can't pass through the paper, so they get left behind.

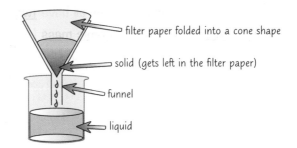

filter paper folded into a cone shape

solid (gets left in the filter paper)

funnel

liquid

Crystallisation Separates a Soluble Solid from a Solution

To separate a solute (dissolved solid) from a solution you'll need to crystallise it...

1) Pour the solution into an evaporating dish and gently heat the solution. This technique is called evaporation.

2) Some of the solvent (which will usually be water) will evaporate and the solution will get more concentrated.

3) Wait until about half of the solvent has evaporated, or when you see crystals start to form. Then remove the dish from the heat and leave the solution to cool.

You could evaporate off all the solvent, but you'd end up with tiny crystals and the heat could break your substance down.

evaporating dish

4) The salt should start to form crystals as it becomes insoluble in the cool, highly concentrated solution.

5) Filter the crystals out of the solution, and leave them in a warm place to dry. (Or you could dry them in a special piece of drying equipment, like a drying oven or a desiccator.)

Choose the Right Purification Method

The best technique to separate a mixture will depend on the properties of the substances in the mixture. For example:

A mixture is made up of two substances, X and Y.

Substance X is a liquid at room temperature. Its melting point is 5 °C and its boiling point is 60 °C.
Substance Y is a solid at room temperature. Its melting point is 745 °C and its boiling point is 1218 °C.
Substance Y dissolves completely in substance X.

- To get X on its own, you'd need to distil it from the solution. You can use simple distillation here — there's no need for fractional distillation as there's only one liquid in the solution.

- To get Y on its own means separating a soluble solid from a solution, so you'd use crystallisation.

You wouldn't be able to use filtration to separate the two substances — substance Y dissolves in substance X so they would both pass through the filter paper.

Revise mixtures — just filter out the important bits...

The product of separation may not be completely pure first time, so scientists may carry out the same technique a couple of times before it's pure enough. Or they'll use a number of techniques to remove all the impurities.

Q1   Describe how you could produce pure crystals of copper sulfate from a copper sulfate solution.   [5 marks]

Relative Mass

The mass of an atom is really, really tiny. To make it easier to calculate with and compare the masses of different atoms, you usually use relative masses instead of their actual masses.

Elements have a Relative Atomic Mass, A_r

1) In the periodic table, the elements all have two numbers next to them.
2) The bigger one is the relative atomic mass (A_r) of the element.

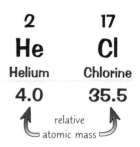

2	17
He	**Cl**
Helium	Chlorine
4.0	35.5

relative atomic mass

~There's more about the relative atomic masses of elements, including how to calculate them, on page 92.~

Compounds have a Relative Formula Mass, M_r

The relative formula mass, M_r (or RFM), of a compound is all the relative atomic masses in its formula added together.

~For simple covalent compounds, the relative formula mass is often called the relative molecular mass (RMM).~

EXAMPLE: Find the relative formula mass of magnesium chloride, $MgCl_2$.

1) Use the periodic table to find the relative atomic masses of magnesium and chlorine. A_r of Mg = 24.3 A_r of Cl = 35.5

2) Add up the relative atomic masses of each atom in the compound.

$$M_r \text{ of } MgCl_2 = A_r \text{ of Mg} + (2 \times A_r \text{ of Cl})$$
$$= 24.3 + (2 \times 35.5)$$
$$= 24.3 + 71.0 = 95.3$$

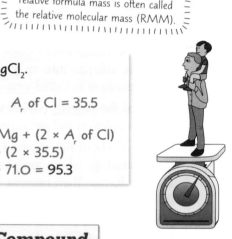

You Can Calculate the % Mass of an Element in a Compound

You might need to work out the percentage mass of an element in a compound. Thankfully, there is a handy formula to help you...

$$\text{Percentage mass of an element in a compound} = \frac{A_r \text{ of element} \times \text{number of atoms of element in compound}}{M_r \text{ of the compound}} \times 100$$

EXAMPLE:

a) Find the percentage mass of sodium in sodium carbonate, Na_2CO_3.

A_r of sodium = 23.0, A_r of carbon = 12.0, A_r of oxygen = 16.0

M_r of Na_2CO_3 = $(2 \times 23.0) + 12.0 + (3 \times 16.0)$ = 106.0

$$\text{Percentage mass of Na} = \frac{A_r \text{ of Na} \times \text{number of atoms of Na}}{M_r \text{ of } Na_2CO_3} \times 100 = \frac{23.0 \times 2}{106.0} \times 100 = \mathbf{43.4\%}$$

b) Use your answer to part a) to calculate the mass of sodium in 5.00 g of sodium carbonate.

% mass of sodium in sodium carbonate = 43.4%

mass of sodium in 5.00 g of sodium carbonate = 43.4% of 5.00 g = $5.00 \times \frac{43.4}{100}$ = **2.17 g**

Have you mastered this page? Relatively...

The best way to get to grips with all this stuff is by practising. Start by having a go at these questions...

Q1   Calculate the relative formula mass (M_r) of: a) H_2O b) LiOH   c) H_2SO_4 [3 marks]

Q2   Calculate the percentage mass of potassium in potassium hydroxide (KOH).   [2 marks]

Conservation of Mass

You've probably realised by now that you can't <u>magic</u> stuff out of thin air. It can't magically <u>disappear</u>, either.

In a Chemical Reaction, Mass Always Stays the Same

1) During a chemical reaction <u>no atoms are lost</u> and <u>no atoms are made</u>.

2) This means there are the <u>same numbers</u> and <u>types</u> of atoms on each side of a reaction equation.

> For example: $2Li + F_2 \rightarrow 2LiF$
> In this reaction, there are <u>2 lithium atoms</u> and <u>2 fluorine atoms</u> on <u>each side</u> of the equation.

3) Because of this, no mass is lost or gained — mass is <u>conserved</u> (stays the same) in a reaction.

4) You can see that mass stays the same if you <u>add up</u> the relative formula masses of the substances on each side of a <u>balanced symbol equation</u>.

5) The total M_r of the reactants will be the <u>same</u> as the total M_r of the products.

If you're not sure what the large and small numbers in reaction equations mean, see p.78-79.

EXAMPLE:

Show that mass is conserved in this reaction: $2Li + F_2 \rightarrow 2LiF$
Relative atomic masses (A_r): Li = 6.9, F = 19.0

1) Add up the relative formula masses on the <u>left-hand side</u> of the equation.

$2 \times A_r(Li) + 2 \times A_r(F) = (2 \times 6.9) + (2 \times 19.0)$
$= 13.8 + 38.0 = 51.8$

2) Add up the relative formula masses on the <u>right-hand side</u> of the equation.

$2 \times M_r(LiF) = 2 \times (6.9 + 19.0)$
$= 2 \times 25.9 = 51.8$

The total M_r on the left-hand side of the equation is the same as the total M_r on the right-hand side. So mass is conserved.

You can Calculate the Mass of a Reactant or Product

1) You can use the idea of conservation of mass to <u>work out</u> the mass of a reactant or product in a reaction.

2) You need to know the masses of <u>all</u> the reactants and products except for <u>one</u>.

3) You can work out the <u>total mass</u> of everything on one side of the equation.

4) You can also work out the total mass of everything on the other side of the equation, <u>except</u> for the thing you don't know the mass of.

5) The mass of the thing you <u>don't</u> know is the <u>difference</u> between these two totals.

EXAMPLE:

6 g of magnesium completely reacts with 4 g of oxygen in the following reaction:
$2Mg + O_2 \rightarrow 2MgO$
What mass of magnesium oxide is formed?

1) Find the <u>total mass</u> of reactants.

Mass of reactants = 4 + 6 = 10 g

2) Magnesium oxide is the <u>only product</u>. So the <u>mass of products</u> you do know is 0 g.

Mass of magnesium oxide = 10 − 0 = 10 g

Leaving all the potatoes on your plate — that's mash conservation...

Never, ever forget that, in a reaction, the total mass of reactants is the same as the total mass of products.

Q1 When 6.00 g of calcium carbonate is heated, it breaks down to form carbon dioxide and 3.36 g of calcium oxide. Calculate the mass of carbon dioxide that forms. [2 marks]

More on Conservation of Mass

Even though mass is always conserved in a reaction, sometimes you might do an experiment where the mass of a reaction mixture in an unsealed container changes. Time to find out why...

If the Mass Seems to Change, There's Usually a Gas Involved

In some experiments, the mass of an unsealed reaction container might change during a reaction. This usually happens for one of two reasons...

1) If One of the Reactants is a Gas, the Mass Could Go Up

If the mass goes up, it's probably because one of the reactants is a gas found in the air (e.g. oxygen) and all the products are solids, liquids or in solution.

1) Before the reaction, the gas is floating around in the air. It's there, but it's not trapped in the reaction container. This means you can't measure its mass.

2) When the gas reacts, its atoms become part of the product, which is held inside the reaction container.

3) So the total mass of the stuff inside the reaction container goes up. For example:

> • When a metal reacts with oxygen in an unsealed container, the mass of the reaction mixture goes up.
>
> • This is because the mass of the oxygen atoms isn't measured when they're part of the gas, but it is when they're in the metal oxide.
>
> $$metal_{(s)} + oxygen_{(g)} \rightarrow metal\ oxide_{(s)}$$

2) If One of the Products is a Gas, the Mass Could Go Down

If the mass goes down, it's probably because one of the products is a gas and all the reactants are solids, liquids or in solution.

1) Before the reaction, all the reactants are held in the reaction container.

2) If the container isn't sealed, then the gas can escape as it's formed.

3) It's no longer trapped in the container, so you can't measure its mass.

4) This means the total mass of the reaction mixture goes down. For example:

> • When a metal carbonate is heated, it can break down to form a metal oxide and carbon dioxide gas.
>
> • If you do this reaction in an unsealed container, the mass of the reaction mixture will go down because the carbon dioxide escapes.
>
> • But really, the mass of the metal oxide and the carbon dioxide formed will be the same as the mass of the metal carbonate.
>
> $$metal\ carbonate_{(s)} \rightarrow metal\ oxide_{(s)} + carbon\ dioxide_{(g)}$$

Remember from the particle theory on page 76 that a gas will spread out to fill any container it's in. So if the reaction container isn't sealed, the gas will escape into the air.

My friend and I talked about grams — it was a mass conversation...

If all this information is escaping from your brain, have another read of the page and then try these questions...

Q1   During a reaction, the mass of a reaction mixture increases.
      What does this tell you about the states of matter of the products and reactants?   [2 marks]

Q2   A scientist carries out the reaction shown below in an unsealed container.
      $$2Na_{(s)} + 2HCl_{(aq)} \rightarrow 2NaCl_{(aq)} + H_{2(g)}$$
      Predict how the mass of the reaction mixture will change as the reaction takes place.   [1 mark]

Acids, Alkalis and Standard Solutions

Acids and alkalis — some people love 'em, some people hate 'em. I'm fairly <u>neutral</u>, to be honest.

Acids and Alkalis Neutralise Each Other

1) An <u>acid</u> is a substance that dissolves in water to release H^+ ions.
Common acids include <u>hydrochloric acid</u>, <u>sulfuric acid</u> and <u>nitric acid</u>.

2) An <u>alkali</u> is a substance that produces <u>hydroxide (OH⁻) ions</u> when it <u>dissolves in water</u>.
Common alkalis include <u>sodium hydroxide</u>, <u>potassium hydroxide</u> and <u>calcium hydroxide</u>.

3) Acids and alkalis react together in <u>neutralisation reactions</u>:

$$acid + alkali \rightarrow salt + water$$

There's more on acids and alkalis on page 140.

4) The salt that forms contains the <u>negative ion</u> from the <u>acid</u> and the <u>positive ion</u> from the <u>alkali</u>.

<u>Examples</u>: $HCl + NaOH \rightarrow NaCl + H_2O$ The salt made is sodium chloride.
$H_2SO_4 + Ca(OH)_2 \rightarrow CaSO_4 + 2H_2O$ The salt made is calcium sulfate.
$HNO_3 + KOH \rightarrow KNO_3 + H_2O$ The salt made is potassium nitrate.

5) Neutralisation reactions between acids and alkalis can be seen in terms of a reaction between H^+ and OH^- ions like this:

$$H^+_{(aq)} + OH^-_{(aq)} \rightarrow H_2O_{(l)}$$

A Standard Solution Has a Known Concentration

1) The <u>amount</u> of a substance in a given <u>volume</u> of a solution is called its <u>concentration</u>.

2) A <u>standard solution</u> is a solution with a <u>known concentration</u>. You can prepare one in the lab:

- Put a <u>weighing container</u> on a <u>mass balance</u> and reset it to <u>zero</u>. <u>Add</u> the correct mass of the solute (the solid you want to dissolve).
- Add the solid to a beaker containing some <u>deionised</u> (pure) water. <u>Stir</u> until all the solute has <u>dissolved</u>.
- Use some more deionised water to <u>wash</u> the weighing container. Pour the water into the beaker — this makes sure that all the solid has been transferred.
- Tip the solution into a <u>volumetric flask</u> of the right size. Use a <u>funnel</u> to make sure it all goes in.
- <u>Rinse</u> the beaker and stirring rod with deionised water and add that to the <u>flask</u> too. This makes sure there's no solute stuck to the beaker or rod.
- Top the flask up to the <u>correct volume</u> with more deionised water. Make sure the <u>bottom</u> of the <u>meniscus</u> is on the <u>line</u> (see p.234). When you get close to the line, use a <u>dropping pipette</u> to add the last bit of water one drop at a time.
- <u>Stopper</u> the flask and turn it upside down a few times to <u>mix</u> the solution.

3) You can also make a standard solution by <u>diluting</u> a <u>more concentrated</u> solution.

4) The method for doing this is similar to the one above, except that you start by measuring out a volume of the concentrated solution using a <u>pipette</u>, rather than weighing out a mass of the solute.

Katherine's solution was premium, but mine was only standard...

Standard solutions are really useful in titrations. There's more on titrations on the next page.

Q1   A student reacts sulfuric acid with a solution of the alkali sodium hydroxide. Write a word equation for this reaction.   [1 mark]

Titrations

Titrations are used to work out the <u>concentrations</u> of solutions, so they're pretty important. I secretly love them...

Titrations are Used to Find Out Concentrations

<u>Titrations</u> let you find out how much acid is needed to <u>neutralise</u> a quantity of alkali or vice versa.
You can then use this result to work out the <u>concentration</u> of the acid or alkali. For example:

1) Say you want to find out the concentration of some <u>alkali</u>. Using a <u>pipette</u> and <u>pipette filler</u>, add a set volume of the alkali to a <u>conical flask</u>. Add two or three drops of an <u>indicator</u> too (see below).

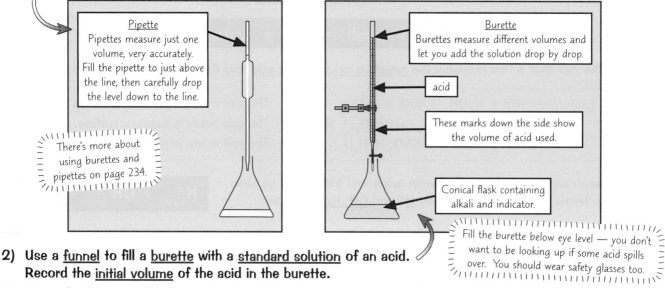

Pipette
Pipettes measure just one volume, very accurately.
Fill the pipette to just above the line, then carefully drop the level down to the line.

There's more about using burettes and pipettes on page 234.

Burette
Burettes measure different volumes and let you add the solution drop by drop.

acid

These marks down the side show the volume of acid used.

Conical flask containing alkali and indicator.

Fill the burette below eye level — you don't want to be looking up if some acid spills over. You should wear safety glasses too.

2) Use a <u>funnel</u> to fill a <u>burette</u> with a <u>standard solution</u> of an acid.
Record the <u>initial volume</u> of the acid in the burette.

3) Using the <u>burette</u>, add the <u>acid</u> to the alkali a bit at a time. Give the conical flask a regular <u>swirl</u>.

4) The indicator will <u>change colour</u> at the exact point when <u>all</u> the alkali has been <u>neutralised</u>.

5) You should go especially <u>slowly</u> when you think the <u>end-point</u> (colour change) is about to be reached — add the acid <u>one drop at a time</u> when you get to this stage.

6) To work out when this is going to be, do a <u>rough titration</u> first. For this, don't worry about recording the <u>exact</u> end point, just note <u>roughly how much</u> acid you need.
Then go <u>slowly</u> as you get <u>near</u> this amount on the next runs.

7) <u>Record</u> the <u>final volume</u> of acid in the burette.
You can use this volume, along with the initial reading,
to calculate the volume of acid used to <u>neutralise</u> the alkali.

This value could then be used to find the concentration of the alkali.

Use Single Indicators for Titrations

1) During a titration you want to see a <u>sudden colour change</u> at the end-point.

2) So you need to use a <u>single indicator</u> that gives a clear colour change. For example:
    • <u>litmus</u> (blue in alkalis and red in acids).
    • <u>methyl orange</u> (yellow in alkalis and red in acids).
    • <u>phenolphthalein</u> (pink in alkalis and colourless in acids).

litmus   methyl orange   phenolphthalein

alkali acid   alkali acid   alkali acid

3) <u>Universal indicator</u> (see p.140) is no good here — it changes colour <u>too gradually</u>.

How do you get thin molecules? Feed them tight rations...

Titrations might seem a bit tricky, but the main thing is just to make sure you do them as carefully as you can.

Q1   How do you know when the end-point of a titration has been reached?   [1 mark]

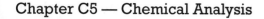

Evaluating Titration Data

If you're going to do titration experiments, you need to be able to talk about the quality of your results too.

Repeating Titrations Helps Make Your Results More Accurate

1) You will need to repeat your titration experiment several times.
This will help make your titration more accurate and help you spot any outliers.

An outlier is a result that doesn't fit in with your other results (see page 225).

2) The first titration you do should be a rough titration.
This will give you a rough idea of the end-point.

3) Then repeat the whole thing a few times, making sure you get pretty much the same answer each time.
You should keep going until you have three results that are within 0.10 cm³ of each other.

4) Finally, calculate a mean (average) of your results, ignoring the rough titration and any outliers.

EXAMPLE: Use the data in the table to calculate the mean volume of acid needed to neutralise the alkali. Ignore any outliers (results not within 0.10 cm³ of each other).

Repeat number:	1	2	3	4
Initial burette reading (cm³)	15.00	15.00	15.00	15.00
Final burette reading (cm³)	29.95	29.50	29.45	29.55
Volume of acid used (cm³)	14.95	14.50	14.45	14.55

You work out the volume of acid used by taking the initial burette reading away from the final burette reading.

1) Find the volumes of acid used that are within 0.10 cm³ of each other.
Repeat 2 (14.50 cm³), repeat 3 (14.45 cm³) and repeat 4 (14.55 cm³).

2) Use these values to calculate a mean.
(14.50 + 14.45 + 14.55) ÷ 3 = 43.50 ÷ 3 = 14.50 cm³

5) If you've followed the correct method, the results of your titration should be valid (see p.223).

6) Getting the same result more than once shows that your results are repeatable.

7) They'll also be precise if the values are very similar to each other.
Using precise equipment such as burettes and pipettes will help with the precision of your results.

8) Taking a mean from the results which are in close agreement (not including outliers) should help to reduce any random errors in the individual results. This makes your overall result more accurate.

The Way You Choose Samples can be Important

1) You can use titrations to work out how much of a certain chemical is present in a substance.
For example, you might want to know how much acid there was in a particular make of fruit drink.

2) When you do tests like this, you usually can't test the whole substance.
Instead, you'd need to take some samples from the substance to test.

Taking samples also means you'll have some of the substance left to carry out other tests on.

3) You should pick the samples from your substance at random.
This should mean that they're representative — your samples should reflect any differences between different bits of the substance.

For example: imagine you were asked to check the concentration of hydrochloric acid present in river water near a waste pipe coming out of a factory. You'd need to take a number of samples of water from slightly different places near the pipe and test them all.

If I had to rate the bit about means, I'd say it was pretty average...

If you do several repeats of a titration, it makes it easy to spot any results that don't fit in with the others.
You can ignore these outliers in your calculations.

Q1 The table on the right shows the volume of nitric acid used to neutralise a solution of sodium hydroxide in three titration repeats. Calculate the mean volume of nitric acid used.

Repeat	1	2	3
Volume of acid (cm³)	16.40	16.45	16.35

[1 mark]

Chapter C5 — Chemical Analysis

Acids, Alkalis and pH

Testing the pH of a solution means using an <u>indicator</u> — and that means pretty <u>colours</u>...

The pH Scale Goes From 0 to 14

For more about acids and alkalis see page 137.

1) You can tell how <u>acidic</u> or <u>alkaline</u> a solution is from its <u>pH</u>.
2) <u>Acidic</u> solutions have a <u>pH less than 7</u>.
3) <u>Alkaline</u> solutions have a pH <u>greater than 7</u>.
4) A <u>neutral</u> substance has <u>pH 7</u>.
5) <u>Acids</u> form H^+ ions in water.
    <u>Alkalis</u> form OH^- ions (hydroxide ions) in water.
6) As the <u>concentration</u> of hydrogen ions <u>increases</u>, the <u>pH</u> <u>decreases</u>. The higher the hydrogen ion concentration, the <u>more acidic</u> something is, so the lower the pH.

Why don't you just make 10 the highest pH?

These go to 14.

Acids are found in lots of everyday products. They're used in cleaning products, added to food to stop mould from growing and can be used in medicines.

You Can Measure the pH of a Solution

You've already met indicators back on page 138.

1) You can measure the <u>pH</u> of a solution using an <u>indicator</u> or a <u>pH meter</u>.
2) An <u>indicator</u> is a <u>dye</u> that <u>changes colour</u> depending on whether it's <u>above or below a certain pH</u>.
3) First, you <u>add a few drops</u> of indicator to the solution you're testing. Then compare the <u>colour</u> the solution goes to a <u>pH chart</u> for that indicator.
4) Here's a <u>pH chart</u> for Universal indicator:

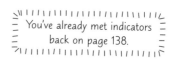

pH 0 1 2 3 4 5 6 7 8 9 10 11 12 13 14

ACIDS   NEUTRAL   ALKALIS

5) A <u>pH probe</u> attached to a <u>pH meter</u> can be used to measure pH <u>electronically</u>.
6) The probe is placed in the solution you are measuring. The pH appears on a <u>digital display</u>. (This gives you a more <u>accurate</u> pH value than an indicator.)
7) When you use a pH probe, it's important to <u>set it up (calibrate) correctly</u>. Before you start, make sure the display shows (very close to) <u>pH 7</u> if you put the probe in deionised (pure) water.
8) Also, you should <u>rinse</u> the probe with deionised water in between readings.

pH probe

pH meter

Indie 'gators — hipster crocodiles...

pHew, you got to the end of the page, so here's an interesting(ish) fact — your skin is slightly acidic (pH 5.5).

Q1   a) The pH of an unknown solution is found to be 6. Is the solution acidic or alkaline?   [1 mark]
      b) A student added Universal indicator to a solution of pH 2. What colour did the solution go?   [1 mark]

Reactions of Acids

You saw on p.137 that acids react with alkalis to form a <u>salt</u> and <u>water</u>. Here's some more on these reactions...

Salts Are Made in Neutralisation Reactions

1) A <u>salt</u> is made in a <u>neutralisation reaction</u> (p.137).
2) You can work out what type of salt will be formed from the <u>acid</u> used.
3) You need to be able to <u>remember</u> what happens when you add <u>acids</u> to different substances...

Name of Acid	Name of Salt
hydrochloric	chloride
sulfuric	sulfate
nitric	nitrate

Acid + Metal Hydroxide → Salt + Water

<u>Examples:</u>
$HCl + NaOH \rightarrow NaCl + H_2O$
$H_2SO_4 + Zn(OH)_2 \rightarrow ZnSO_4 + 2H_2O$
$HNO_3 + KOH \rightarrow KNO_3 + H_2O$

<u>Salt formed:</u>
Sodium chloride
Zinc sulfate
Potassium nitrate

Neutralisation reactions are used in industry to make salts for things such as fertilisers.

Acid + Metal → Salt + Hydrogen

<u>Examples:</u>
$2HCl + Mg \rightarrow MgCl_2 + H_2$
$H_2SO_4 + Mg \rightarrow MgSO_4 + H_2$

<u>Salt formed:</u>
Magnesium chloride
Magnesium sulfate

Some metals, such as copper and silver, are very unreactive. They don't react with acids at all.

Acid + Metal Carbonate → Salt + Water + Carbon Dioxide

<u>Examples:</u>
$2HCl + Na_2CO_3 \rightarrow 2NaCl + H_2O + CO_2$
$H_2SO_4 + K_2CO_3 \rightarrow K_2SO_4 + H_2O + CO_2$
$2HNO_3 + ZnCO_3 \rightarrow Zn(NO_3)_2 + H_2O + CO_2$

<u>Salt formed:</u>
Sodium chloride
Potassium sulfate
Zinc nitrate

You can Make Soluble Salts Using Acid + Alkali Reactions

PRACTICAL

1) You can make <u>soluble salts</u> (salts that dissolve in water) by reacting an <u>acid</u> with an <u>alkali</u>.
2) But you can't just add an <u>excess</u> (more than you need) of the acid to the alkali. This is because you'd end up with a <u>mixture</u> of the salt and the acid rather than just a salt solution.
3) You have to add <u>exactly</u> the right amount of acid to <u>neutralise</u> (react with) the alkali.
4) A <u>titration</u> (see page 138) using an <u>indicator</u> will let you work out <u>how much</u> acid you need to react exactly with all the alkali.
5) Then do the reaction again using the <u>right amounts</u> of alkali and acid, but <u>no indicator</u> (so the salt doesn't contain any indicator).
6) The solution that remains when the reaction is <u>finished</u> will only contain <u>salt</u> and <u>water</u>.
7) To get pure, dry crystals of the salt, you'll need to <u>evaporate</u> some of the water by <u>warming</u> up the solution. Then leave it to <u>crystallise</u> (see page 133 for more on crystallisation).
8) <u>Filter</u> the crystals out of the solution and then <u>dry</u> the salt. You could do this by leaving the salt in a fume cupboard, or you could put it in a <u>drying oven</u> or a hot <u>sand bath</u>.

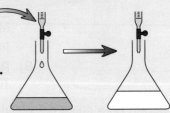

Nitrates — much cheaper than day-rates...

In the exam you might be given the names of some reactants and asked to predict what products they'll form. So, you need to know the names of the salts that the acids make — see the table at the top of the page.

Q1   Name the products that form when hydrochloric acid reacts with sodium.   [2 marks]

PRACTICAL	# Making Salts

You met one method for <u>making salts</u> on the previous page. Time for some more...

Making Soluble Salts Using an Acid and an Insoluble Reactant

1) You can make soluble salts by reacting an <u>acid</u> with a <u>metal</u>, or an <u>insoluble base</u> (like an insoluble <u>metal carbonate</u> or <u>metal hydroxide</u>).

2) Add the insoluble reactant to the <u>acid</u>. They will react to form a <u>soluble salt</u>.

3) You can tell that the reaction has <u>finished</u> when <u>excess solid</u> starts to <u>sink</u> to the bottom of the flask.

4) <u>Filter</u> off the <u>excess</u> solid. You get a solution containing only <u>salt</u> and <u>water</u>.

5) <u>Gently heat the solution</u> to <u>evaporate</u> off some of the water. Then, leave the solution to cool to <u>crystallise</u> the salt (see page 133).

6) Filter off the solid and leave it to <u>dry</u>. And there you have it — a <u>soluble salt</u>.

Making Insoluble Salts — Precipitation Reactions

To make an <u>insoluble</u> salt, you can use a <u>precipitation reaction</u>.

This is where you react two <u>soluble salts</u> together to make your <u>insoluble salt</u>.

Soluble salts dissolve in water. Insoluble salts don't.

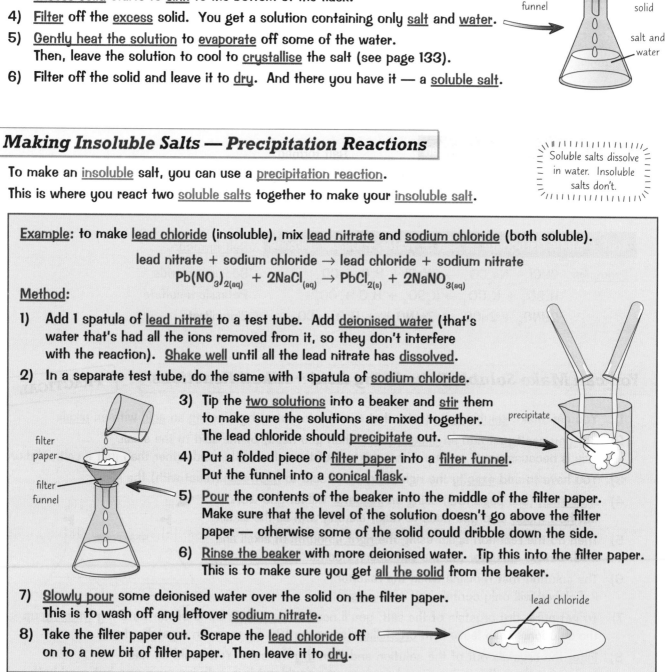

<u>Example</u>: to make <u>lead chloride</u> (insoluble), mix <u>lead nitrate</u> and <u>sodium chloride</u> (both soluble).

lead nitrate + sodium chloride → lead chloride + sodium nitrate

$$Pb(NO_3)_{2(aq)} + 2NaCl_{(aq)} \rightarrow PbCl_{2(s)} + 2NaNO_{3(aq)}$$

<u>Method</u>:

1) Add 1 spatula of <u>lead nitrate</u> to a test tube. Add <u>deionised water</u> (that's water that's had all the ions removed from it, so they don't interfere with the reaction). <u>Shake well</u> until all the lead nitrate has <u>dissolved</u>.

2) In a separate test tube, do the same with 1 spatula of <u>sodium chloride</u>.

3) Tip the <u>two solutions</u> into a beaker and <u>stir</u> them to make sure the solutions are mixed together. The lead chloride should <u>precipitate</u> out.

4) Put a folded piece of <u>filter paper</u> into a <u>filter funnel</u>. Put the funnel into a <u>conical flask</u>.

5) <u>Pour</u> the contents of the beaker into the middle of the filter paper. Make sure that the level of the solution doesn't go above the filter paper — otherwise some of the solid could dribble down the side.

6) <u>Rinse the beaker</u> with more deionised water. Tip this into the filter paper. This is to make sure you get <u>all the solid</u> from the beaker.

7) <u>Slowly pour</u> some deionised water over the solid on the filter paper. This is to wash off any leftover <u>sodium nitrate</u>.

8) Take the filter paper out. Scrape the <u>lead chloride</u> off on to a new bit of filter paper. Then leave it to <u>dry</u>.

I was attacked by a nasty lead chloride — it was a-salt...

The theory may seem boring, but you'll probably get to make some nice salts in your class, and that's pretty cool.

Q1 Describe how you would make the soluble salt copper chloride from hydrochloric acid and copper carbonate.

[5 marks]

Rates of Reactions

Reactions can be <u>fast</u> or <u>slow</u> — you've probably already realised that. It's exciting stuff. Honest.

Particles Must Collide with Enough Energy in Order to React

1) The <u>rate of a reaction</u> is how <u>quickly</u> a reaction happens.
2) Particles have to <u>collide</u> (<u>bump into each other</u>) to react.
   So, the <u>rate</u> of a reaction depends on how <u>often</u> the particles <u>collide</u>.
3) The <u>more frequent</u> the collisions are, the <u>faster</u> the reaction is.
4) The particles also have to <u>bump into</u> each other with <u>enough energy</u> for a collision to be <u>successful</u>.
5) A <u>successful</u> collision is one where the particles react together.
6) The <u>minimum</u> amount of energy that particles need to react is called the <u>activation energy</u> (see p.81).

The More Successful Collisions, the Higher the Rate of Reaction

If you <u>increase</u> the <u>frequency</u> of collisions between particles, the reaction happens <u>more quickly</u> (the rate increases). The <u>three</u> factors below all lead to more frequent collisions:

Increasing the Temperature Increases Rate

1) When it gets <u>hotter</u>, particles <u>move faster</u>.
2) If the particles move faster, they will collide <u>more frequently</u>.
3) Higher temperatures also increase the <u>energy</u> of the collisions. So <u>more</u> particles will <u>collide</u> with <u>enough energy</u> to react.
4) So <u>increasing</u> the temperature <u>increases</u> the rate of reaction.

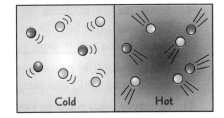

Increasing Concentration (or Pressure) Increases Rate

1) If a <u>solution</u> is made more <u>concentrated</u>, it means there are more particles in the same space.
2) Because there are more particles, collisions happen <u>more often</u>. So the reaction rate <u>increases</u>.
3) In a <u>gas</u>, increasing the <u>pressure</u> means that the particles are <u>more crowded</u>.
4) This means that the particles will bump into each other <u>more often</u>. So the rate of reaction will <u>increase</u>.

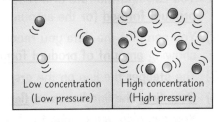
Low concentration (Low pressure) | High concentration (High pressure)

Smaller Solid Particles (or Higher Surface Area) Means a Higher Rate

1) The <u>surface area</u> to <u>volume</u> ratio tells you how much of a substance is <u>on the surface</u>, compared to its total <u>size</u>.
2) Breaking a solid into <u>smaller</u> chunks <u>increases</u> its surface area to volume ratio.
3) The particles around it will have <u>more area to hit</u>. So the frequency of collisions will <u>increase</u>.
4) This means that the rate of reaction is <u>faster</u> for solids with a larger <u>surface area to volume</u> ratio.

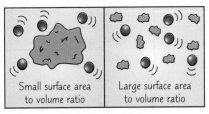
Small surface area to volume ratio | Large surface area to volume ratio

Increase your concentration — burn through that exam paper...

Increasing the temperature increases the speed of particles <u>and</u> it means they have more energy. So, they stand a much better chance of colliding with enough energy to react. Lucky things...

Q1 How will breaking up a solid into small pieces affect the rate at which it reacts with a liquid? [1 mark]

Reaction Rates and Catalysts

Catalysts increase reaction rate and reduce energy costs. Makes them worth learning about I suppose...

Using a Catalyst Increases the Rate

1) A catalyst is a substance that speeds up a reaction, but isn't used up itself.

2) This means that you get the catalyst back unchanged at the end. You should have the same mass of the catalyst that you started with. It will usually look the same too.

3) Catalysts work by providing a new reaction pathway. The new pathway will have a lower activation energy than the old one.

4) Catalysts can speed up the rate of a reaction without having to use high temperatures or pressures.

5) This is useful in industry as you need less energy to get the right reaction conditions. It makes the process cheaper and more environmentally friendly.

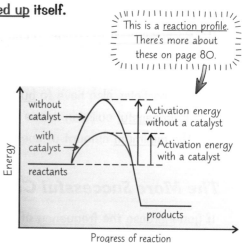

This is a reaction profile. There's more about these on page 80.

Enzymes Control Cell Reactions

1) Enzymes are proteins that act as biological catalysts. They catalyse the chemical reactions in cells.

2) Enzymes work best under certain conditions. If the temperature or pH are too low or too high, the enzyme won't work properly. It could even be damaged and stop working.

3) Some industrial processes use enzymes as catalysts. They can speed up the reaction at fairly low temperatures. This saves a lot of energy.

4) However, you have to keep the reaction conditions just right for the enzymes to work properly.

You Need to Understand Graphs for the Rate of Reaction

1) You can find the rate of a reaction by observing the amount of product formed (or the amount of reactant used up) over time.

2) You can plot the data you record on a graph showing amount of product formed against time.

3) The steeper the line on the graph, the faster the rate of reaction.

4) Over time the line becomes flat as the reactants are used up.

5) You can also use graphs to show how the reaction rate changes if you change the reaction conditions.

The line goes flat when the reaction finishes.

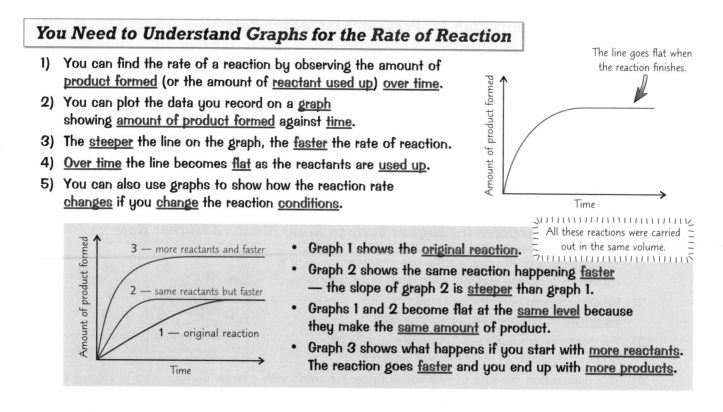

- Graph 1 shows the original reaction.

- Graph 2 shows the same reaction happening faster — the slope of graph 2 is steeper than graph 1.

- Graphs 1 and 2 become flat at the same level because they make the same amount of product.

- Graph 3 shows what happens if you start with more reactants. The reaction goes faster and you end up with more products.

All these reactions were carried out in the same volume.

Catalysts are chemical stars — but success won't change them...

Catalysts aren't just in science labs. Enzymes are in all our cells, catalysing the reactions we need for life.

Q1   What is a catalyst?   [2 marks]

Measuring Reaction Rates PRACTICAL

All this talk about reaction rates is nice, but you've got to have a way of <u>measuring</u> them.

A Change in Mass Tells You How Quickly The Product is Being Made

1) If one of the <u>products</u> of a reaction is a <u>gas</u>, you can measure the rate of reaction using a <u>mass balance</u>.

2) As the gas is given off, the <u>mass</u> of the reaction mixture <u>decreases</u>. If the reaction mixture is placed on a <u>mass balance</u>, the reading on the balance will <u>go down</u> during the reaction.

3) <u>Faster</u> reactions <u>lose</u> mass <u>quicker</u> than slower reactions.

4) If you take measurements at <u>regular intervals</u>, you can plot a <u>graph</u> of <u>mass lost</u> against <u>time</u>.

5) This is the <u>most accurate</u> of the methods on this page, because the mass balance is very accurate.

6) One <u>disadvantage</u> of this method is that the <u>gas</u> is released straight into the <u>room</u>. So if the gas produced by the reaction was <u>toxic</u>, you'd need to do the whole experiment in a <u>fume cupboard</u>.

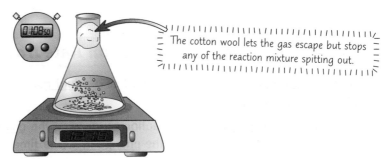

The cotton wool lets the gas escape but stops any of the reaction mixture spitting out.

You Can Also Measure the Volume of Gas Given Off

1) You can measure the <u>volume</u> of gas <u>given off</u> during a reaction using a <u>gas syringe</u>.

2) The <u>more</u> gas given off during a set period of time, the <u>faster</u> the reaction.

3) Gas syringes usually give volumes to the nearest cm^3, so they're quite <u>accurate</u>.

4) If you take measurements at <u>regular intervals</u>, you can plot a <u>graph</u> of <u>volume of gas produced</u> against <u>time</u>.

gas syringe

5) You could also measure the volume of gas given off by bubbling it into an <u>upside-down measuring cylinder</u> filled with <u>water</u> (there's more about how to do this on page 239).

I'd rate these reaction measurements as 8/10...

Make sure you've learnt both of the different methods on this page, then have a go at this question:

Q1   Describe one method that could be used to measure the volume of gas given off during a reaction.   [1 mark]

Finding Reaction Rates from Graphs

You might remember a bit about how to <u>interpret</u> graphs on reaction rate from page 144.
Well this page shows you how to <u>calculate</u> the rate of reaction from a graph.

Use This Formula to Find the Rate of a Reaction:

Mean Rate of Reaction = $\dfrac{\text{Amount of reactant used or amount of product formed}}{\text{Time}}$

This is the <u>mean</u> (average) rate of reaction. To find the rate of a reaction at one particular moment, you'll have to plot a graph and find the gradient of the line at that point (see next page).

1) When the product or reactant is a <u>solid</u> you measure the amount in <u>grams</u> (<u>g</u>). If the product's a <u>gas</u>, then you usually use <u>cm^3</u>.

2) Time is usually measured in <u>seconds</u> (<u>s</u>).

3) This means that the <u>units</u> are likely to be <u>g/s</u> or <u>cm^3/s</u>.

You can Calculate the Mean Reaction Rate from a Graph

1) A <u>rate of reaction graph</u> shows the amount of <u>product made</u> (or <u>reactant used up</u>) on the <u>y-axis</u>.

2) <u>Time</u> goes on the <u>x-axis</u>.

3) You can find the <u>mean rate</u> of the reaction by dividing the <u>change in y</u> (the total <u>amount</u> of product made or reactant used) by the <u>change in x</u> (the <u>time</u> that the reaction took to finish).

EXAMPLE: The graph shows the volume of gas released by a reaction over time. Find the mean rate for the whole reaction.

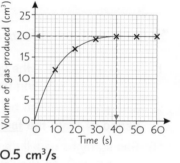

1) To find the <u>change in y</u> (the amount of gas produced by the reaction), draw a line across to the y-axis from the point where the graph goes flat.
Change in y = 20 cm^3

2) To find the <u>change in x</u> (how long the reaction took to finish), draw a line down to the x-axis from the point where the graph goes flat.
Change in x = 40 s

3) Mean rate of reaction = change in y ÷ change in x = 20 cm^3 ÷ 40 s = 0.5 cm^3/s

4) You can also use this method to find the <u>mean rate</u> between <u>any two points</u> in time:

EXAMPLE: The graph shows the volume of gas released by a reaction over time. Find the mean rate of reaction between 20 s and 40 s.

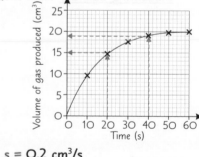

1) Draw lines from the <u>x-axis</u> up to the graph at <u>20 s</u> and <u>40 s</u>. Then, read across to the <u>y-axis</u> to find the <u>y-value</u> at these times. At 20 s, y = 15 cm^3. At 40 s, y = 19 cm^3.

2) Use these values to find the <u>change in y</u> between 20 s and 40 s. Change in y = 19 cm^3 − 15 cm^3 = 4 cm^3.

3) Use the times from the question to find the <u>change in x</u>. Change in x = (40 s − 20 s) = 20 s

4) Mean rate of reaction = change in y ÷ change in x = 4 cm^3 ÷ 20 s = 0.2 cm^3/s

Calculate your reaction to this page. Boredom? How dare you...

There's only one way to learn this stuff properly — practise. So you'd better get going with this question.

Q1 Look at the graph in the first example above. Find the mean rate of reaction between 0 and 10 s. [2 marks]

Using Tangents to Find Reaction Rates

So, it's possible to work out the mean rate of a reaction. But what if you want to know how fast it's going at one exact point? That's where <u>tangents</u> come in. Don't worry, they're not as scary as they sound...

A Tangent Tells You the Slope at a Particular Point on a Curve

1) The <u>gradient</u> of a line tells you how <u>steep</u> the line is.

2) The <u>gradient</u> of a straight line is <u>the same</u> all the way along it.

3) The <u>gradient</u> of a <u>curved</u> line <u>changes</u> as you move along it.

4) You can use a <u>tangent</u> to find how <u>steep</u> a <u>curved</u> line is at a particular point.

5) A tangent is a <u>straight</u> line that touches the curve at a single <u>point</u>. The tangent doesn't <u>cross</u> the curve.

6) Because a <u>tangent</u> is a straight line, you can find its <u>gradient</u>.

7) The <u>gradient</u> of the <u>tangent</u> will be the same as the <u>gradient</u> of the <u>curve</u> at that <u>point</u>.

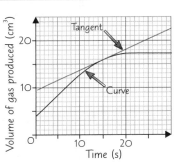

You could use the tangent on this graph to find the gradient of the curve at time = 15 s.

Draw a Tangent to Find the Reaction Rate at a Particular Point

If you want to find the <u>rate</u> of reaction at a particular point in time, you need to find the <u>gradient</u> of the curve at that point. You can do this by drawing a <u>tangent</u>.

EXAMPLE: The graph below shows the mass of reactant used up during a chemical reaction. What was the rate of reaction at 3 minutes?

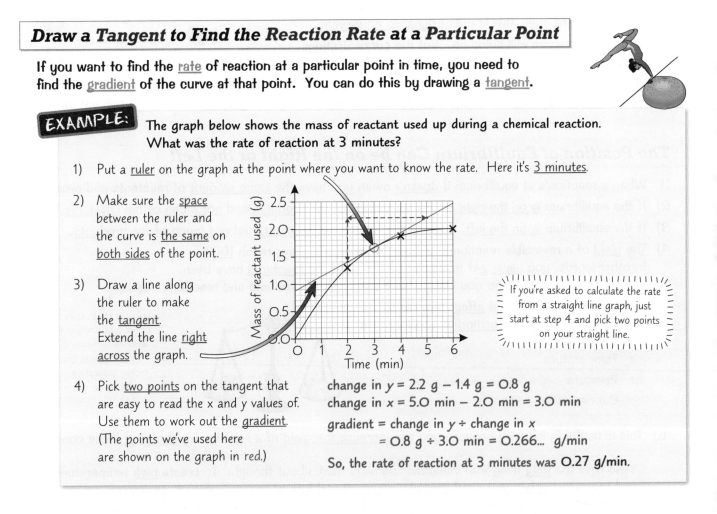

1) Put a <u>ruler</u> on the graph at the point where you want to know the rate. Here it's <u>3 minutes</u>.

2) Make sure the <u>space</u> between the ruler and the curve is <u>the same</u> on <u>both sides</u> of the point.

3) Draw a line along the ruler to make the <u>tangent</u>. Extend the line <u>right</u> <u>across</u> the graph.

4) Pick <u>two points</u> on the tangent that are easy to read the x and y values of. Use them to work out the <u>gradient</u>. (The points we've used here are shown on the graph in red.)

If you're asked to calculate the rate from a straight line graph, just start at step 4 and pick two points on your straight line.

change in y = 2.2 g − 1.4 g = 0.8 g
change in x = 5.0 min − 2.0 min = 3.0 min

gradient = change in y ÷ change in x
= 0.8 g ÷ 3.0 min = 0.266... g/min

So, the rate of reaction at 3 minutes was 0.27 g/min.

I saw my chemistry teacher on holiday — he was a tanned gent...

There's only one way to learn this stuff properly — practise. So you'd better get going with this question.

Q1 During a reaction, a gas was produced and collected. The volume of gas produced was recorded at 10 second intervals in the table on the right.

Time (s)	0	10	20	30	40	50	60
Volume of gas (cm³)	0	24	32	36	38	39	40

a) Plot these results on a graph and draw a line of best fit. [2 marks]

b) Find the rate of the reaction at time = 26 s. [4 marks]

Dynamic Equilibrium

<u>Reversible reactions</u> are funny things. They can go forwards as well as backwards...

Reversible Reactions can go Forwards and Backwards

A <u>reversible reaction</u> is one where the <u>products</u> can react with each other to form the original <u>reactants</u>. In other words, <u>it can go both ways</u>.

A + B ⇌ C + D

The '⇌' shows that the reaction goes both ways.

Reversible Reactions Will Reach Dynamic Equilibrium

1) As the <u>reactants</u> (A and B) react, they get used up and their <u>concentrations decrease.</u> This <u>slows down</u> the <u>forward reaction</u>.

2) As more of the <u>products</u> (C and D) are made, their <u>concentrations increase</u>. This <u>speeds up</u> the <u>backward reaction</u>.

3) After a while the backward reaction reaches the <u>same rate</u> as the forward one. This is called <u>dynamic equilibrium</u>.

4) <u>Both</u> reactions are still going on. But the <u>concentrations</u> of the reactants and products <u>don't change</u>.

5) You can only get an equilibrium if the reversible reaction is in a '<u>closed system</u>'. A <u>closed system</u> means that nothing can <u>get out</u> and nothing can <u>get in</u>.

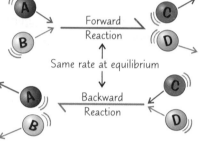

The Position of Equilibrium Can be on the Right or the Left

1) When a reaction's at equilibrium it <u>doesn't</u> mean you have the <u>same amount</u> of reactants and products.

2) If the equilibrium <u>is on the right</u>, there will be <u>lots</u> of the <u>products</u> and <u>not much</u> of the <u>reactants</u>.

3) If the equilibrium <u>is on the left</u>, there will be <u>lots</u> of the <u>reactants</u> but <u>not much</u> of the <u>products</u>.

4) The <u>yield</u> of a reversible reaction in a <u>closed system</u> will <u>never</u> reach <u>100%</u>. In other words, you <u>never</u> get to a point where <u>all of the reactants</u> have been turned into <u>products</u> — so you always have a <u>mixture</u> of products and reactants.

5) There are three things that <u>affect</u> how far to the <u>left</u> or the <u>right</u> the <u>position of equilibrium</u> is:

- **Temperature**
- **Pressure** (only for reactions involving gases)
- **Concentration**

This is a problem in industry, because it means that you have to spend time and money separating out your product from the reactants.

6) This is useful in industry because you can <u>increase the yield</u> of a reaction by <u>changing</u> these conditions.

Yield isn't the <u>only</u> thing that industrial chemists think about though. To create <u>high</u> temperatures and pressures <u>safely</u> you need <u>special equipment</u> and <u>lots of energy</u>, which is <u>expensive</u>. So <u>lower</u> temperatures and pressures are often used, even if it makes the yield a bit lower. The <u>rate</u> of a reaction is important too — it's no use getting a very high yield if it takes <u>ages</u>.

Dynamic equilibrium — lots of activity, but not to any great effect...*

Keep an eye out for that arrow that shows you that a reaction is reversible. I'd hate you to miss it.

Q1   Explain what is meant by a 'reversible reaction'. [1 mark]

Q2   Name three things which can affect the position of equilibrium. [3 marks]

*Much like the England football team...

Revision Questions for Chapters C5 & C6

Chapters C5 and C6 were quite an adventure, and it's not over yet. Time to test what you remember...
- Try these questions and tick off each one when you get it right.
- When you've done all the questions for a topic and are completely happy with it, tick off the topic.

Purity and Mixtures (p.129-133) ☑

1) Give the definition of a pure substance in chemistry. ☑
2) What is a formulation? ☑
3) What are the names of the two phases in chromatography? ☑
4) Give the equation for calculating the Rf value of a spot in paper chromatography. ☑
5) What kind of mixture would you use fractional distillation to separate? ☑
6) Describe how you could separate an insoluble solid from a liquid. ☑

Masses (p.134-136) ☑

7) How do you calculate the relative formula mass, M_r, of a substance? ☑
8) What does it mean if mass is conserved in a reaction? ☑
9) Suggest why the mass of a reaction mixture in an open container might decrease during a reaction. ☑

Solutions and Titrations (p.137-139) ☑

10) What is an acid? ☑
11) Write the general equation for the reaction between H^+ and OH^- ions in a neutralisation reaction. ☑
12) Describe how you would prepare a standard solution from a solid solute. ☑
13) Describe the steps involved in carrying out a titration. ☑
14) Why is it better to use a single indicator in a titration instead of universal indicator? ☑
15) When you do a titration, why should you take a mean from your results (ignoring any outliers)? ☑

Acids, Alkalis and pH (p.140-142) ☑

16) What is the pH of a neutral solution? ☑
17) Describe a method that you could use to measure the pH of a solution. ☑
18) What are the products of a reaction between a metal and an acid? ☑
19) Briefly describe a method you could use to make a pure, insoluble salt from two soluble salts. ☑

Rates of Reactions (p.143-147) ☑

20) Explain why increasing the temperature of a reaction increases its rate. ☑
21) Name two factors other than temperature that affect the rate of a reaction. ☑
22) Describe how a catalyst increases the rate of a reaction. ☑
23) In a reaction, a gas is formed. Describe a method you could use to track the rate of reaction. ☑
24) Give the formula for finding the mean rate of a reaction. ☑
25) Describe how you could use a tangent to find the rate of a reaction at a
particular point on a graph showing product formed against time. ☑

Reversible Reactions and Dynamic Equilibrium (p.148) ☑

26) What symbol is used to show that a reaction is reversible? ☑
27) If a reaction is at dynamic equilibrium, what can you say about the rates
of the forward and backward reactions? ☑

Waves Basics

Waves <u>transfer energy</u> from one place to another <u>without</u> transferring any <u>matter</u> (stuff).

Waves Transfer Energy in the Direction They are Travelling

1) A <u>wave</u> is a <u>regular disturbance</u> (a <u>set pattern</u> of <u>movement</u>) that <u>transfers energy</u>.

2) When a wave <u>travels through</u> a medium, the particles (p.213) of the <u>medium vibrate</u>.

3) The particles <u>transfer energy</u> between each other as they vibrate.

4) <u>BUT</u> overall, the particles stay in the <u>same places</u> — <u>only energy</u> is transferred, <u>not matter</u>.

A medium is just whatever a wave is travelling through (e.g. water, air).

- For example, if you drop a twig into calm water, <u>ripples</u> (water waves) spread out. The ripples <u>don't</u> carry the <u>water</u> (or the twig) away with them though.
- And if you strum a <u>guitar string</u>, the sound waves don't carry the <u>air</u> away from the guitar. If they did, you'd feel a <u>wind</u> whenever there was a sound.

All Waves are Either Transverse or Longitudinal

1) In <u>transverse waves</u>, the disturbance of the medium is at <u>right angles</u> (90°) to the <u>direction</u> the wave <u>travels</u>.

2) <u>Examples</u> of transverse waves are <u>electromagnetic waves</u> (p.156), ripples on <u>water</u> (see p.152) and waves on a <u>rope</u>.

3) Transverse waves can travel <u>on the surface</u> of a liquid, but they <u>can't</u> travel <u>through liquids</u>.

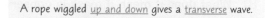

A rope wiggled <u>up and down</u> gives a <u>transverse</u> wave.

Wave travels this way.

Disturbances go up and down.

4) In <u>longitudinal waves</u>, the disturbance of the medium is <u>parallel</u> to (in the <u>same direction</u> as) the <u>direction</u> the wave travels.

5) Longitudinal waves have <u>compressions</u> (where the particles squish together), and <u>rarefactions</u> (where they spread out).

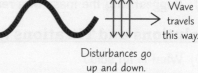

If you <u>push</u> and <u>pull</u> the end of a spring, you can see <u>compression pulses</u> travel down the spring. This is a <u>longitudinal</u> wave.

compressions

rarefactions

Disturbances in the same direction as the wave travels.

6) A <u>sound wave</u> in <u>air</u> is a longitudinal wave. The air particles <u>collide</u> (<u>hit</u> each other), causing them to <u>bunch up</u> and <u>spread out</u> as the wave travels through the air.

You Need to Know these Words to Describe Waves

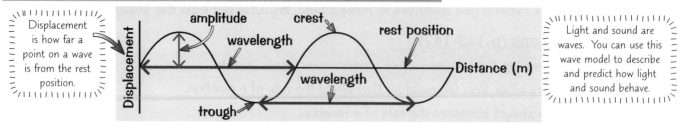

Displacement is how far a point on a wave is from the rest position.

amplitude   crest   rest position
wavelength
Displacement
wavelength
Distance (m)
trough

Light and sound are waves. You can use this wave model to describe and predict how light and sound behave.

1) The <u>amplitude</u> is the <u>maximum displacement</u> of a point on the wave from the <u>undisturbed (rest) position</u>.

2) The <u>wavelength</u> is the distance between <u>one point</u> on a wave (one disturbance) and the <u>same point</u> on the <u>next wave</u> (the next disturbance). E.g. from <u>crest to crest</u>. It is <u>one</u> complete wave.

3) <u>Frequency</u> is the <u>number of complete waves</u> made by a source (the thing making the waves) <u>each second</u>. It's also the <u>number of complete waves</u> that <u>pass</u> a certain point <u>each second</u>. It's measured in <u>hertz</u> (<u>Hz</u>).

4) <u>Period</u> is the amount of <u>time</u> it takes for <u>one</u> complete wave to <u>pass</u> a certain point.

So, that's the wave basics...

Make sure you've got all this clear in your head, otherwise the rest of the topic will just be a blur of nonsense.

Q1   State what is meant by the wavelength of a wave.   [1 mark]

Wave Speed

If you know the <u>frequency</u> and <u>wavelength</u> of a wave, you can work out its <u>speed</u> as well. How neat is that?

Wave Speed = Frequency × Wavelength

1) The <u>wave speed</u> is how fast the <u>wave</u> is moving.

2) It is the speed at which <u>energy is being transferred</u> through the <u>medium</u>.

3) The <u>wave speed equation</u> can be used for <u>all types</u> of wave, including <u>water</u>, <u>sound</u> and <u>electromagnetic waves</u>.

> wave speed (m/s) = frequency (Hz) × wavelength (m)

There's more on changing units on p.190.

4) Wave frequencies are often given in <u>kHz</u> (kilohertz) or <u>MHz</u> (megahertz).

5) Change them to <u>Hz</u> to use them in the equation. <u>1 kHz = 1000 Hz</u>, <u>1 MHz = 1 000 000 Hz</u>.

EXAMPLE: A radio wave has a frequency of 12 MHz.
Find its wavelength. (The speed of radio waves in air is 3.0×10^8 m/s.)

1) Change the frequency into <u>hertz</u>. $12 \times 1\,000\,000 = 12\,000\,000$ Hz

2) <u>Rearrange</u> the wave speed equation for <u>wavelength</u>.   wavelength = wave speed ÷ frequency

3) Put in the <u>values</u> you've been <u>given</u>. $= (3.0 \times 10^8) \div (12\,000\,000)$
Watch out — the speed is in <u>standard form</u> (p.126). $= 25$ m

Use an Oscilloscope to Measure the Speed of Sound

1) Connect <u>two microphones</u> to an <u>oscilloscope</u> (a device which shows waves on a screen).

2) Connect a <u>signal generator</u> to a speaker and <u>turn it on</u>.
This will let you generate <u>sound waves</u> at a <u>set frequency</u>.

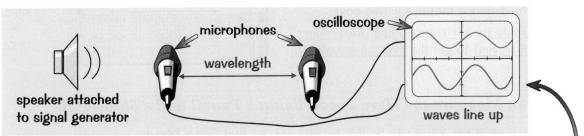

3) Set up the oscilloscope so the <u>waves</u> reaching each microphone are shown <u>separately</u>.

4) Start with <u>both microphones</u> next to the speaker. The waves on the oscilloscope <u>should line up</u>.

5) Slowly <u>move one microphone</u> away. Stop when the two waves <u>line up</u> again on the display.

6) This means the microphones are now <u>exactly one wavelength apart</u>.

7) Measure the <u>distance between the microphones</u> to find the <u>wavelength</u>.

8) Find the <u>speed</u> of the <u>sound waves</u> passing through the <u>air</u> using the equation above.

9) The <u>frequency</u> is whatever you set the <u>signal generator</u> to.

10) The speed of sound in air is around <u>330 m/s</u>.
Check your results <u>roughly agree</u> with this.

330 m/s might sound fast, but it's actually loads slower than electromagnetic waves travel.

Looks like the perfect setup for a karaoke duet...

Make sure you understand each step of that method above — you could be tested on it in the exams.

Q1   A wave has a speed of 0.15 m/s and a wavelength of 0.75 m. Calculate its frequency.   [3 marks]

PRACTICAL Wave Experiments

Ever wanted an excuse to watch a <u>cork</u> bob about in water? No, me neither, but that's what's coming up...

You can Measure Speed, Frequency and Wavelength with a Ripple Tank

1) You can generate <u>waves</u> in a <u>ripple tank</u> using a <u>motor</u> attached to a <u>dipper</u>.
2) The dipper moves up and down to create <u>water waves</u>.
3) You can measure the <u>frequency</u>, <u>speed</u> and <u>wavelength</u> of water waves in a ripple tank.

You can Measure the Frequency of Water Waves Using a Cork and a Stopwatch

1) <u>Float</u> a cork in the ripple tank.
   It should <u>oscillate</u> (<u>bob up and down</u>) as the waves pass it.
2) When the cork is at the <u>top</u> of a 'bob', <u>start the stopwatch</u>.
3) <u>Time</u> how long the cork takes to complete <u>10 bobs</u>.
4) <u>Divide</u> this <u>time</u> by 10 to get the time for <u>one bob</u>.
   This is the <u>period</u> of the water waves.
5) Calculate the <u>frequency</u> (p.150)
   using the formula:

   frequency = 1 ÷ period

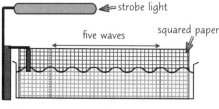

EXAMPLE:

Calculate the frequency of a wave with a period of 0.5 s.
frequency = 1 ÷ period = 1 ÷ 0.5 = 2 Hz

You can use a Strobe Light to Measure Wavelength

1) Place a card covered with <u>centimetre-squared paper</u> behind the ripple tank.
2) Turn on the <u>strobe light</u>. <u>Adjust its frequency</u>
   until the waves appear to <u>stop moving</u>.
3) Using the squared paper, measure
   the <u>distance</u> that <u>five</u> waves cover.
4) <u>Divide</u> the <u>distance</u> by <u>five</u> (the <u>number</u>
   <u>of waves</u>) to get the <u>average wavelength</u>.

Mr. Turner never missed
the chance to throw
some shapes when the
strobe light was on...

You can Measure the Wave Speed Using a Pencil and a Stopwatch

1) You need <u>two people</u> to do this experiment, so first <u>find a friend</u>.
2) Place a <u>large piece of paper</u> next to the tank.
3) <u>Follow one crest</u> as it moves
   from <u>one end</u> of the tank to the <u>other</u>.
4) <u>Track the path</u> of the crest on the paper using
   a <u>pencil</u> and a <u>ruler</u> as it moves across the tank.
5) Get your friend to <u>time</u> how long it takes you to
   draw a line of a <u>certain length</u>, e.g. 20 cm.
6) <u>Calculate wave speed</u> by plugging the <u>length of the line</u>
   (the distance) and the <u>time taken</u> to draw it into the formula
   <u>average speed = distance ÷ time</u> (see page 189).

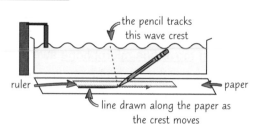

You could also calculate the wave speed from
the wavelength and frequency you calculated
above, using the equation from page 151.

Disco time in the physics lab...

...followed by bath time. A cork just isn't as exciting to play with as my rubber duck Fred though. Ah well...

Q1   Describe a method to measure the frequency of a water wave.   [4 marks]

Reflection

Now it's time for some reflection on reflection...

Waves Are Absorbed, Transmitted and Reflected at Boundaries

When any wave meets a boundary between two materials, three things can happen:

1) The wave is ABSORBED by the second material — it transfers all its energy and disappears.
2) The wave is TRANSMITTED (carries on travelling) through the second material.
3) The wave is REFLECTED — the wave is 'sent back' away from the second material.

What happens to an electromagnetic wave (p.156) depends on its wavelength.

A boundary between materials is sometimes called a 'material interface'.

Reflection is When Waves Bounce Back

1) Rays are straight lines that point along the direction the wave is moving.
2) The diagram on the right shows a light ray hitting a mirror (the incident light ray) and being reflected (the reflected light ray).
3) The normal is an imaginary line (drawn with a dotted line) at right angles to the boundary at the point the ray hits it.
4) There's one rule for all reflected waves: ➤ **Angle of Incidence = Angle of Reflection**
5) Each angle is measured from the normal to the incident or reflected ray.
6) When water waves hit an object, they are reflected by it.
7) But unlike light and sound waves, you can actually see water waves.
8) So you can use water waves in a ripple tank to model light and sound waves.

You can Investigate Reflection Using a Ray Box and a Mirror | PRACTICAL

1) To investigate reflection, you'll need a ray box, a plane (flat) mirror and a piece of white paper.
2) Take the piece of paper and draw a straight solid line across it using a ruler.
3) Then draw a straight, dotted line at a right angle to the solid line. This dotted line is the normal.
4) Place the mirror so its shiny surface lines up with the solid line.
5) Using the ray box, shine a thin beam of light at the mirror. The light should hit the mirror where the normal meets the mirror. This is the incident light ray.
6) Your set-up should look something like this:
7) Trace the path that the light takes with a sharp pencil and a ruler.
8) Measure the angle of incidence and the angle of reflection using a protractor.
9) Repeat steps 5)-8), changing the angle of incidence each time.
10) You'll find that the angle of incidence ALWAYS equals the angle of reflection.
11) Keep your test fair by keeping other variables the same. For example, use the same mirror and keep the width and brightness of the beam the same every time.

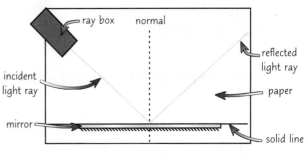

Do this experiment in a dark room so you can see the light beams clearly.

Mirror mirror on the wall, make it the fairest test of all...

That's how to investigate reflection with a mirror and a ray box. For my next trick, I'll pull a question out of my hat...

Q1   The angle of incidence for a reflected light beam is 27°. State the angle of reflection.   [1 mark]

Refraction

Grab a glass of water and put a straw in it. The straw looks like it's <u>bent</u>. But it's not magic, it's <u>refraction</u>.

Refraction — When Waves Change Direction as They Cross a Boundary

1) When a wave travels <u>from one material into another</u> it can <u>change direction</u>. This is <u>refraction</u>.

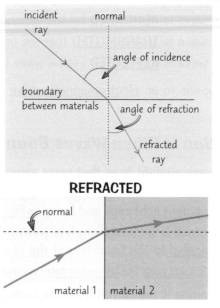

- The <u>normal</u> is an <u>imaginary line</u> that's <u>perpendicular</u> (at 90°) to the boundary.
- <u>The angle of incidence</u> is the angle between the <u>incoming</u> (<u>incident</u>) <u>ray</u> and the <u>normal</u>.
- <u>The angle of refraction</u> is the angle between the <u>refracted ray</u> and the normal.

2) Whether a wave changes direction depends on the <u>angle</u> at which it hits the <u>boundary</u>:

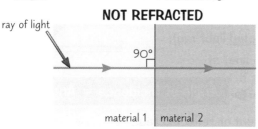

If a wave hits the boundary at <u>90°</u> (<u>along the normal</u>), then the wave <u>won't change direction</u>.

If the wave hits the boundary at <u>any</u> other <u>angle</u>, it <u>will</u> change direction.

How a Wave Refracts Depends on the Materials it Travels Between

<u>How much</u> a wave <u>refracts</u> depends on the <u>densities</u> (p.212) of the materials.

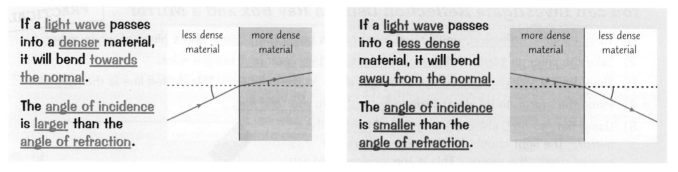

If a <u>light wave</u> passes into a <u>denser</u> material, it will bend <u>towards the normal</u>.

The <u>angle of incidence</u> is <u>larger</u> than the <u>angle of refraction</u>.

If a <u>light wave</u> passes into a <u>less dense</u> material, it will bend <u>away from the normal</u>.

The <u>angle of incidence</u> is <u>smaller</u> than the <u>angle of refraction</u>.

You can Model Refraction of Light and Sound Using Water Waves

1) <u>Light</u> and <u>sound</u> can <u>refract</u> when they cross a boundary between <u>different materials</u>.

2) You can <u>model</u> this refraction with <u>water waves</u>.

3) Instead of passing through materials with different densities, the water waves travel across water with <u>different depths</u>.

4) When water waves pass between areas of water with <u>different depths</u> at an <u>angle to the normal</u>, they <u>change direction</u>.

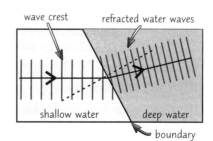

Help, my wave isn't refracting! Well, that's perfectly normal...

Refraction has loads of uses (e.g. in glasses, cameras and telescopes). So make sure you really understand it.

Q1   State what is meant by refraction.   [1 mark]

Investigating Refraction   PRACTICAL

Hurrah — it's time to whip out your ray box and get some refraction going on.

You Can Use a Rectangular Glass Block to Investigate Refraction of Light

1) Place a rectangular glass prism (a glass block) on a piece of paper and trace around it.

2) Use a ray box to shine a ray of light at the middle of one side of the block at an angle.

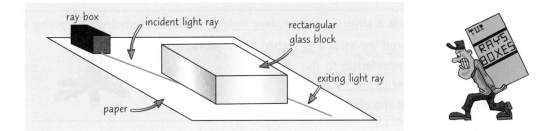

ray box   incident light ray   rectangular glass block

exiting light ray

paper

3) Trace the ray as it enters and exits the block.

4) Remove the block and join up the incident ray and the exiting ray with a straight line.

5) This shows the path of the refracted ray through the block.

6) Draw the normal at the point where the light ray entered the block.

7) Use a protractor to measure the angle of incidence, I (the angle between the incident ray and the normal).

8) Then measure the angle of refraction, R (the angle between the refracted ray and the normal).

9) Then draw the normal at the point where the light ray exited the block.

10) Measure the angle of incidence (in this case, this is between the ray that's travelling through the block and the normal).

11) Then measure the angle of refraction (here, it's the angle between the exiting ray and the normal).

12) Repeat steps 8), 10) and 11) three times, keeping the angle of incidence as the ray enters the block the same.

13) Calculate an average for each of the angles.

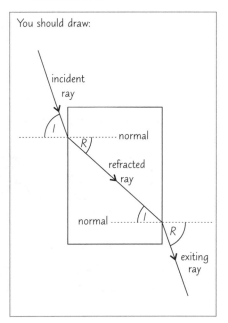

You should draw:

incident ray

I

R   normal

refracted ray

normal   I

R

exiting ray

You Should Notice a Few Things...

1) You should see that:

   • The ray of light bends towards the normal as it enters the glass block (see page 154).

   • The ray of light bends away from the normal as it leaves the glass block.

2) Light is an electromagnetic wave (p.156) — so this investigation shows one type of electromagnetic wave being refracted.

3) In fact, all electromagnetic waves can be refracted.

Lights, camera, refraction...

This experiment isn't the fanciest, but you still have to be able to describe how to do it, so make sure you learn it.

Q1   Describe an experiment you could do to investigate the refraction of light when it enters a glass block.

[3 marks]

The Electromagnetic Spectrum

The light waves that we see are just one small part of a big group of electromagnetic waves...

Electromagnetic Waves Transfer Energy

1) Electromagnetic (EM) waves are transverse waves (p.150).

2) EM waves are a type of radiation (see p.206), so they are sometimes called EM radiation.

3) They transfer energy from a source to an absorber some distance away.

> 1) A campfire is a source. It transfers energy to its surroundings by giving out infrared waves.
> 2) These infrared waves are absorbed by objects.
> 3) Energy is transferred to the objects' thermal energy stores (p.161).
> 4) This causes the objects to warm up.
>
> You might see this explanation of how energy is transferred by radiation called a radiation model. It can be used to predict what a process will cause to happen.

4) All EM waves travel at the same speed through space.

5) This speed is very fast, but finite (the waves still take some time to travel from one point to another).

Different Electromagnetic Waves Have Different Wavelengths

1) EM waves can have different wavelengths and frequencies.

2) There are EM waves of every wavelength within a certain range.

3) EM waves are split up into seven groups based on wavelength and frequency.

4) The seven groups together make up the electromagnetic spectrum:

| RADIO WAVES | MICRO WAVES | INFRA RED | VISIBLE LIGHT | ULTRA VIOLET | X-RAYS | GAMMA RAYS |

Long wavelength, low frequency, low energy → Short wavelength, high frequency, high energy

5) Our eyes can only detect (see) a small part of this spectrum — visible light.

6) Different colours of visible light have different wavelengths.
From longest to shortest wavelength, the colours are: red, orange, yellow, green, blue, indigo, violet.

EM Waves are Emitted by Atoms and Molecules

A wide range of EM waves can be emitted (given out) and absorbed by atoms or molecules (p.205.)

1) Changes in nuclei can cause gamma rays to be emitted (p.206).

2) Visible light, ultraviolet (UV) radiation and X-rays can be emitted when electrons in atoms lose energy (see next page).

3) Molecules can absorb and emit infrared waves.

4) When any EM wave is absorbed, it ceases to exist as (stops being) radiation and usually causes heating.

5) UV waves from the Sun are absorbed by oxygen molecules in the Earth's upper atmosphere, forming ozone.

6) This ozone absorbs large amounts of UV waves from the Sun, protecting living things (especially animals) from its damaging effects (see the next page).

Learn about the EM spectrum and wave goodbye to exam stress...

Here's a way to remember the order of EM waves: 'Rock Music Is Very Useful for eXperiments with Goats'.

Q1   State the type of electromagnetic wave that has the lowest frequency.   [1 mark]

Chapter P1 — Radiation and Waves

Energy Levels in Atoms

Electrons don't need bouncy castles, <u>EM radiation</u> is enough to make them <u>jump about</u> in atoms...

Electrons Can be Excited to Higher Energy Levels

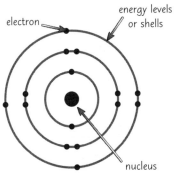

energy levels or shells

electron

nucleus

1) <u>Electrons</u> in an atom sit in <u>different energy levels</u> or shells.
2) Each <u>energy level</u> is a <u>different distance</u> from the <u>nucleus</u>.
3) The <u>further</u> an <u>energy level</u> is from the <u>nucleus</u>, the <u>more energy</u> an electron in that energy level has.
4) An electron can <u>move to a higher</u> energy level if it <u>absorbs electromagnetic (EM) radiation</u>.
5) If this happens the electron is said to be '<u>excited</u>'.
6) The excited electron will then <u>fall back</u> to its starting <u>energy level</u>.
7) It will <u>emit EM radiation</u> with the same amount of <u>energy</u> it <u>absorbed</u>.

Remember EM radiation and EM waves are the same thing.

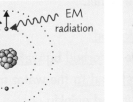

An electron can move to a <u>higher</u> energy level (further from the nucleus) when it <u>absorbs</u> electromagnetic radiation.

EM radiation

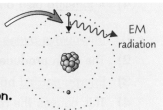

An excited electron can move to a <u>lower</u> energy level (closer to the nucleus) by <u>releasing</u> electromagnetic radiation.

EM radiation

An Atom is Ionised if it Loses an Electron

1) <u>Electrons</u> in the <u>highest energy level</u> of an atom are called <u>outer electrons</u>.
2) If an <u>outer electron</u> absorbs radiation with <u>enough energy</u>, it can <u>leave the atom</u>.
3) This process is called <u>ionisation</u>. If an atom <u>loses</u> one electron (or more), it becomes a (<u>positive</u>) <u>ion</u>.
4) The ion can go on to <u>take part</u> in <u>other chemical reactions</u> (see p.77).

Some EM Waves Can be Damaging

1) Some EM waves can be <u>absorbed</u> by body tissues (see p.56).
2) <u>High energy ultraviolet radiation</u>, <u>X-rays</u> and <u>gamma rays</u> are all types of <u>ionising radiation</u>.
3) This means they have enough <u>energy</u> to cause the <u>ionisation of atoms</u> or <u>molecules</u>.
4) Being <u>exposed</u> to a <u>large amount</u> of ionising radiation (having radiation <u>hit</u> or <u>enter</u> your body) can cause <u>damage</u> to living cells (p.209).
5) Exposure to <u>lower amounts</u> of radiation can <u>change</u> cells making them more likely to grow in an <u>uncontrolled way</u>. This may cause <u>cancer</u>.

- <u>Ultraviolet</u> (<u>UV</u>) is <u>absorbed</u> by the skin, where it can cause <u>damage</u> to <u>cells</u> and may lead to <u>skin cancer</u>.
- It can also damage your <u>eyes</u> and possibly even cause <u>blindness</u>.
- <u>X-rays</u> and <u>gamma rays</u> can cause mutations (changes) and damage cells too (which can lead to cancer).
- They can also pass <u>through the skin</u> and be absorbed by <u>deeper tissues</u>.
- They can be very dangerous as they transfer <u>a lot of energy</u>.

What's an atom's favourite chore? Ioning...

Ionising radiation is pretty scary stuff — it's important to protect yourself from it as much as possible (see page 209).

Q1 Name two types of EM radiation that can cause ionisation when they are absorbed by atoms. [2 marks]

Uses of EM Radiation

How EM waves <u>behave</u> in materials varies (p.153), which means we use <u>different types</u> in <u>different ways</u>...

Radio Waves are Used Mainly for Communication

1) <u>Radio</u> and <u>TV</u> signals can be sent by radio waves.
2) <u>Very short wavelength</u> radio waves are used for FM radio and TV.
3) <u>Longer wavelength</u> radio waves can be used to send radio signals <u>around the world</u>.

Microwaves are Used for Satellites and Cooking

1) Communication with <u>satellites</u> uses microwaves, e.g. for <u>satellite TV</u> and <u>mobile phones</u>.
2) A signal is sent into <u>space</u> to a satellite dish <u>high</u> above the Earth.
3) The satellite <u>sends</u> the signal back to Earth in a different direction.
4) A <u>satellite dish</u> on the ground receives the signal.

1) <u>Microwave ovens</u> use microwaves to <u>cook food</u>.
2) The oven produces microwaves, which are <u>absorbed</u> by <u>water</u> in the food.
3) <u>Energy carried</u> by the microwaves is <u>transferred to</u> the water molecules, causing them to <u>heat up</u>.
4) This causes the rest of the <u>food</u> to heat up and quickly <u>cook</u>.

Infrared Radiation Can be Used to Heat Things

1) <u>Infrared</u> (IR) radiation is <u>given out</u> by <u>all objects</u>.
2) The <u>hotter</u> the object, the <u>more</u> infrared radiation it gives out.
3) When an object <u>absorbs</u> infrared radiation, <u>energy is transferred</u> to the object's <u>thermal energy store</u>. This makes it <u>warm up</u>.
4) Infrared radiation can be <u>used</u> in many ways:

   1) <u>Infrared cameras</u> detect IR radiation and create a <u>picture</u>.
   2) This is useful for seeing where a house is <u>losing energy</u>.
   3) It can also allow you to see <u>hot objects</u> in the <u>dark</u>.

   1) Infrared radiation can also be used to <u>warm things</u>.
   2) <u>Electric heaters</u> release lots of IR radiation to warm a room.
   3) <u>Food</u> can be <u>cooked</u> using infrared radiation.

The different colours mean different amounts of IR radiation are being detected from those areas. Here, the redder the colour, the more infrared radiation is being detected.

Optical Fibres Use Visible Light to Send Data

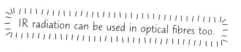
IR radiation can be used in optical fibres too.

1) <u>Light</u> is used to <u>see things</u>, but it's also used for <u>communication</u>.
2) <u>Optical fibres</u> are thin <u>glass or plastic tubes</u> that can <u>carry data</u> over long distances.
3) They're often used to send information to <u>telephones</u> or <u>computers</u>.
4) Information is sent <u>as light rays</u> that bounce <u>back and forth</u> along the fibre.
5) Optical fibres are also used to <u>see inside</u> a person's body during surgery.

Optical fibre
Light ray

Surfers hate microwaves...

Who knew we used microwaves for more than cooking chips in less than 3 minutes? Turns out, they're dead handy.

Q1   State one use of radio waves.   [1 mark]

More Uses of EM Radiation

Even more <u>uses of EM radiation</u>. But it's not all fun and games <u>using EM waves</u>, it can be a <u>risky</u> business.

Ultraviolet Radiation Gives You a Suntan

1) When some materials <u>absorb UV light</u>, they <u>give off visible light</u>. This can be pretty useful:

> 1) <u>Energy-efficient lights</u> use <u>UV radiation</u> to produce <u>visible light</u>.
> 2) <u>Security pens</u> can be used to <u>mark</u> property with your name (e.g. laptops).
> 3) Under <u>UV light</u> the ink will <u>glow</u>, but it's <u>invisible</u> otherwise.
> 4) This can help the police find out who <u>stolen property</u> belongs to.

2) <u>Ultraviolet radiation (UV)</u> is also produced by the Sun. It's what gives you a <u>suntan</u>.

3) <u>UV lamps</u> can be used to give people a <u>suntan</u> without the Sun (but this can be <u>dangerous</u>).

X-rays and Gamma Rays are Used in Medicine

1) X-rays pass <u>easily through flesh</u> but not through <u>bones</u> or <u>metal</u>.

2) So they can be used to create an <u>X-ray image</u> to check for <u>broken bones</u>.

3) They can pass through many materials easily, so they can also be used to <u>see inside</u> other objects, e.g. airports use them to look inside suitcases.

4) <u>X-rays</u> can also treat people with <u>cancer</u>.

5) This is because they can <u>kill cells</u> (p.209). They are aimed at the <u>cancer cells</u> to kill them.

> 1) <u>Gamma rays</u> (p.206) can also <u>kill cells</u>.
> 2) They can be used to <u>treat cancer</u> in the same way as X-rays.
> 3) They can also be used to <u>sterilise</u> (remove germs from) food and medical equipment. The food or equipment is <u>blasted</u> with <u>gamma rays</u> which <u>kills</u> any <u>living</u> things on it.
> 4) Gamma rays are also used in <u>medical imaging</u> to <u>see inside</u> your body (see p.211).

There are Risks and Benefits to Using EM Waves

1) We've made <u>technology</u> (machines) that use <u>every part</u> of the EM spectrum.

2) We also keep trying to develop (make) <u>new technology</u> and <u>new ways</u> of <u>using EM waves</u>.

3) EM waves are very <u>useful</u>. BUT they can also be <u>dangerous</u> (p.157).

4) It's very important that any <u>risks</u> involved with using them are properly <u>thought about</u>.

> • For example, some airports brought in <u>X-ray body scanners</u> to improve airport safety.
> • The scanners were thought to be <u>safe</u> when they were first used.
> • Some scientists then claimed that the body scanners <u>can increase</u> a person's <u>risk</u> of getting <u>cancer</u>.
> • This has led to this type of scanner being <u>banned</u> in many countries.

5) Some people have <u>strong opinions</u> on whether or not a new technology should be used.

6) But <u>decisions</u> about <u>whether or not</u> to use <u>new technology</u> need to made based on <u>scientific evidence</u> (p.231), not just <u>people's opinions</u>.

Don't lie to an X-ray — they can see right through you...

I hate to say it, but go back over the last few pages and read all of the uses for EM waves again to really learn 'em.

Q1 State two uses of X-rays. [2 marks]

Temperature and Radiation

All objects, including yourself, emit (give out) radiation constantly. No wonder I'm so tired all the time...

All Objects Emit Electromagnetic Radiation

1) Objects don't just emit one type of EM radiation.
2) They emit EM radiation with lots of different wavelengths.
3) You can measure the intensity of each wavelength of radiation emitted from an object.
4) Intensity is a measure of the amount of energy transferred from an object by radiation.
5) The wavelength of EM radiation with the highest intensity is called the principal wavelength.
6) If you plot a graph of intensity against wavelength for an object, you get a curve with a peak at the principal wavelength.
7) This graph shows you the distribution (spread) of radiation emitted by the object.

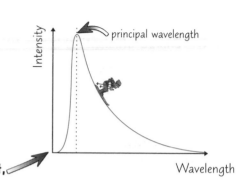

Remember, gamma rays are the lowest wavelength EM waves and radio waves have the highest wavelength (p.156).

The Intensity of Each Wavelength Emitted Depends on Temperature

1) The distribution of radiation emitted by an object depends on its temperature.
2) As the temperature of an object increases, the intensity of every emitted wavelength increases.
3) However, the intensity increases more for shorter wavelengths than longer wavelengths.
4) This is because shorter wavelengths of EM radiation transfer more energy (see p.156).
5) This causes the principal wavelength to decrease (and the graph to change shape).
6) So as objects get hotter, the principal wavelength gets shorter.

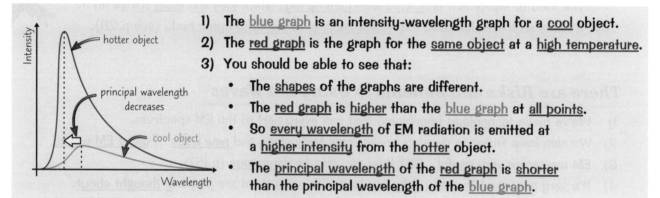

1) The blue graph is an intensity-wavelength graph for a cool object.
2) The red graph is the graph for the same object at a high temperature.
3) You should be able to see that:
   - The shapes of the graphs are different.
   - The red graph is higher than the blue graph at all points.
   - So every wavelength of EM radiation is emitted at a higher intensity from the hotter object.
   - The principal wavelength of the red graph is shorter than the principal wavelength of the blue graph.

The Principal Frequency Emitted Increases with Temperature

1) The frequency of radiation with the highest intensity is called the principal frequency.
2) The principal frequency increases as the temperature of an object increases.
3) This is because higher frequency EM radiation transfers more energy.
4) This is the opposite to how the principal wavelength changes with temperature.

How much ice cream I eat increases with temperature...

The principal wavelength of radiation you emit is about 9.5×10^{-6} m — and you thought this page was dull...

Q1   State how the principal wavelength of radiation emitted by an object will change as it gets hotter.   [1 mark]

Energy Stores and Conservation of Energy

Energy is a tricky little beast. For one thing, it can be stored in lots of different ways.

Energy is Held in Energy Stores

Here are the energy stores you need to learn:

1) **KINETIC** — anything moving has energy in its kinetic energy store, p.201.

2) **THERMAL** — all objects have energy in this store. The hotter the object, the more energy in the store.

3) **NUCLEAR** — the nucleus of an atom releases energy from this store in nuclear reactions.

4) **GRAVITATIONAL POTENTIAL** — any object raised above ground level has energy in this store, p.201.

5) **ELASTIC POTENTIAL** — anything stretched has energy in this store, like springs and rubber bands, p.219.

6) **ELECTROSTATIC** — e.g. two charges that attract or repel each other have energy in this store.

7) **ELECTROMAGNETIC** — e.g. two objects that exert a magnetic force on each other have energy in this store.

8) **CHEMICAL** — anything that can release energy by a chemical reaction has energy in this store, e.g. food.

When a System Changes, Energy is Transferred

1) A system is just the single object or a group of objects that you're interested in.

2) When a system changes, the store energy is in often changes too.

3) A system can be changed by heating or by working (see p.162).

4) Closed systems are systems where no matter (stuff) or energy can enter or leave.

5) When a closed system changes, the total energy of the system stays the same (there is no net change).

> **For example...**
> - A cold spoon sealed in a flask of hot soup is a closed system.
> - Energy is transferred from the thermal energy store of the soup to the thermal energy store of the spoon by heating.
> - But no energy leaves the system. The total energy stays the same.

You Need to Know the Law of Conservation of Energy

> Energy can be transferred usefully, stored or dissipated, but can never be created or destroyed.

Dissipated is a fancy way of saying the energy is spread out into useless energy stores (so that it is unusable).

1) This means that whenever a system changes, energy is just moved between stores. It never disappears.

2) Even when energy is dissipated (or wasted), it isn't gone (see p.163).

3) It's just been transferred to an energy store that's less useful.

4) Usually dissipated energy ends up in thermal energy stores.

Energy can't be created or destroyed — only talked about a lot...

Energy stores pop up everywhere in physics. Make sure you understand them before you read the next page.

Q1   A spring is stretched. Name the type of store the energy is stored in.   [1 mark]

Energy Transfers

Energy just loves to keep moving... It is transferred between energy stores <u>by heating</u> or <u>by doing work</u>.

Energy can be Transferred by Heating...

1) Energy transfer <u>by heating</u> is where energy is transferred from a <u>hotter region</u> to a <u>colder region</u>.

2) For example, when a pan of water is <u>heated</u> on a hob.

3) Energy can also be transferred by <u>radiation</u>, e.g. electromagnetic waves (p.153) or sound waves.

4) The energy is often transferred directly to <u>thermal energy stores</u>.

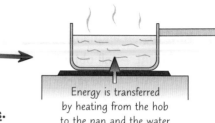

Energy is transferred by heating from the hob to the pan and the water

Energy can also be Transferred by doing Work

<u>Work done</u> is just another way of saying <u>energy transferred</u> — they're the <u>same thing</u>.

Work can be done Mechanically...

<u>Work</u> can be done <u>mechanically</u> (an object moving due to a <u>force</u> doing work on it).

<u>A ball falling from a height</u>
1) The ball is <u>accelerated</u> by the <u>constant force</u> of <u>gravity</u>.
2) Energy is <u>transferred mechanically</u> from the ball's <u>gravitational potential energy</u> store to its <u>kinetic energy</u> store.

F

... or Electrically

1) Work can be done <u>electrically</u> on devices (a charge doing <u>electrical work</u> against resistance, e.g. a charge moving round a circuit). For example:

<u>A battery-operated torch</u>
- Energy is transferred <u>electrically</u> from the <u>chemical</u> energy store of the <u>battery</u> to the <u>thermal</u> energy store of the filament (wire) in the bulb.
- This energy is then transferred to the <u>surroundings</u> by <u>heating</u> and <u>radiation</u> in the form of light.

2) <u>Electricity</u> from the <u>mains</u> often <u>transfers energy</u> from the <u>chemical energy stores</u> of <u>fossil fuels</u> that have been <u>burnt</u> in a power station (see p.165).

3) One advantage of transferring energy by electricity is it can travel over <u>long distances</u> from power stations to consumers.

4) Electricity can be <u>used</u> in many ways, e.g. driving motors or heating.

All this work, I can feel my energy stores being drained...

You might be asked to explain the examples above — make sure you understand them.

Q1   Describe the energy transfers that occur in a battery-operated motor.   [3 marks]

Efficiency and Power

More! More! Tell me more about <u>energy transfers</u> please! Oh go on then, since you insist...

Energy Transfers Involve Some Wasted Energy

1) <u>No device</u> is 100% efficient — whenever <u>work is done</u>, some of the energy transferred is <u>always</u> wasted.

2) The <u>less energy</u> that is <u>wasted</u>, the <u>more efficient</u> the device is said to be.

3) The efficiency for any energy transfer can be <u>worked out</u> using this equation:

$$\text{efficiency} = \frac{\text{useful energy transferred}}{\text{total energy transferred}}$$

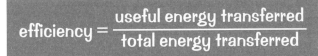

You can give efficiency as a <u>decimal</u> or you can <u>multiply</u> your answer by 100 to get a <u>percentage</u>, i.e. <u>0.75</u> or <u>75%</u>.

EXAMPLE: A food blender is 70% efficient. 6000 J of energy is transferred to it.
Calculate the useful energy transferred by the blender.

1) Change the <u>efficiency</u> from a <u>percentage</u> to a <u>decimal</u>.   efficiency = 70 ÷ 100 = 0.7
2) <u>Rearrange</u> the equation for <u>useful energy transferred</u>.   useful energy transferred
3) <u>Stick in</u> the numbers you're given.   = efficiency × total energy transferred
   = 0.7 × 6000 = **4200 J**

Energy Transferred Depends on the Power

1) <u>Power</u> is the rate of <u>energy transfer</u>, i.e. how much energy is transferred between stores <u>per second</u>.

2) The <u>total</u> energy transferred by an appliance depends on <u>how long</u> the appliance is on for and its <u>power</u>.

3) So the <u>more</u> energy it transfers in a <u>given time</u>, the <u>higher</u> its power.

4) The amount of <u>energy transferred electrically</u> is given by:

$$\text{energy transferred (J)} = \text{power (W)} \times \text{time (s)}$$

EXAMPLE: A 2200 W hair dryer is used for 200 seconds. How much energy does it transfer?

<u>Substitute</u> the numbers into the equation   energy transferred = power × time
to find the <u>energy transferred</u>.   = 2200 × 200 = **440 000 J**

5) <u>Energy</u> is usually measured in <u>joules</u>, but for <u>electrical devices</u> you may also see it given in <u>kilowatt-hours</u>.

6) A kilowatt-hour is the amount of energy a device with a <u>power of 1 kW</u> (1000 W) <u>transfers</u> in <u>1 hour</u>.

7) To calculate the energy transferred in kilowatt-hours (kWh), you need <u>power</u> in <u>kW</u>, and the <u>time</u> in <u>hours</u>.

EXAMPLE: A 100 W motor ran for 1.5 hours.
Calculate the energy transferred in this time. Give your answer in kWh.

1) <u>Convert</u> the watts to <u>kilowatts</u>.   100 W ÷ 1000 = 0.1 kW
2) Then just <u>substitute</u> into the equation.   energy transferred = power × time = 0.1 × 1.5 = **0.15 kWh**

8) The <u>power rating</u> of a device tells you the <u>power</u> it works at.
This is <u>how much</u> energy is <u>transferred</u> when the device is used.

9) An device with a <u>higher power rating</u> will <u>cost more</u> in a given time, as it will transfer <u>more energy</u>.

I've got the power...

Make sure you get your head around kWh, they can be a bit tough until you've practised using them.

Q1   A motor transfers 4.8 kJ of energy in 120 seconds. Calculate its power in watts.   [3 marks]

Reducing Unwanted Energy Transfers

There are many ways you can __reduce__ the amount of energy that is __wasted__ during a process. __Lubrication__ and __thermal insulation__ are two that you need to know about.

You can Show How Much Energy is Wasted Using Sankey Diagrams

1) You can use diagrams to show the different energy transfers made by a device.

2) These diagrams are also useful for calculating the efficiency of a device.

3) The width of the arrows shows how much energy is being transferred. The length has nothing to do with it.

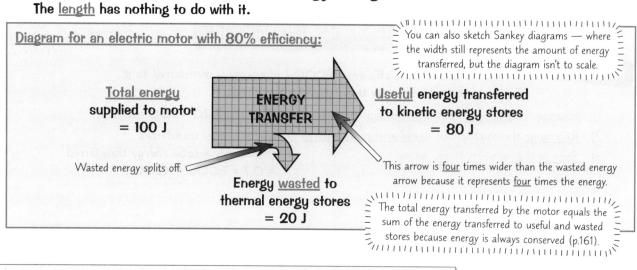

Diagram for an electric motor with 80% efficiency:

You can also sketch Sankey diagrams — where the width still represents the amount of energy transferred, but the diagram isn't to scale.

Total energy supplied to motor = 100 J

ENERGY TRANSFER

Useful energy transferred to kinetic energy stores = 80 J

Wasted energy splits off.

Energy wasted to thermal energy stores = 20 J

This arrow is four times wider than the wasted energy arrow because it represents four times the energy.

The total energy transferred by the motor equals the sum of the energy transferred to useful and wasted stores because energy is always conserved (p.161).

Lubrication Reduces Energy Transferred by Friction

1) For objects that are touching each other, lubricants can be used to reduce the friction (p.187) between moving parts.

2) Lubricants are usually liquids (like oil), so they can flow easily between objects and coat them.

Thermal Insulation Reduces the Rate of Energy Transfer by Heating

1) Energy can be transferred through some materials by heating much more easily than others.

2) All materials have a thermal conductivity — it describes how well a material transfers energy by heating.

3) The lower the thermal conductivity of a material, the slower the rate of energy transfer through it.

The rate of energy transfer is how fast energy passes through a material.

Thermal Insulation is Important in Buildings

1) The walls of buildings are made from materials with a low thermal conductivity.

2) This reduces the amount of energy lost from the buildings.

3) Thicker walls help too — the thicker the walls, the slower the rate of energy transfer from the buildings to the surroundings.

4) The slower the rate of energy transfer, the slower the rate of cooling of the buildings.

Don't waste energy — turn the TV off while you revise...

Unwanted energy transfers can cost you a lot in energy bills. It's why so many people buy home insulation.

Q1   Suggest one way to reduce unwanted energy transfers in an electric motor.   [1 mark]

Energy Resources

We use <u>A LOT</u> of electricity — the energy to power all our gadgets has to come from <u>somewhere</u>...

Non-Renewable Energy Sources Will Run Out One Day

1) We get <u>most</u> of our energy from <u>non-renewable</u> sources.

2) These are sources that will <u>run out</u> one day.

3) The main non-renewables are the three <u>fossil fuels</u> (<u>coal</u>, <u>oil</u> and <u>gas</u>) and <u>nuclear fuels</u> (<u>uranium</u> and <u>plutonium</u>).

> Peat is often called a non-renewable source too, because it can't be quickly replaced.

Most Power Stations Use Steam to Drive a Turbine

1) <u>Non-renewable power stations</u> usually <u>heat water</u> to produce <u>steam</u>.

   • <u>Fossil fuels</u> are <u>burnt</u> and the energy released is used to make <u>steam</u>.

   • <u>Nuclear fuels</u> produce energy in a <u>nuclear reactor</u> which is used to make <u>steam</u>.

2) The steam causes a <u>turbine</u> to turn.

3) The turbine drives a <u>generator</u> which spins a <u>magnet near a wire</u> to produce <u>electricity</u>.

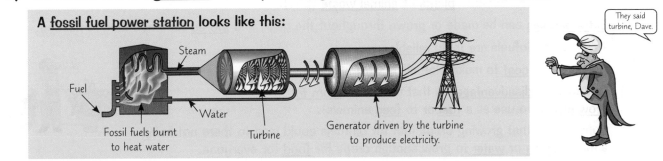

A <u>fossil fuel power station</u> looks like this:

Steam

Fuel

Water

Fossil fuels burnt to heat water

Turbine

Generator driven by the turbine to produce electricity.

> They said turbine, Dave.

4) A <u>fossil fuel</u> power station has high set-up costs but its <u>running costs</u> are low.

Non-Renewables are Reliable (For Now)

1) <u>Fossil fuels</u> and <u>nuclear energy</u> are <u>reliable</u>.

2) There are enough <u>fossil</u> and <u>nuclear fuels</u> to meet <u>current demand</u>.

3) We always have some in <u>stock</u> so power plants can respond <u>quickly</u> to <u>changes in demand</u>.

4) However, these fuels are <u>slowly running out</u>.

> If an energy source is reliable, it means it can be trusted to provide enough power at any time.

Non-Renewable Sources Cause Environmental Problems

1) All three <u>fossil fuels</u> (coal, oil and gas) release <u>carbon dioxide</u> (CO_2) when they burn.

2) This CO_2 contributes to <u>climate change</u> and <u>global warming</u> (see p.84).

3) Burning coal and oil releases <u>sulfur dioxide</u>, which causes <u>acid rain</u>.

4) <u>Coal mining</u> makes a <u>mess</u> of the landscape.

5) <u>Oil spillages</u> cause <u>serious environmental problems</u>, e.g. killing mammals and birds.

6) <u>Nuclear waste</u> (from nuclear power stations) is very <u>dangerous</u> and difficult to <u>dispose of</u>.

7) <u>Nuclear power</u> also carries the risk of a <u>major nuclear accident</u>.

> Global warming is where greenhouse gases cause the Earth to warm up.

It all boils down to steam...

Steam engines were invented as long ago as the 17th century, yet we're still using that idea to produce most of our electricity over 300 years later. Pretty impressive, eh?

Q1   Describe how a fossil fuel power station generates electricity.   [3 marks]

Renewable Energy Resources

Time for the first page on <u>renewable energy resources</u>. You've probably heard about a few of these already.

Renewable Energy Sources Will Never Run Out

1) <u>Renewable</u> energy sources, unlike non-renewables, <u>will never run out</u>.
2) Most of them do some <u>damage to the environment</u>, but in <u>less nasty</u> ways than non-renewables.
3) They <u>don't</u> provide as much energy as <u>non-renewables</u> and the <u>weather-dependent</u> ones can be <u>unreliable</u>.
4) Renewable sources include <u>biofuels</u>, <u>wind</u> power, the <u>Sun</u>, <u>hydroelectricity</u> and the <u>tides</u>.
5) <u>Hydroelectric</u>, <u>tidal</u> and <u>wind</u> power all turn turbines <u>directly</u> with wind or water.
6) <u>Biofuels</u> are <u>burnt</u> like fossil fuels (see previous page) to <u>make steam</u> in order to produce electricity.

Biofuels are Made from Plant Products and Animal Waste

1) <u>Biofuels</u> can be burnt to produce <u>electricity</u> or used to run <u>cars</u> in the same way as <u>fossil fuels</u>.
2) They're made from either <u>plants</u> or <u>animal waste</u> (poo).
3) <u>Extra biofuels</u> can be made or grown throughout the year, and <u>stored</u> for when they're needed.
4) This means biofuels are fairly <u>reliable</u>.
5) However the <u>cost</u> to make biofuels is very <u>high</u>.
6) One of their <u>disadvantages</u> is that you need <u>room to grow crops</u> (to use as a <u>fuel</u> or to <u>feed</u> animals).

7) Some worry that growing crops just for biofuels could lead to there not being enough <u>space</u> or <u>water</u> to grow enough crops for <u>food</u> for everyone.
8) In some places, large areas of <u>land</u> have been <u>cleared of vegetation</u> (plants and trees) to grow <u>crops</u>.
9) This leads to other <u>animals and plants</u> losing their <u>habitats</u> (where they live).
10) The <u>decay</u> and <u>burning</u> of cleared vegetation releases CO_2 and methane, leading to <u>global warming</u>.
11) Biofuels also <u>release CO_2</u> when they're burnt, but the <u>crops</u> for biofuels <u>absorb</u> CO_2 while <u>growing</u>.
12) There's <u>debate</u> about whether there's <u>any net (overall) change</u> in the amount of CO_2.

Wind Power — Lots of Little Wind Turbines

1) Each wind turbine has a <u>generator</u> inside it.
2) The rotating <u>blades</u> turn the generator and produce <u>electricity</u>.
3) There's <u>no pollution</u> once they're built.
4) But some people think they <u>spoil the view</u>. And they can be <u>very noisy</u>.
5) They <u>only</u> work when it's <u>windy</u>, so they can't always <u>supply</u> electricity, or respond to <u>high demand</u>.
6) They have quite a <u>high set-up cost</u> but <u>no fuel costs</u>.

Burning poo... lovely...

Given our electricity-guzzling ways, it's pretty important we find ways to generate electricity without destroying the planet. Burning cow pats may not be the ultimate fix, but it's a start. See the next page for more ways.

Q1 State two renewable energy sources. [2 marks]

Q2 State two disadvantages of using wind power to generate electricity. [2 marks]

Chapter P2 — Sustainable Energy

More on Energy Resources

Three more <u>renewable energy sources</u> to learn, then we'll look at <u>trends</u> in the crazy world of energy production.

Solar Cells — Expensive but No Environmental Damage

1) Solar cells generate <u>electricity</u> from <u>sunlight</u>.
2) There's <u>no pollution</u> (although they do use quite a lot of energy to make).
3) Solar cells are mainly used to generate electricity on a <u>small scale</u>, e.g. in <u>homes</u>.
4) The set-up costs of solar cells are <u>high</u>. But after that the energy is <u>free</u> and the <u>running costs are almost zero</u>.
5) Solar power is most suitable (best to use) for <u>sunny countries</u>, but it can be used in <u>cloudy countries</u>, such as Britain.
6) And of course, you <u>can't</u> make solar power at <u>night</u> or <u>make more</u> when there's extra demand.

Time to recharge.

Hydroelectricity — Building Dams and Flooding Valleys

1) <u>Producing hydroelectricity</u> usually involves <u>flooding</u> a <u>valley</u> by building a <u>big dam</u>.
2) <u>Rainwater</u> is caught and flows out <u>through turbines</u>.
3) Hydroelectric plants don't release any <u>pollution</u> once they're up and running.
4) But there is a <u>big impact</u> on the <u>environment</u> due to the flooding of the valley.
5) Plants in the water rot and release <u>greenhouse gases</u>, which lead to global warming (see p.84).
6) Animals and plants also lose <u>their habitats</u>.
7) There's no problem with <u>reliability</u> in countries that get rain regularly.
8) And more water can easily be let through when there's <u>extra demand</u> for electricity.
9) <u>Start-up costs are often high</u>, but there are <u>low running costs</u> and it's a <u>reliable</u> energy source.

You might see hydroelectricity referred to as HEP — this just stands for hydroelectric power.

Tidal Barrages — Using the Tides of the Sea

1) <u>Tidal barrages</u> are also <u>big dams</u> with <u>turbines</u> in them.
2) They're built across <u>tidal rivers</u> or <u>estuaries</u> (where rivers meet the sea).
3) <u>Water</u> passing through the <u>turbines</u> generates electricity.
4) There is <u>no pollution</u> but they <u>change the habitat</u> for wildlife, e.g. wading birds and sea creatures, and affect <u>boat access</u>.
5) The <u>amount of energy</u> generated <u>changes</u> with the <u>tides</u>.
6) And they <u>can't</u> produce <u>more energy</u> when there's an <u>increase in demand</u>.
7) But tidal barrages are pretty <u>reliable</u> as we can <u>predict</u> the tides (we know what they're going to do).

None shall pass!

Do, re, mi, fa, so-lar, ti-dal...

Make sure you can describe the energy resources above and the effect on the environment when using them.

Q1   Give one advantage and one disadvantage of generating electricity using solar power.   [1 mark]

Q2   Describe the negative effects on the environment caused by hydroelectricity.   [2 marks]

Trends in Energy Use

Over time, the types of energy resources we use change. There are many reasons for this...

There are Disadvantages and Benefits for Each Energy Resource

1) The risks, drawbacks and benefits need to be weighed up when deciding the best energy resource to use.

2) Which resources are easily available, their cost and their reliability must be thought about.

3) The environmental impact and any opportunities (e.g. jobs) they create must also be looked at.

4) Of course, everyone has different concerns (worries) and opinions.

5) This means that there's often no 'right' answer — so decisions about which resources to use vary depending on the situation. For example:

- The government may decide nuclear fuel is a good, clean and reliable energy resource to use.
- Setting up and shutting down a nuclear power station provides many jobs but is difficult and costly.
- Nuclear power also always carries the small risk of a major disaster.
- Some say the benefits outweigh the risk, whilst others say the potential damage isn't worth it.

Our Energy Demands are Changing

1) The world demand for energy is continually (always) increasing.

2) This is because of the population increasing and people using more electrical devices than they used to.

3) The growing demand raises questions over how we will be able to keep up with it.

4) For example, people are worried about if certain energy resources will be available in the future.

5) People are questioning how sustainable different energy resources are.

6) Sustainable energy resources are those that we can keep on using in the long term (like renewables).

7) There has been an increase in the use of renewable energy resources over time. This has been down to:

- Some people making changes in their everyday lives to try and use less energy or to use energy from renewable energy resources.
- Many countries now having targets for using renewable resources.
- Research being done to find new sustainable energy resources, as well as looking at improving the ways we use our current ones.

> The research and development of new energy resources provides jobs, as does the building of any new power stations.

Currently in the UK we mostly use fossil fuels for generating electricity, heating and transport.
This is because they're relatively cheap, efficient and reliable.
But they're not sustainable — we can't keep using them long-term as they'll run out one day.
So slowly, the UK is trying to increase its use of more sustainable energy resources.

8) However, the resources we use won't change overnight. Research and development take time and money.

9) Governments need to balance spending money on this research with spending money on other things their country needs, e.g. schools and health care.

10) Just like many of our current energy resources, new energy resources may also bring with them new technological and environmental challenges.

11) For example, before countries could use nuclear fuel to generate electricity, technology had to be created to make the process work and be safe.

12) Using nuclear fuel to generate electricity also created the problem of having to deal with very harmful waste.

Going green is on-trend this season...

So energy demands are increasing, and the energy sources we're using are changing. Just not particularly quickly.

Q1   Suggest two reasons why a government may choose to invest in nuclear power.   [2 marks]

Chapter P2 — Sustainable Energy

The National Grid

Once electricity has been produced using energy resources (p.165), it has to be transported to consumers (you).

Electricity is Distributed via the National Grid

1) The national grid is a giant system of cables and transformers (p.182) that covers the UK.

2) It transfers electrical power from power stations to consumers (anyone using electricity) across the UK.

3) Transformers are used to increase the generated electricity to a very high voltage (a high potential difference, p.171) before it is transmitted through the network of the national grid.

4) Transferring electrical power at a very high p.d. helps to reduce energy losses (see p.182).

5) The p.d. is then reduced by another transformer to a level that is safe for us to use.

Alternating Voltage Keeps Changing Direction

1) An alternating current (a.c.) is produced by an alternating voltage (or alternating potential difference, p.d.).

2) Alternating just means that the p.d. and current constantly change direction.

3) The UK mains electricity (in your home) is a.c. at 50 Hz and around 230 V.

4) Direct current (d.c.) is produced by a direct voltage. The current and the p.d. don't change direction.

5) You get d.c. from batteries and cells.

Most Plugs Contain Three Wires

Mains appliances usually have a 3-core cable, which contains three wires.

NEUTRAL WIRE — blue.

1) The neutral wire completes the circuit.

2) Electricity normally flows in through the live wire and out through the neutral wire.

3) The neutral wire is always at 0 V.

LIVE WIRE — brown.

1) The live wire carries the current into the appliance.

2) It alternates between a high positive and negative voltage of about 230 V.

EARTH WIRE — green and yellow.

1) The earth wire is for safety.

2) It carries the current away if something goes wrong.

3) It's also at 0 V.

1) There is a p.d. between the live wire and your body (which is at 0 V).

2) Touching the live wire can cause a current to flow through your body.

3) This can give you a dangerous electric shock.

4) Even if a switch is turned off (the switch is open), touching the live wire is still dangerous. This is because it still has a p.d. of 230 V.

5) Any connection between the live and earth wires can be dangerous. The p.d. could cause a huge current to flow, which could result in a fire.

Why are earth wires green and yellow — when mud is brown..?

Make sure you can explain why touching a live wire is dangerous. It's all to do with our old pal, potential difference.

Q1   Explain the difference between alternating potential difference and direct potential difference.   [2 marks]

Q2   State the potential difference of the live, neutral and earth wires in an appliance.   [3 marks]

Revision Questions for Chapters P1 & P2

Hope you've still got some energy left to have a go at these revision questions to see what you've learnt.
- Try these questions and <u>tick off each one</u> when you <u>get it right</u>.
- When you've done <u>all the questions</u> for a topic and are <u>completely happy</u> with it, tick off the topic.

<u>Wave Basics (p.150-152)</u> ☑

1) Describe a difference between a transverse wave and a longitudinal wave.
   Give one example of each type of wave. ☑

2) Describe the following features of a wave: a) amplitude   b) wavelength   c) frequency   d) period ☑

3) State the wave speed equation. ☑

4) Describe an experiment to measure the speed of sound in air. ☑

5) Describe an experiment to measure the wavelength of a water wave. ☑

<u>Reflection and Refraction (p.153-155)</u> ☑

6) What three things can happen to a wave when it hits a boundary between two different materials? ☑

7) Describe an experiment for investigating the reflection of light. ☑

8) Give two conditions that must occur for refraction to happen. ☑

<u>Uses and Dangers of Electromagnetic Waves (p.156-160)</u> ☑

9) True or False? The speed at which an EM wave travels through space depends on its wavelength. ☑

10) List the groups of waves in the EM spectrum, in order of increasing wavelength. ☑

11) What is emitted when an electron drops down an energy level? ☑

12) What is meant by ionising radiation? ☑

13) Give one use of: a) infrared radiation   b) visible light   c) ultraviolet radiation   d) gamma rays ☑

14) True or false? All objects emit electromagnetic radiation. ☑

<u>Energy Stores, Energy Transfers and Efficiency (p.161-164)</u> ☑

15) Name the eight energy stores. ☑

16) True or false? The net change in the total energy of a closed system is always zero. ☑

17) In which energy store does wasted energy eventually end up? ☑

18) How can energy be transferred between stores? ☑

19) Write down the equation that links energy transferred, power and time. ☑

20) What does the thickness of an arrow in a Sankey diagram represent? ☑

21) True or false? Thicker walls make a house cool down quicker. ☑

<u>Energy Sources and Trends in their Use (p.165-168)</u> ☑

22) Name four non-renewable energy resources. ☑

23) What is the difference between renewable and non-renewable energy resources? ☑

24) Describe the benefits and drawbacks of using biofuels. ☑

25) Compare the reliability of solar power and tidal barrages. ☑

26) Explain why the UK plans to use more renewable energy resources in the future. ☑

<u>The National Grid (p.169)</u> ☑

27) What is the national grid? ☑

28) State the frequency and potential difference of the UK mains supply. ☑

29) Why is it dangerous to create a link between the live wire and the ground? ☑

Current, Potential Difference and Resistance

If the word <u>current</u> makes you think of delicious cakes instead of physics, that's all about to change.

Current can Only Flow Around a Closed Circuit

1) <u>Electric current</u> is the <u>rate of flow</u> of <u>charge</u> (how <u>fast</u> the charge flows around a circuit).
2) Current is measured in <u>amperes</u>, **A.**
3) Charge is measured in <u>coulombs</u>, **C.**
4) Charge will <u>only flow</u> round a complete (closed) circuit if something is providing a <u>potential difference</u>, e.g. a battery.
5) <u>Potential difference</u> (p.d.) is the 'driving force' that <u>pushes</u> the charge around a circuit.
6) The <u>unit</u> of potential difference is the <u>volt</u>, **V.**
7) <u>Resistance</u> is anything that slows down the <u>flow of charge</u>.
8) Resistance is measured in <u>ohms</u>, Ω.
9) <u>All</u> circuit <u>components</u> (p.172) have a <u>resistance</u>.
10) You can usually <u>ignore</u> the resistance from the <u>wires</u> connecting components together as it's so small.

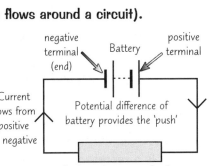

Current flows from positive to negative

negative terminal (end)   Battery   positive terminal

Potential difference of battery provides the 'push'

Resistance opposes the flow

The parts in a circuit e.g. bulbs, resistors, etc. are called 'components'.

Current, Resistance and P.d. are Linked

1) Resistance, current and potential difference are all <u>related</u> (see p.172).
2) If the <u>potential difference</u> of the power supply is <u>increased</u> while the <u>resistance</u> of the circuit <u>stays the same</u>, then the <u>current will increase</u>.
3) If the <u>resistance</u> of a circuit is <u>increased</u> while the power supply's <u>potential difference stays the same</u>, the <u>current</u> will <u>decrease</u>.

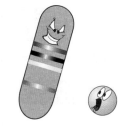

Total Charge Through a Circuit Depends on Current and Time

1) <u>Metal conductors</u> (e.g. components and wires) have <u>lots of charges</u> that are free to move.
2) A <u>battery</u> (or other p.d. source) in a circuit is what <u>causes</u> these charges to flow.
3) Charges going round a circuit flow in a <u>continuous loop</u> — they keep going <u>around</u> the circuit <u>again and again</u>.
4) The charges are <u>not used up</u>, but transfer energy to components as they do <u>work</u> (p.162).
5) So, in a <u>single</u>, closed <u>loop</u> the current is the same <u>everywhere</u> in the circuit (see p.178).
6) <u>Charge</u>, <u>current</u> and <u>time</u> are related by this <u>equation</u>:

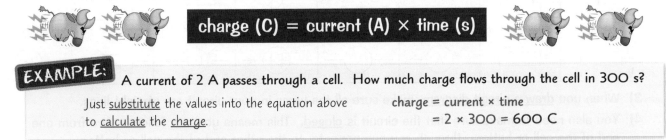

charge (C) = current (A) × time (s)

EXAMPLE: A current of 2 A passes through a cell. How much charge flows through the cell in 300 s?

Just <u>substitute</u> the values into the equation above to <u>calculate</u> the <u>charge</u>.

charge = current × time
= 2 × 300 = 600 C

I think it's about time you took charge...

Current, resistance and potential difference are super important in electricity. Make sure you understand them.

Q1   1500 C of charge passes through a resistor in 500 s. Calculate the current through the resistor.   [3 marks]

Describing and Drawing Circuits

Here comes an <u>important equation</u> you'll use lots, as well as some handy <u>symbols</u> to help you <u>draw circuits</u>.

You Can Use A Model to Describe Circuits

1) You can think of an <u>electric circuit</u> as being like a set of <u>pipes</u>.
2) The <u>current</u> is the <u>how fast water flows</u> around the pipes.
3) The <u>potential difference</u> is the <u>water pump</u> pushing the water around.
4) <u>Resistance</u> is any sort of <u>narrowing</u> of the pipes that makes it <u>harder</u> for the water to <u>flow</u>.
5) If you turn up the <u>pump</u> (increase the <u>p.d.</u>), more <u>force</u> is provided and the flow (current) <u>increases</u>.
6) If you add more <u>narrow sections</u> (increase the <u>resistance</u>), the flow <u>decreases</u>.
7) This is a <u>representational model</u> (p.222).
8) It can be used to <u>predict</u> how current, resistance and p.d. will <u>behave</u> in a circuit.
9) But it has some <u>limitations</u> — e.g. it can't tell you how the current will <u>change with temperature</u>.

There's a Formula Linking P.d., Resistance and Current

1) <u>Current</u>, <u>potential difference</u> and <u>resistance</u> are all linked by this <u>formula</u>:

$$\text{potential difference (V)} = \text{current (A)} \times \text{resistance } (\Omega)$$

2) You can use this equation for <u>whole circuits</u> or <u>single components</u>.

> **EXAMPLE:**
> A 4.0 Ω resistor in a circuit has a current of 1.5 A flowing through it. Calculate the potential difference across the resistor.
>
> <u>Substitute</u> the values you have into the equation, and work out the potential difference.
>
> potential difference = current × resistance
> potential difference = 1.5 × 4.0 = 6.0 V

Learn these Circuit Diagram Symbols

There's more about a.c. and d.c. on p.169.

1) You need to be able to <u>understand circuit diagrams</u> and <u>draw them</u> using the <u>correct symbols</u>.
2) These are the <u>symbols</u> you need to know:

cell	battery	open switch	closed switch	filament lamp	fuse	LED	power supply
resistor	variable resistor	ammeter	voltmeter	diode	LDR	thermistor	motor

3) When you <u>draw a circuit diagram</u>, make sure all the <u>wires</u> in your circuit are <u>straight lines</u>.
4) You also need to make sure that the circuit is <u>closed</u>. This means you can follow a wire from one end of the <u>cell</u> or <u>battery</u>, through any <u>components</u>, to the other end of the cell or battery.

In the end you'll have to learn this — resistance is useless...

Make sure you learn that equation. It crops up a lot in this topic, so you won't get far without it.

Q1   A component has a p.d. of 32 V across it and a 4 A current through it. Calculate its resistance. [3 marks]

Investigating Resistance

PRACTICAL

Ooh experiments, you've gotta love 'em. And good news, there's a few coming up in this section.
Here's an experiment for investigating resistance and how it changes with the length of a wire.

You Can Investigate How Wire Length Affects Resistance

1) The resistance of a component can depend on a number of different things (e.g. its material or size).

2) One thing you can easily investigate is how the length of a wire affects the wire's resistance.

3) You can do this using this circuit:

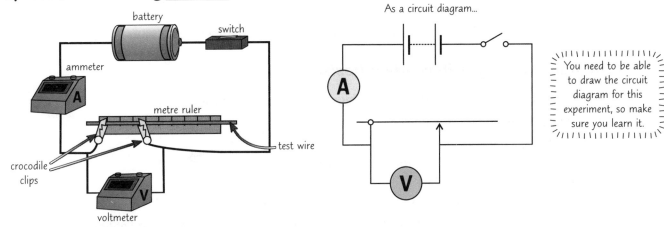

As a circuit diagram...

You need to be able to draw the circuit diagram for this experiment, so make sure you learn it.

Measure Potential Difference and Current for Different Lengths

1) Attach a crocodile clip to the wire, level with 0 cm on the ruler.

2) Attach the second crocodile clip to the wire a short distance from the first clip (e.g. 10 cm).

3) Write down the length of the wire between the clips.

4) Close the switch, then record the current through the wire from the ammeter and the p.d. across it from the voltmeter (p.241).

5) Use your measurement of current and p.d. to calculate the resistance for each length of wire.

A thin wire will give you the best results. Make sure it's as straight as possible so your length measurements are accurate.

6) Use the equation resistance = potential difference ÷ current (p.172).

7) Open the switch and move the second crocodile clip along the wire.

8) Repeat steps 3 to 6 for a range of wire lengths.

Plot a Graph of your Results

1) Plot a graph of resistance against length of wire.

2) Draw a line of best fit through your points.

3) Your graph should be a straight line through the origin (where length and resistance are both zero).

4) This means resistance is directly proportional to length — as the length doubles, the resistance doubles.

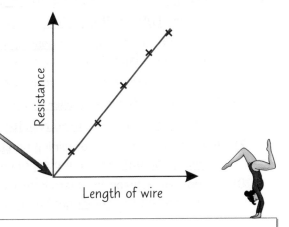

Measure gymnastics — use a vaultmeter...

You could also investigate how the thickness or material of the wire affects its resistance. What fun.

Q1   A student wants to investigate how the resistance of a wire changes with its length.
      Draw a circuit diagram of a circuit she could use to do this.

[3 marks]

LDRs and Thermistors

LDRs and thermistors are special resistors whose resistance can change. Turns out, this is really useful.

You can Use a d.c. Circuit to Test LDRs and Thermistors

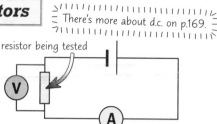
There's more about d.c. on p.169.

1) The resistance of some resistors depends on its surroundings.
2) If you set up the circuit shown on the right, you can test how their resistance changes as the environment (surroundings) change.
3) Each time you make a change (see below), record the p.d. across and the current through the resistor (the LDR or thermistor).
4) Then calculate the resistance using resistance = potential difference ÷ current.

resistor being tested

LDR Stands for Light-Dependent Resistor

1) An LDR's resistance depends on the intensity (brightness) of light.
2) In bright light, the resistance is low.
3) In darkness, the resistance is high.
4) You can test this using the circuit above. Cover up the LDR with a piece of thick paper, a few mm at a time.
5) Find the resistance each time you cover up more of the LDR.
6) LDRs have lots of applications including automatic night lights and outdoor lighting.

resistance / dark — light intensity — light

A Thermistor is a Type of Temperature-Dependent Resistor

1) The resistance of a thermistor depends on its temperature.
2) In hot conditions, the resistance of a thermistor drops.
3) In cool conditions, the resistance goes up.
4) You can test this by placing the thermistor into a beaker of hot water.
5) Calculate the resistance each time the water (and so the thermistor) cools by 5 °C.
6) Thermistors are used as temperature detectors, in things like irons and car engines.

resistance / cool — temperature — hot

You Can Use LDRs and Thermistors in Sensing Circuits

1) Sensing circuits can be used to monitor (keep track of) changes in the surroundings.
2) They use LDRs or thermistors to change the p.d. across other components in the circuit.
3) The circuit on the right is a sensing circuit in a hob on a cooker, which uses a lamp to tell you when the hob is hot.
4) As the hob gets hotter, the resistance of the thermistor decreases.
5) This means it takes a smaller share of the p.d. from the power supply (see p.178).
6) So the p.d. across the fixed resistor and the lamp rises, and the lamp gets brighter.
7) For a sensing circuit containing an LDR, you usually want to increase the p.d. across a component as it gets darker.
8) To do this, replace the thermistor with an LDR. Then connect the component across the LDR instead of across the fixed resistor.

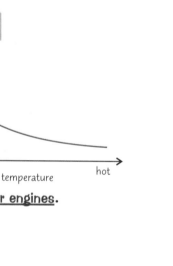

thermistor

fixed resistor

filament lamp

Permistors — resistance decreases with curliness of hair...

Thermistors and LDRs may seem a bit weird, but they're really useful, so make sure you know how they work.

Q1   Describe how the resistance of an LDR changes with light intensity.   [1 mark]

I-V Characteristics

And we're not done with the <u>experiments</u> just yet. Time to draw some sweet <u>*I-V* characteristics</u>...

I-V Characteristics Can Show How Resistance Changes with Current

1) An '<u>*I-V* characteristic</u>' is a <u>graph</u> showing how the <u>current</u> (*I*) flowing through a component changes as the <u>potential difference</u> (*V*) across it changes.

You can read values from the graph and use the equation on page 172 to find the resistance at a given point.

2) The <u>shape</u> of a component's <u>*I-V* characteristic</u> shows how its <u>resistance changes with current</u>.

3) Some components have *I-V* characteristics that are a <u>straight line</u> (e.g. a <u>fixed resistor</u> at a <u>fixed temperature</u>).

4) These components are <u>linear components</u>.

5) Their <u>resistance is constant</u> as the <u>current changes</u>.

6) Other components have <u>curved</u> *I-V* characteristics (e.g. a <u>heating element</u> or a <u>filament lamp</u>).

7) These are <u>non-linear</u> components.

8) Their resistance <u>changes</u> depending on the size of the <u>current</u> flowing through them.

You Can Investigate *I-V* Characteristics   PRACTICAL

You should do this experiment for <u>different components</u>, including: a <u>resistor</u>, a <u>filament lamp</u>, a <u>diode</u>, an <u>LDR</u> and a <u>thermistor</u>.

The <u>conditions</u> (temperature, light levels, etc.) of the circuit should be kept <u>constant</u> for this experiment.

This circuit is a series circuit (p.178) and it uses a direct current (p.169).

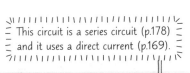

1) Set up the <u>test circuit</u> shown on the right.

2) The <u>variable resistor</u> is used to <u>change</u> the <u>current</u> in the circuit. This changes the <u>potential difference</u> across the <u>component</u>.

3) Now you need to get <u>sets</u> of <u>current</u> and <u>potential difference</u> readings:
   • Set the <u>resistance</u> of the variable resistor.
   • Measure the <u>current through</u> and <u>p.d. across</u> the component.
   • Take measurements at a number of <u>different</u> resistances.

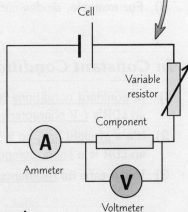

4) <u>Swap</u> over the wires connected to the cell to reverse the <u>direction of the current</u>. The ammeter should now display <u>negative readings</u>.

5) <u>Repeat</u> step 3 to get results for <u>negative values</u> of current.

6) Plot a <u>graph</u> with <u>current</u> on the *y*-axis and <u>potential difference</u> on the *x*-axis.

7) The <u>*I-V* characteristics</u> you should get for the <u>components</u> are shown below and on the next page.

A Fixed Resistor is a Linear Component

1) The *I-V* characteristic of a <u>fixed resistor</u> is a <u>straight line</u>.

2) This shows that a fixed <u>resistor</u> is <u>linear component</u>.

3) Its <u>resistance stays constant</u> as the <u>current</u> through it <u>changes</u>.

4) So they can be used in circuits to provide a <u>constant resistance</u>.

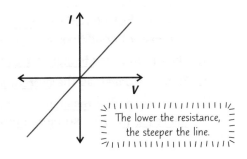

The lower the resistance, the steeper the line.

This experiment can be pretty electrifying...

When it comes to components and *I-V* characteristics, remember: linear = straight line, non-linear = bendy. Sorted.

Q1   State what happens to the resistance of a linear component when the current through it changes.   [1 mark]

Circuit Devices and *I-V* Characteristics

So, now you can plot an *I-V characteristic*, it's time to really look at what they're telling you.

Filament Lamps Have a Curved I-V Characteristic

1) A filament lamp's *I-V* characteristic is <u>curved</u>, so it is a <u>non-linear component</u>.
2) This is because the <u>temperature</u> of the filament lamp <u>increases</u> as <u>current increases</u>.
3) The increase in temperature causes the <u>resistance</u> of the lamp to <u>increase</u>.
4) This makes it <u>harder</u> for current to flow, so the graph gets <u>less steep</u>.
5) As the <u>temperature</u> and <u>resistance increase</u>, the wire (filament) in the lamp <u>glows</u>.
6) This is why filament lamps can be used to <u>produce light</u>.

Current Only Flows in One Direction Through a Diode

1) The *I-V characteristic* of a diode looks like this:
2) The graph is <u>curved</u>, so a diode is a <u>non-linear component</u>.
3) When the <u>p.d.</u> is <u>positive</u>, the graph is steep, showing a large <u>current can flow</u>.
4) When the <u>p.d.</u> is <u>negative</u>, the graph is a flat line at *I* = 0, showing that <u>no current</u> can flow.
5) This shows there's a very high resistance in the <u>reverse</u> direction.
6) So a diode lets current flow through it in <u>one direction</u>, but <u>not</u> in the other.
7) Diodes can be really useful in <u>electronic circuits</u>.
8) For example, diodes can be used to get <u>direct current</u> from an <u>alternating</u> supply (see p.169).

current flows this way

In Constant Conditions, LDRs are Linear Components

1) In <u>constant conditions</u> (p.175) an LDR's *I-V characteristic* looks like <u>this</u>:
2) It's a <u>straight line</u>, so in <u>constant conditions</u>, an LDR is a <u>linear component</u>.
3) This means its <u>resistance doesn't change</u> with current.

The Resistance of a Thermistor Decreases as Current Increases

1) In <u>constant conditions</u>, a thermistor's *I-V characteristic* looks like this:
2) The *I-V* characteristic is <u>curved</u>, so a thermistor in constant conditions is a <u>non-linear component</u>.
3) The graph gets <u>steeper</u> as <u>current increases</u>.
4) This is because as the <u>current increases</u>, the thermistor <u>warms up</u>.
5) This causes the <u>resistance</u> of the thermistor to <u>decrease</u> (p.174), so <u>more current</u> can flow.

All this talk of I-V... Good job they're not poisonous...

Draw out those graphs and make sure you can tell whether they're showing a linear or non-linear component.

Q1 Draw the *I-V* characteristic for: a) an LDR in constant conditions b) a filament lamp. [4 marks]

Energy in Circuits

All electrical devices <u>transfer energy</u>. These energy transfers are all down to <u>charges</u> doing <u>work</u>.

Charges do Work as They Move Around a Circuit

1) When a <u>charge moves</u> around a circuit, <u>energy</u> can be transferred <u>to</u> or <u>from</u> the charge.

2) <u>Energy is transferred</u> because <u>work is done</u> (p.162).

3) A <u>power supply</u> does <u>work</u> on a <u>charge</u> and so transfers <u>energy</u> to it.

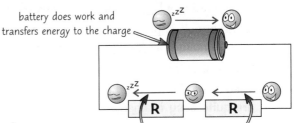

battery does work and transfers energy to the charge

4) The <u>charge does work</u> against the <u>resistance</u> of <u>components</u> or <u>devices</u> as it <u>flows through them</u>.

5) So <u>energy is transferred</u> from a <u>power supply</u> to a component as a <u>current flows</u> through the component.

6) Some of this <u>energy</u> is <u>always transferred electrically</u> to the <u>thermal energy store</u> of the <u>component</u>. This is why <u>wires</u> and <u>components heat up</u> when a current flows.

charges transfer energy to the resistors (by doing work)

7) Energy is then transferred away to the <u>surroundings</u>.

8) You have to be able to <u>describe the energy transfers</u> that happen in <u>devices</u> and <u>components</u>:

> • When a <u>current flows</u> through a fan, it <u>does work</u> against the <u>resistance</u> of the fan's <u>motor</u>.
>
> • Energy is transferred <u>electrically</u> from the <u>battery's chemical energy store</u> to the <u>kinetic energy store</u> of the fan's <u>motor</u>.
>
> • Some energy is also transferred <u>electrically</u> to the <u>thermal energy stores</u> of the <u>motor</u>.
>
> • Energy is then transferred <u>by heating</u> to the <u>thermal energy store</u> of the <u>surroundings</u>.

Potential Difference is the Work Done Per Unit Charge

1) The <u>potential difference</u> between two points is equal to the <u>work done per unit of charge</u> flowing between those two points.

2) It is the <u>energy transferred</u> to or from <u>each coulomb</u> of charge that passes between those points.

3) A power supply with a <u>bigger p.d.</u> will do <u>more work</u> on each charge.

4) So it will transfer <u>more energy</u> to the circuit for every <u>coulomb</u> of charge which flows round it.

5) The <u>potential difference</u>, the <u>work done</u> (either <u>on</u> or <u>by</u> charges) and the total <u>charge</u> passing through the potential difference are <u>linked</u> by:

> The unit for potential difference is V, the unit for work done is J and the unit for charge is C.

potential difference = work done (energy transferred) ÷ charge

6) You can rearrange this equation to find the <u>energy transferred</u> to a <u>component</u> in an <u>electric circuit</u>:

energy transferred (work done) = charge × potential difference

EXAMPLE:

An electric toothbrush contains a 3.0 V battery. 140 C of charge passes through the toothbrush as it is used. Calculate the energy transferred to the toothbrush.

Just put the <u>charge</u> and <u>p.d.</u> values into the energy equation.

energy transferred = charge × potential difference
= 140 × 3.0 = 420 J

Have a break from all this work — or you'll have no energy left...

Re-read this page, then cover it up and see what you can remember. It's important you get this stuff in your head.

Q1   90 C of charge does 810 J of work as it passes through a resistor.
        Calculate the potential difference across the resistor.

[2 marks]

Series Circuits

There's a difference between connecting components in <u>series</u> and <u>parallel</u> — first up, <u>series circuits</u>.

Series Circuits — All or Nothing

1) In <u>series circuits</u>, the different components are connected <u>in a line</u> between the ends of the battery.

2) If the circuit is <u>broken</u>, e.g. if a component breaks or is removed, <u>all the components</u> stop working.

3) Series circuits are often designed and built to <u>test</u> and <u>measure components</u>.

4) They're useful for this because the potential difference, current and resistance are quite easy to <u>change</u>, <u>measure</u> and <u>calculate</u> (see p.172).

Current is the Same Anywhere

1) The <u>same charge</u> passes through <u>every component</u>.

2) So the <u>same current</u> flows through <u>all components</u>.

3) The size of the current depends on the <u>total potential difference</u> and the <u>total resistance</u> of the circuit.

4) For a given p.d., the <u>larger</u> the <u>total resistance</u>, the <u>smaller</u> the <u>current</u> in the whole circuit.

5) So if the <u>resistance</u> of any component <u>increases</u>, the <u>current decreases</u>.

6) And if the <u>resistance</u> of any component <u>decreases</u>, the <u>current increases</u>.

Potential Difference is Shared

1) The <u>charges</u> in a series circuit have to <u>flow</u> through <u>every component</u>.

2) So the <u>work done</u> by the <u>battery</u> on each charge <u>equals</u> the <u>total work done</u> by each charge on the <u>components</u>.

3) This means the <u>potential difference</u> of the battery is <u>shared</u> between components.

4) The bigger a component's <u>resistance</u>, the bigger its <u>share</u> of the <u>total p.d.</u> (p.172).

5) If the <u>resistance</u> of one component <u>changes</u>, the <u>p.d.</u> across <u>every component</u> will <u>change</u>.

6) This is because the <u>total</u> potential difference across components has to <u>equal</u> the <u>battery's p.d.</u>.

Resistance Adds Up

1) When you <u>add</u> a resistor in series, the <u>charges</u> have to <u>go through</u> (and do work against) another component.

2) The battery has a <u>fixed p.d.</u> and so can only supply the same 'push' to each charge.

3) So the new resistor makes the charges flow around the circuit <u>more slowly</u>.

4) This <u>decreases the current</u> in the circuit.

5) So the <u>net (total) resistance</u> of the circuit has <u>gone up</u>.

6) The <u>net resistance</u> is the <u>SUM</u> of the <u>resistances</u> of all the <u>components</u> in the circuit.

You might see the net resistance called the equivalent or effective resistance.

EXAMPLE:

A series circuit contains a cell and a 2 Ω and a 4 Ω resistor. Calculate the net resistance of the circuit.

net resistance = 2 Ω + 4 Ω = 6 Ω

Series circuits — they're no laughing matter...

Get those rules straightened out in your head, then have a go at this question to test what you can remember.

Q1   A series circuit contains two 3 Ω resistors and a cell. Calculate the net resistance of the circuit.   [2 marks]

Parallel Circuits

Move over series circuits, it's time for parallel circuits to have their say.

Parallel Circuits — Everything is Independent

1) In parallel circuits, components are on branches that are connected separately to the ends of the battery.

2) If you take out one of the branches in a parallel circuit, the components in the other branches will keep working.

3) This means components in parallel can be switched on and off without affecting each other.

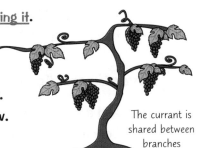

A branch
Another branch
A junction

Current is Split Between Branches

1) Current splits at junctions, and is shared between branches.

2) The total current going into a junction has to equal the total current leaving it.

3) So the total current flowing around the circuit is equal to the sum of all the currents through the separate branches.

4) Since a charge can only flow through one branch at a time, the current in a branch is the same as if it was the only branch in the circuit.

5) The smaller the resistance of a branch, the easier it is for charges to flow.

6) So a larger current flows through a branch with a smaller resistance.

7) If the resistance of a branch changes, the current through that branch will change.

8) But the current through all other branches will stay the same.

The currant is shared between branches

Potential Difference is the Same on Every Branch

1) Each charge can only pass down one branch of the circuit.

2) So it must transfer all the energy supplied to it by the battery to whatever's on that branch.

3) This means all branches have the same potential difference across them as the battery.

4) If the resistance of a branch changes, the p.d. across the branch stays the same.

Net Resistance Decreases in Parallel Circuits

1) The net resistance of the circuit decreases as you add resistors in parallel.

2) If you add a resistor in parallel, both resistors still have the same potential difference across them as across the battery.

3) This means the 'pushing force' making the current flow is still the same.

4) But by adding another loop, the current has more than one direction to go in.

5) More current can flow around the circuit, so the total current increases.

6) This means the net resistance of the circuit is lower (as resistance = p.d. ÷ current).

After this page, your circuits knowledge will be unparalleled...

Remember, in parallel circuits, each branch has the same p.d., but the total current is shared between branches.

Q1   Two identical bulbs are connected in parallel to a 3.5 V battery. State the p.d. across each bulb.   [1 mark]

Chapter P3 — Electric Circuits

Investigating Series and Parallel Circuits

Time for another <u>experiment</u>. And, lucky you, this one is all about <u>series and parallel circuits</u>.
If you're not a fan of these circuits yet, this page is sure to <u>make you like them</u>. Maybe.

You Can Investigate Series and Parallel Circuits using Bulbs | PRACTICAL

1) The <u>brightness</u> of a <u>bulb</u> (filament lamp) depends on how much <u>energy</u> is being transferred to it.
2) The <u>more energy transferred</u> to the bulb, the <u>brighter it is</u>.
3) The energy transferred depends on the <u>p.d.</u> across it and the <u>amount of charge</u> flowing through it (p.177).
4) As current is the <u>rate of flow of charge</u>, energy transferred depends on <u>current</u> too.
5) You can use bulbs to test out <u>the rules</u> of <u>series</u> and <u>parallel circuits</u>.

First Set Up the Basic Circuit

1) Find at least four <u>identical (exactly the same) bulbs</u>.
2) Build the <u>basic circuit</u> shown on the right.
3) Use a <u>voltmeter</u> to measure the <u>p.d.</u> across the bulb.
4) Read the <u>current</u> in the circuit from the <u>ammeter</u>.

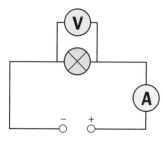

Investigate Adding Bulbs in Series...

1) <u>Add</u> a second bulb <u>in series</u> with the first.
2) Connect a <u>voltmeter</u> across the second bulb.
3) Record the <u>p.d.</u> across <u>each bulb</u>, and the <u>current</u> in the circuit.
4) <u>Repeat steps 1)-3)</u> until you have added all the bulbs.
5) You should see that the bulbs <u>all get dimmer</u> each time you add a bulb.
6) This is because the <u>source potential difference</u> is <u>shared</u> between each of the bulbs in the circuit.
7) So the <u>potential difference</u> across each bulb <u>falls</u> when another is added.
8) The <u>current falls</u> each time you add a bulb, because you increase the <u>net resistance</u> of the circuit.
9) <u>A lower current</u> and <u>a lower p.d.</u> means the bulbs get <u>dimmer</u>.

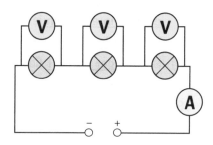

... and in Parallel

1) Build the <u>basic circuit</u> again, using the same equipment.
2) <u>Add</u> a bulb <u>in parallel</u> with the first bulb.
3) Connect a <u>voltmeter</u> across the bulb, and connect an <u>ammeter</u> on the <u>branch</u>.
4) Record the <u>p.d.</u> across <u>each bulb</u>, and the <u>current</u> in each branch.
5) <u>Repeat steps 2)-4)</u> until all the bulbs are added.
6) You should find that the bulbs <u>don't get dimmer</u> as you add more to the circuit.
7) The potential difference across <u>each bulb</u> is <u>equal</u> to the <u>source p.d.</u>, for any number of bulbs.
8) The <u>current</u> on each branch is <u>the same</u>, and it <u>doesn't change</u> when you add more bulbs.
9) As the <u>p.d. and current</u> for each bulb <u>stays the same</u>, the <u>brightness</u> of each bulb <u>doesn't change</u>.

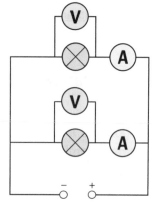

I can't resist a good practical...

Make sure you're completely happy building circuits from diagrams — this experiment is good practice.

Q1   Describe how the brightness of a bulb in a circuit changes as more bulbs are added in series.   [1 mark]

Electrical Power

The <u>power</u> of a device tells you how <u>quickly</u> it <u>transfers energy</u>.

Power is the Rate of Energy Transfer

1) Electrical devices have <u>power ratings</u>.
2) Power ratings tell you the <u>rate</u> (how quickly) that energy is transferred <u>to them</u> from a <u>power supply</u>.
3) Some of this energy will be transferred to the <u>surroundings</u>.
4) Power is measured in <u>watts</u>, <u>W</u>.
5) You can calculate the <u>power transfer</u> in a <u>device</u> from the <u>amount of energy transferred</u> to the <u>device</u> in a given amount of <u>time</u> using:

The power rating of a device is actually the maximum power at which the device can work at. You can usually assume that devices are working at their maximum powers.

$$\text{power (W)} = \text{energy (J)} \div \text{time (s)}$$

EXAMPLE: 240 000 J of energy is transferred from the mains to a microwave in 5 minutes. Calculate its power rating.

1) <u>Convert</u> the time into <u>seconds</u>. time = 5 × 60 = 300 s
2) <u>Substitute</u> the numbers into the equation to find the <u>power</u>. power = energy ÷ time = 240 000 ÷ 300 = 800 W

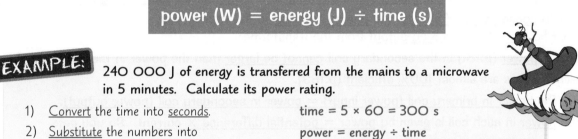

Power in a Circuit Depends on Current and Potential Difference

1) The <u>higher</u> the <u>potential difference</u> across a component, the <u>more energy</u> each charge passing through it will have (p.177).
2) A higher p.d. also makes the charges move <u>faster</u> (i.e. a higher current).
3) This means there will be <u>more energy</u> transferred in a <u>given time</u>, so the device's <u>power</u> will be <u>higher</u>.
4) So you can calculate the <u>power</u> of an electrical device using:

$$\text{power (W)} = \text{potential difference (V)} \times \text{current (A)}$$

5) You can also find the power using:

$$\text{power (W)} = (\text{current})^2 \, (A)^2 \times \text{resistance } (\Omega)$$

EXAMPLE: A motor with a power of 1250 W has a resistance of 50 Ω. Calculate the current flowing through the motor.

Your calculator should have a '√' (square root) button to help with these calculations.

1) First <u>rearrange</u> power = current² × resistance to find the current:
   - <u>Divide</u> both sides by resistance.
   - Find the <u>square root</u> of both sides.

   power = current² × resistance
   current² = power ÷ resistance
   current = √power ÷ resistance

2) Now just <u>plug in</u> the numbers. current = √(1250 ÷ 50) = √25 = 5 A

You have the power — now use your potential...

There are a lot of equations to get your head around here — practise using them until you can remember them all.

Q1 A hairdryer is plugged into the mains supply. The p.d. of the mains supply is 230 V. The current through the hairdyer is 3.0 A. Calculate the power of the hairdryer. [2 marks]

Transformers

Transformers are dead useful — we use them in the national grid to make transmitting electricity more efficient.

Transformers Change the P.d. of Electricity Supplies

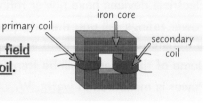

primary coil
iron core
secondary coil

- Transformers have two coils of wire, the primary coil and the secondary coil, joined by an iron core.
- When a current flows through the primary coil, the magnetic field it produces (see p.184) causes a current in the secondary coil.
- You DON'T need to know how this works though — phew.

1) Transformers are used to change the potential difference of electricity.

2) So the p.d. across the secondary coil is different to the p.d. across the primary coil.

3) Due to conservation of energy, the energy supplied to the transformer must be equal to the energy output from the transformer.

4) So the power (p.181) in the secondary coil cannot be larger than the power in the primary coil.

5) Transformers are almost 100% efficient (p.163).

6) So, the power in primary coil (power input) = power in secondary coil (power output).

7) The power in each coil is given by power = potential difference × current. So you get:

$$\text{p.d. across primary coil (V)} \times \text{current in primary coil (A)} = \text{p.d. across secondary coil (V)} \times \text{current in secondary coil (A)}$$

8) If the transformer increases the p.d. (p.d. is bigger across the secondary coil than across the primary coil), the current decreases (current is smaller in the secondary coil than in the primary coil).

9) If the transformer decreases the p.d., the current increases.

Transformers Are Used in the National Grid

1) Once the electricity has been produced, it goes into the national grid (p.169).

2) The national grid has to transfer loads of energy each second.

3) So the national grid transmits electricity at a really high power.

4) This means the electricity must have either a high p.d. or a high current (p.181).

'Potential difference' is sometimes called 'voltage'.

1) If power is transmitted through the national grid at a high current, the wires heat up.

2) This causes a lot of energy to be dissipated (see p.161), so it isn't very efficient (p.163).

3) To stop this happening, step-up transformers at power stations increase the p.d. of the electricity up really high.

4) As the p.d. is increased, the current is decreased.

5) So electricity is transmitted through the national grid at a really high p.d. and a lower current.

6) With a lower current, less power is dissipated.

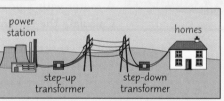

power station
homes
step-up transformer
step-down transformer

7) Step-down transformers bring the p.d. back down before it reaches homes and businesses.

8) This is far more efficient than just transmitting the electricity at a low potential difference.

Transformers — NOT robots in disguise...

You don't need to learn that big equation (it's given to you in the exam), but make sure you know how to use it.

Q1   The current in the primary coil of a transformer is 160 A. The power output is 320 W.
Find the potential difference across the primary coil of the transformer.   [3 marks]

Permanent and Induced Magnets

I think magnetism is an <u>attractive</u> subject, but don't get <u>repelled</u> by the exams — <u>revise</u>.

Magnetic Forces Can Be Attractive or Repulsive

1) <u>All</u> magnets have a <u>north pole</u> (N) and a <u>south pole</u> (S).

2) Two magnetic poles that are the <u>same</u> (<u>like poles</u>) <u>repel</u> each other (push each other apart).

3) Two <u>different</u> (<u>unlike</u>) magnetic poles <u>attract</u> each other.

4) The <u>attraction</u> or <u>repulsion</u> between the poles of two magnets is caused by the <u>magnetic fields</u> around the magnets <u>interacting</u>.

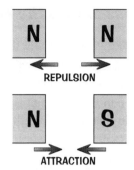

Magnets Produce Magnetic Fields

1) All magnets have a <u>magnetic field</u> around them.

2) This is the <u>region</u> (area) where <u>other magnets</u> experience a <u>force</u>.

3) The <u>magnetic effect</u> (the <u>strength</u> of the magnetic field) is <u>strongest</u> at the <u>poles</u>.

4) The <u>further away</u> from a magnet you get, the <u>weaker</u> its field is.

5) The <u>strength</u> and <u>direction</u> of magnetic fields can be shown with <u>magnetic field lines</u>.

> ### Magnetic Field Lines
> * Field lines <u>always</u> point from a <u>north pole</u> to a <u>south pole</u>.
> * They show the <u>direction</u> of the <u>force</u> that a <u>north pole</u> of a small magnet would feel <u>at that point</u>.
> * The <u>closer together</u> the lines are, the <u>stronger</u> the magnetic field is in that place.

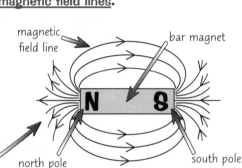

6) You can use these rules to <u>draw the field</u> around a <u>bar magnet</u>.

Magnets Can be Permanent or Induced

1) <u>Permanent magnets</u> produce their <u>own</u> magnetic field.

2) So permanent magnets <u>always</u> have a magnetic field around them.

3) <u>Induced magnets</u> are <u>magnetic materials</u> that <u>turn into</u> a magnet when they're put into a <u>magnetic field</u>.

4) When you <u>take away</u> the magnetic field, induced magnets <u>stop producing</u> a magnetic field.

5) So when they're <u>removed from a magnetic field</u>, <u>permanent</u> magnets <u>keep</u> their <u>magnetisation</u>, but <u>induced</u> magnets <u>lose it</u>.

6) Some <u>magnetic materials</u> that can become <u>induced magnets</u> are <u>iron</u>, <u>steel</u>, <u>nickel</u> and <u>cobalt</u>.

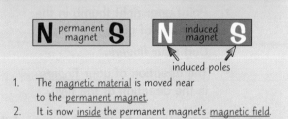

1. The <u>magnetic material</u> is moved near to the <u>permanent magnet</u>.
2. It is now <u>inside</u> the permanent magnet's <u>magnetic field</u>.
3. The <u>magnetic material</u> becomes an <u>induced magnet</u>.
4. It now has its <u>own poles</u> and <u>magnetic field</u>.

Magnets are like farmers — surrounded by fields...

Magnetism can get pretty darn tough. Learn these basics — you'll need them for the rest of the chapter.

Q1 State where the magnetic field produced by a bar magnet is strongest. [1 mark]

Q2 Describe the difference between permanent and induced magnets. [1 mark]

Magnetism and Electromagnetism

On this page you'll see that a magnetic field is also found around a wire that has a current passing through it.

A Compass Shows the Direction of a Magnetic Field

1) The needle of a compass is a tiny bar magnet.

2) The north pole of this magnet is attracted to the south pole of any other magnet it is near.

3) So you can use a compass to see and trace magnetic field lines, like the bar magnet on the right.

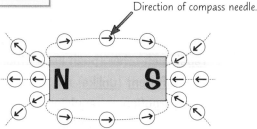
Direction of compass needle.

The Earth has a Magnetic Field

1) When they're not near a magnet, compasses always point north.

2) This is because the Earth produces its own magnetic field (which looks a lot like the field of a big bar magnet).

3) This is evidence that the inside (core) of the Earth must be magnetic.

- The N-pole of the compass is attracted towards the Magnetic North Pole.
- The Magnetic North Pole is the magnetic pole near to the geographic North Pole (the place at the top of the Earth).
- The Magnetic North Pole has a confusing name — it is actually the south pole of the Earth's magnetic field.
- But it is called 'north' because it's close to the geographic North Pole.
- The north pole of the Earth's magnetic field is near the geographic South Pole.

A Moving Charge Creates a Magnetic Effect

1) A current-carrying wire (a wire with an electric current flowing through it) has a magnetic field around it.

2) The field lines are circles around the wire (see below).

3) You can see the direction of the field by placing a compass near to the wire.

4) As you move the compass, the needle will move to point in the direction of the field.

5) You can also use the right-hand thumb rule to quickly work out which way the field goes:

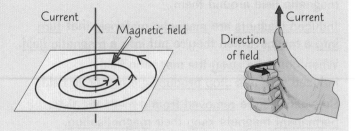

The Right-Hand Thumb Rule
- Point your right thumb in the direction of current.
- Curl your fingers.
- The direction of your fingers is the direction of the field.

Current
Magnetic field
Direction of field
Current

6) Reversing (swapping) the direction of the current reverses the direction of the magnetic field.

7) The closer to the wire you are, the stronger the magnetic field gets.

8) So the closer you are to the wire, the closer together the field lines are.

9) And the larger the current through the wire is, the stronger the field is.

Give me one good raisin why I should make the currant joke...

Practise using the right-hand thumb rule. At least you shouldn't forget which hand to use — it's in the name.

Q1   Draw the magnetic field for a current-carrying wire, with the current coming out of the page.   [2 marks]

Solenoids and Electromagnets

And now, a sudden twist... You can <u>increase the strength</u> of the <u>magnetic field</u> around a wire by winding it into a <u>coil</u>. And if you stick a block of iron in it, you create an <u>electromagnet</u>. Fancy.

A Solenoid is a Coil of Wire

1) You can <u>wind</u> a <u>current-carrying wire</u> into a <u>coil</u> called a <u>solenoid</u>.

2) The magnetic field <u>around</u> the coil is just like the one around a <u>bar magnet</u>.

3) Wrapping a wire into a solenoid <u>increases the strength</u> of the magnetic field produced by the current in the wire.

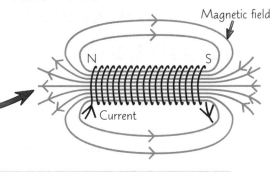
Magnetic field
N   S
Current

- This is because the <u>field lines</u> around <u>each turn</u> of wire <u>line up</u> with each other.
- So <u>lots</u> of <u>field lines</u> end up <u>close</u> to each other and pointing in the <u>same direction</u>.
- The <u>closer together</u> field lines are, the <u>stronger the field</u> is.
- So the <u>field lines</u> can be thought of as <u>adding together</u> to make a <u>stronger magnetic field</u>.

You Can Increase The Strength of a Solenoid

1) The <u>magnetic effect</u> (field strength) of a solenoid can be <u>increased</u> by:
   - Increasing the <u>current</u> through the coil.
   - Increasing the <u>number of turns</u> but keeping the <u>length</u> the <u>same</u>.
   - <u>Decreasing</u> the <u>cross-sectional area</u> of the solenoid (making the solenoid thinner).

2) You can <u>increase</u> the field strength <u>even more</u> by putting a block of <u>iron</u> inside the coil.

3) The <u>iron core</u> becomes an <u>induced</u> magnet whenever current is flowing.

4) A <u>current-carrying solenoid with an iron core</u> is an <u>ELECTROMAGNET</u>.

5) An electromagnet is a magnet whose magnetic field can be turned <u>on</u> and <u>off</u> by turning the <u>current</u> on and off.

Electromagnets Have Led to Improvements in Technology

1) Magnets you can switch on and off are really <u>useful</u>.

2) They're usually used because they're so <u>quick</u> to turn on and off.

3) When electromagnets were discovered in the 19th century (1800s), it quickly led to the creation of <u>lots of devices</u>.

4) One example is the <u>electromagnetic relay</u>.

5) They use <u>electromagnets</u> to <u>switch circuits on and off</u> from a distance.

6) This led to <u>huge advances</u> in how people <u>communicated</u> with each other.

7) For example, electromagnetic relays allowed us to create <u>telegraphs</u>.

8) This is where coded messages can be sent <u>long distances</u> as <u>electrical signals</u>.

9) They are then <u>turned back into words</u> at the other end.

Don't let electromagnets get you all wound up...

Electromagnets are more common than you'd think. They're used in loads of things, from cranes to MRI machines.

Q1   Give two ways you can increase the magnetic effect of a solenoid.   [2 marks]

Revision Questions for Chapter P3

And you've got through to the end of Chapter P3. Have a break, then test what you can remember.

- Try these questions and <u>tick off each one</u> when you <u>get it right</u>.
- When you've done <u>all the questions</u> for a topic and are <u>completely happy</u> with it, tick off the topic.

<u>Circuits (p.171-182)</u> ☐

1) Explain what is meant by electric current. ☑
2) What is the equation that links potential difference, current and resistance? ☐
3) Draw the circuit symbols for: a cell, a filament lamp, a diode, a thermistor and an LDR. ☑
4) Describe an experiment you could do to investigate how the length of a wire affects its resistance. ☐
5) What happens to the resistance of a thermistor as it gets hotter? ☑
6) What is an *I-V* characteristic? ☑
7) True or false? A linear component has a curved *I-V* characteristic. ☑
8) Give two examples of non-linear components. ☑
9) Write down the equation that links potential difference, work done and charge. ☐
10) True or false? The current is shared between components in a series circuit. ☐
11) True or false? The potential difference across every branch of a parallel circuit is the same. ☐
12) What happens to the brightness of a bulb in a circuit as identical bulbs are added in parallel? ☑
13) True or false? Power is the rate of energy transfer. ☐
14) Write down the equation that links power, current and resistance. ☐
15) Explain how using transformers improves the efficiency of transmitting electricity by the national grid. ☐

<u>Magnetism and Electromagnets (p.183-185)</u> ☑

16) True or false? Two magnetic south poles will attract each other. ☑
17) What happens to an induced magnet when it is removed from an external magnetic field? ☑
18) Describe the behaviour of a compass that is far away from any magnets. ☐
19) In the Right-Hand Thumb Rule, what does the direction of the thumb show? ☑
20) What is an electromagnet? ☑

Forces and Newton's Third Law

Clever chap Isaac Newton — he came up with three laws about motion. Let's start with the third...

Forces can be Contact or Non-Contact

1) A force is a push or a pull on an object that is caused by it interacting with another object.
2) Contact forces act between objects that are touching each other.
3) Normal contact forces are the 'push' forces that two touching objects always exert on each other.
4) Friction is a contact force between two objects sliding or trying to slide past each other.
5) Friction acts on both objects in the direction that tries to prevent (stop) motion.

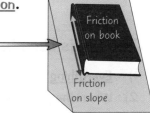

> For example, for a book resting on a slope, friction acts up the slope on the book, and down the slope on the slope to stop the book sliding.

6) Non-contact forces are forces between two objects that aren't touching.
7) These forces are caused by fields around the objects interacting.
8) Some examples of non-contact forces are:

- Gravitational forces (p.188) — e.g. the attractive forces between the Earth and the Sun.
- Electrostatic forces — the attraction or repulsion of charges when their electric fields interact.
- Magnetic forces — the attraction or repulsion between magnets due to their magnetic fields (p.183).

Newton's Third Law is All About Equal and Opposite Forces

1) Whenever two objects interact, they both feel a force. This pair of forces is called an interaction pair.
2) Newton's Third Law says:

> When two objects interact, the two forces in the interaction pair are equal in size and act in opposite directions. They are the same type of force and act on different objects.

3) The tricky bit with Newton's third law is understanding how anything ever goes anywhere.
4) The important thing is that although the forces are equal and opposite, they act on different objects.

> Skater A   Skater B
> - When skater A pushes on skater B, she feels an equal and opposite force from skater B's hand (the 'normal contact' force).
> - Both skaters feel the same sized force, in opposite directions, and so move away from each other (see page 196).

5) It's a bit more complicated for an object in equilibrium (when all forces in it are balanced, see page 195).

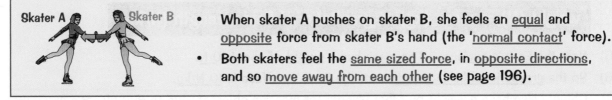

> 1) The weight of the book pulls it down, and the normal contact force from the table pushes it up.
> 2) This is NOT Newton's Third Law. These forces are different types and are both acting on the book.
>
> The pairs of forces due to Newton's Third Law in this case are:
> - The book being pulled down by gravity towards the Earth (W_B). And the Earth being pulled up by the book (W_E).
> - The normal contact force from the table pushing up on the book (N_B). And the normal contact force from the book pushing down on the table (N_T).

Newton's fourth law — revision must be done with cake...

For every action there is an equal and opposite reaction. Like the pain of revision and the joy of passing the exam.

Q1   A man pushes a door with a force of 10 N. State the size of the force the door exerts on the man. [1 mark]

Mass and Weight

The weight is finally over, it's time to talk about mass. And where there's mass, there's gravity.

Everything Made of Matter Has a Mass

1) Mass is just the amount of matter in an object.
2) It's a measure of the total number of atoms that make it up.
3) Mass is measured in kilograms, kg.
4) An object will have the same mass anywhere in the universe.

Gravity is the Force of Attraction Between All Masses

1) Everything that has mass has a gravitational field around it.
2) When the gravitational fields around objects interact, gravitational forces act on the objects.
3) These forces are always attractive (they act towards each other).
4) Isaac Newton was the first person to realise that the force that causes objects to fall on Earth is the same type of force that keeps the Moon orbiting (going around) the Earth.
5) He realised that gravity acted between everything with mass — it is a universal law of nature (it's always true).

This was the first universal law of nature to be discovered.

6) You only usually notice attraction due to gravity when the mass of one object is very large.

Weight is a Downwards Force

1) In everyday situations, objects experience a downwards force due to the gravitational attraction of Earth.
2) This force is called the object's weight. It's measured in newtons (N).
3) The weight of an object is proportional to its mass. The larger its mass, the larger its weight.
4) You can calculate the weight of an object using:

> weight (N) = mass (kg) × gravitational field strength (N/kg)

5) Near the Earth's surface, a 1 kg mass has a weight of about 10 N.
6) So the gravitational field strength near the Earth's surface is 10 N/kg.
7) Objects also have a weight on other planets (or massive objects), due to that planet's gravitational field.
8) An object's weight will be different in different gravitational field strengths.

You Can Measure Weight with a Spring Balance or Top-Pan Balance

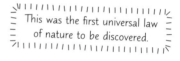

1) Weight can be measured using a spring balance (a newtonmeter).
2) When a mass is put on the hook, the spring in the spring balance extends. The weight can then be read from the scale.
3) Weight can also be measured using a top-pan balance (p.234).

Don't let all this revision weigh you down...

Remember, mass and weight are the not same thing. Make sure you learn the difference.

Q1   A person has a weight of 820 N on Earth. The gravitational field strength of Earth is 10 N/kg.
      Calculate the mass of the person.

[3 marks]

Distance, Displacement, Speed and Velocity

The stuff on this page is pretty darn important. <u>Learn it</u>, don't forget it, and <u>do the question</u> at the end.

Distance and Speed are Scalars, Displacement and Velocity are Vectors

1) An <u>object's motion</u> can be described by its <u>speed</u>, <u>direction</u> of travel and whether its <u>speed is changing</u>.

2) <u>Distance</u>, <u>displacement</u>, <u>speed</u> and <u>velocity</u> are all used to <u>describe</u> an object's motion.

> 1) <u>Distance</u> is just <u>how far</u> an object has moved <u>along the path it has taken</u>.
>
> 2) <u>Displacement</u> is the <u>net distance</u> and <u>direction</u> in a <u>straight line</u> from an object's <u>starting point</u> to its <u>finishing point</u>.
>
> 3) For example, if you walk <u>15 m north</u>, then <u>5 m south</u> your <u>displacement</u> is <u>10 m north</u>, BUT the <u>distance travelled</u> is <u>20 m</u>.

> 1) The <u>speed</u> of an object is <u>how fast</u> it's going — the <u>direction isn't important</u>. E.g. <u>speed = 30 mph</u>.
>
> 2) <u>Velocity</u> describes both the <u>speed and direction</u>. E.g. <u>velocity = 30 mph north</u>.
>
> 3) This means you can have objects travelling at a <u>constant speed</u> but with a <u>changing velocity</u>. This happens when an object is <u>changing direction</u> whilst <u>staying at the same speed</u>.

3) Quantities like <u>speed</u> and <u>distance</u>, that have a <u>size but not a direction</u>, are called <u>scalar</u> quantities.

4) Other examples of scalar quantities are <u>mass</u>, <u>time</u> and <u>temperature</u>.

5) Quantities like <u>velocity</u> and <u>displacement</u>, that have a <u>direction as well as a size</u>, are <u>vector</u> quantities.

6) <u>Force</u> and <u>acceleration</u> are also vector quantities.

Objects Rarely Travel at a Constant Speed

1) When you <u>walk</u>, <u>run</u> or travel in a <u>car</u>, your speed is <u>always changing</u>.

2) Generally, when we talk about speed, we're talking about the <u>average</u> (mean, p.226) speed.

3) You can <u>calculate</u> the average speed using:

$$\text{average speed (m/s)} = \text{distance (m)} \div \text{time (s)}$$

> **EXAMPLE:** A cat walks at an average speed of 0.4 m/s. Find how long it takes to walk 32 m.
>
> 1) <u>Rearrange</u> the equation for <u>time</u>.   time = distance ÷ average speed
> 2) Stick in the values for <u>average speed</u>   time = 32 ÷ 0.4
>   and the <u>distance</u> you've been <u>given</u>.   = 80 s

Learn these Typical Speeds

1) You need to know the <u>typical (usual) speeds</u> of some everyday things.

2) These come in handy when you have to make <u>estimates</u> (p.191).

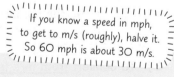

If you know a speed in mph, to get to m/s (roughly), halve it. So 60 mph is about 30 m/s.

- <u>Walking</u> — <u>1.4 m/s</u>
- **Average** <u>wind speed</u> — <u>7 m/s</u>
- <u>Running</u> — <u>3 m/s</u>
- <u>Cars</u> in a <u>built-up area</u> — <u>13 m/s</u>
- <u>Trains</u> — **up to** <u>55 m/s</u>
- <u>Cycling</u> — <u>5.5 m/s</u>
- <u>Cars</u> on a <u>motorway</u> — <u>31 m/s</u>
- **Speed** of <u>sound in air</u> — <u>340 m/s</u>

I feel the need. The need for calculating speed...

Important things to know in life: how to correctly pronounce 'scone' and the difference between scalars and vectors.

Q1   A cyclist travels 600 m in 120 seconds. Calculate the average speed of the cyclist.   [2 marks]

Measuring and Converting Units

If you want to <u>investigate motion</u>, you'll have to take a lot of <u>measurements</u>. And once you've taken those measurements, you need to get them in to the right <u>units</u>. Thankfully, we've got you covered.

You can use Different Equipment to Measure Distance and Time

1) Generally, if you're doing an <u>experiment</u> where you have to measure <u>speed</u>, you do this by <u>measuring distance</u> and <u>time</u>, and then <u>calculating</u> speed (like in the experiment on page 192).

2) The <u>equipment</u> you use for measuring distance and time depends on <u>what you're investigating</u>.

3) When measuring <u>distance</u>, your <u>measuring instrument</u> should be <u>longer</u> than what you're measuring.

4) For example, use a <u>metre stick</u> to measure something that's <u>45 cm long</u>, not a <u>30 cm ruler</u>.

5) To measure times <u>longer than</u> about <u>5 seconds</u>, you can use a <u>stopwatch</u>.

6) Using a stopwatch involves <u>error</u> (p.225) due to things like <u>reaction times</u> (p.197).

7) So to measure <u>shorter times</u>, it's best to use <u>light gates</u> connected to a <u>computer</u> (see page 241).

You Need to be Able to Convert Between Units

1) When using any <u>equation</u>, you <u>need</u> to have your quantities in the <u>right units</u>.

2) For example, in the <u>speed equation</u> on the last page:
   * the <u>speed</u> has to be in <u>m/s</u> (metres per second),
   * the <u>distance</u> has to be in <u>m</u> (metres),
   * the <u>time</u> has to be in <u>s</u> (seconds).

3) You may need to <u>convert</u> (change) the units of a <u>quantity</u> before you put it into an equation.

4) You need to be able to change between <u>hours</u>, <u>minutes</u> and <u>seconds</u>.

> <u>To convert hours into seconds</u>:
> <u>Multiply</u> the number of hours by <u>60</u> to find the number of <u>minutes</u> — e.g. 8 h × 60 = 480 mins
> Then <u>multiply</u> the minutes by <u>60</u> to find the number of <u>seconds</u> — e.g. 480 mins × 60 = 28 800 s

5) To convert other units, you'll need to understand <u>prefixes</u> (see p.228).

6) In the real world speeds are often measured in <u>kilometres per hour, (km/h)</u>.

7) You need to be able to convert <u>km/h</u> into <u>m/s</u>.

> <u>To convert km/h into m/s</u>:
> 1) <u>1 km = 1000 m</u>, so <u>multiply</u> the speed by <u>1000</u> to find the number of <u>metres travelled per hour</u>.   Find 36 km/h in m/s.   <u>36 km/h × 1000 = 36 000 m/h</u>
> 2) Find the <u>number of seconds</u> in an <u>hour</u>.   1 × 60 × 60 = <u>3 600 s</u>
> 3) <u>Divide</u> the number of <u>metres per hour</u> by the number of <u>seconds</u> in an hour, to find the <u>speed in m/s</u>.   36km/h in m/s = 36 000 m/h ÷ 3600   = <u>10 m/s</u>

8) To convert <u>from m/s to km/h</u>, you do the <u>opposite</u>.

9) <u>Multiply</u> the speed by <u>3 600</u> to find the number of <u>metres travelled in an hour</u>.

10) Then <u>divide by 1000</u> to find the speed in <u>km/h</u>.

We are the distance invaders, take us to your ruler...

Make sure you convert your values to the correct units before you make any calculations.

Q1   A man is travelling at an average speed of 2 m/s. Calculate their speed in km/h.   [3 marks]

Acceleration

Acceleration is all about <u>speeding up</u> and <u>slowing down</u>. So let's pick up the pace and dive straight in.

Acceleration is How Quickly You're Speeding Up

1) Acceleration is the <u>change in velocity</u> (see p.189) of an object in a certain amount of <u>time</u>.

2) In <u>most</u> everyday situations, this change in velocity is <u>only</u> a <u>change of speed</u>, <u>not</u> a change in <u>direction</u>.

3) This means you can think of acceleration as the <u>change of speed</u> of an object <u>in a given time</u>.

4) You can find the <u>acceleration</u> of an object using:

> acceleration (m/s^2) = change in speed (m/s) ÷ time taken (s)

Deceleration is just negative acceleration (when something slows down).

You Need to be Able to Estimate Accelerations

You might have to <u>estimate</u> (make a good guess at) the <u>acceleration</u> (or deceleration) of an object. To do this, you'll need to use the <u>typical speeds</u> from page 189 or to <u>estimate a time</u>:

EXAMPLE: A man on a bike accelerates from rest (0 m/s) to a typical speed in 10 seconds. Estimate the acceleration of the bicycle.

1) First, give a <u>sensible speed</u> for the bicycle to be travelling at.

2) Put these numbers into the <u>acceleration equation</u>.

3) The ~ symbol just means it's an <u>approximate</u> answer (it's a <u>rough</u> answer, as we're <u>estimating</u>).

The typical speed of a bike is about 5.5 m/s. The bicycle accelerates in 10 s.

acceleration = change in speed ÷ time taken
= 5.5 ÷ 10 = 0.55 m/s^2

So the acceleration is ~0.55 m/s^2

The equations on this page and the equation on page 189 form a computational model (p.222). You can use them to predict the position or speed of an object that has a constant speed or a constant acceleration.

There's an Equation for Constant Acceleration

1) For any object that is travelling with <u>constant acceleration</u> (sometimes called <u>uniform acceleration</u>), you can use the following <u>equation</u>:

> (final speed)² – (initial speed)² = 2 × acceleration × distance
> $(m/s)^2$ $(m/s)^2$ (m/s^2) (m)

The 'initial speed' is just the starting speed of the object.

2) A <u>common</u> example of <u>constant acceleration</u> is an object in <u>free fall</u> near the Earth's surface.

3) It has a constant acceleration due to gravity of roughly <u>10 m/s^2</u>.

EXAMPLE: An apple is hanging from a branch of a tree 1.8 m above the ground. It falls from the branch and hits the ground. The acceleration due to gravity is 10 m/s^2. Calculate the speed of the apple as it hits the ground.

1) First, <u>rearrange</u> the equation for final speed:
   • <u>Add</u> (initial speed)² to both sides.
   • <u>Square-root</u> both sides.

2) Now, put the <u>numbers</u> in — the <u>initial speed</u> is <u>0 m/s</u>, since the apple started at <u>rest</u>.

(final speed)² = (initial speed)² + (2 × acceleration × distance)

final speed = $\sqrt{\text{(initial speed)}^2 + (2 \times \text{acceleration} \times \text{distance})}$

final speed = $\sqrt{0^2 + (2 \times 10 \times 1.8)}$ = 6 m/s

---

CAUTION! Accelerating through pages means you miss info...

Make sure you're totally happy rearranging and using the equations on this page. They're pretty important.

Q1 A car travels 10 m as it accelerates from 4 m/s to 10 m/s. Calculate the acceleration of the car. [3 marks]

PRACTICAL   # Investigating Motion

Here's an <u>experiment</u> you can do to investigate how <u>distance</u>, <u>speed</u> and <u>acceleration</u> are linked together.

You can Investigate the Motion of a Trolley on a Ramp

1) Set up your <u>apparatus</u> as shown in the diagram below.

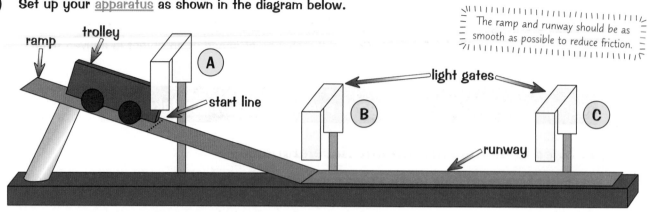

The ramp and runway should be as smooth as possible to reduce friction.

2) Mark a <u>start line</u> on the ramp just before the <u>first light gate</u>.
3) This is to make sure the trolley starts from the <u>same point</u> each time.

There is more on how to use light gates on p.241.

4) Measure the <u>distances</u> between <u>light gates A and B</u>, and between <u>gates B and C</u> using a ruler.
5) Hold the trolley <u>still</u> at the start line. Then <u>let go</u> of the trolley so that it starts to roll down the ramp.
6) As it rolls down the <u>ramp</u>, the trolley will <u>accelerate</u>.
7) When the trolley reaches the <u>runway</u>, it will travel at a <u>constant speed</u> (ignoring any friction).
8) Each <u>light gate</u> will record the <u>time</u> when the trolley passes through it.

You can also measure speed at a point using one light gate.

<u>Calculating the Speed and Acceleration of the Trolley</u>

1) The <u>time taken</u> to travel between <u>light gates A and B</u> can be used to find the <u>average speed</u> of the trolley as it moves <u>down the ramp</u>.
2) The <u>time taken</u> to travel between <u>gates B and C</u> can be used to find the <u>speed</u> on the <u>runway</u>.
3) Use the equation <u>average speed = distance ÷ time</u> (p.189) to calculate these speeds.
4) To find the <u>acceleration</u> of the trolley on the ramp use <u>acceleration = change in speed ÷ time taken</u> (p.191).
5) You'll need to use the following values:
   - The <u>initial speed</u> of the trolley (= 0 m/s).
   - The <u>final speed</u> of the trolley. This is equal to the speed of the trolley on the <u>runway</u> (ignoring <u>friction</u>).
   - The <u>time</u> it takes the trolley to travel between <u>light gates A and B</u>.

You can Change the Trolley's Acceleration and its Speed on the Runway

1) <u>Changing the set up</u> of your experiment will affect the <u>acceleration</u> and <u>final speed</u> of the trolley.
2) For example, you could <u>increase</u> the <u>angle</u> of the ramp.
3) This will <u>increase</u> the trolley's <u>acceleration</u> down the ramp and its <u>speed</u> on the runway.
4) You could also move the <u>start line</u> further up the ramp.
5) As the trolley has a <u>greater distance</u> to accelerate over, its <u>speed</u> on the runway will be higher.

If you want to investigate motion you'll need to invest in gates...

You could be asked about any part of this experiment in the exam, so make sure you really know it before moving on.

Q1   Describe how the speed of an object can be found using two light gates.   [3 marks]

Distance-Time Graphs

Graphs can be rather useful for showing all sorts of things (p.227). First up, we've got distance-time graphs.

Distance-Time Graphs Tell You How Far Something has Travelled

A distance-time graph describes the motion of an object:

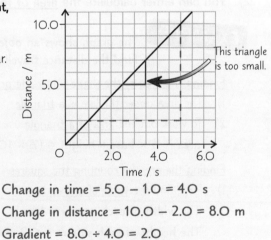

1) The gradient (slope) at any point gives the average speed of the object.
2) A steeper graph means it's going faster.
3) Flat sections are where it's stopped.
4) Curves show acceleration or deceleration.
5) A curve getting steeper (increasing gradient) means it's speeding up (accelerating).
6) A levelling off curve (decreasing gradient) means it's slowing down (decelerating).

The Average Speed of an Object can be Found From a Distance-Time Graph

1) If the graph is a straight line, the average speed at any point during that time is equal to the gradient of the line.

EXAMPLE:

Using the distance-time graph on the right, calculate the average speed of the car.

1) The gradient of the graph is the average speed of the car.

2) Gradient = $\dfrac{\text{change in vertical axis}}{\text{change in horizontal axis}}$.

3) Draw a large triangle, that takes up most of the straight line.

4) Use the horizontal side of the triangle to find the change in time.

5) Use the vertical side of the triangle to find the change in distance.

6) Put the values into the gradient equation above.

This triangle is too small.

Change in time = 5.0 − 1.0 = 4.0 s

Change in distance = 10.0 − 2.0 = 8.0 m

Gradient = 8.0 ÷ 4.0 = 2.0

So average speed = 2.0 m/s

2) If the graph is curved, you can find the average speed at a certain time by drawing a tangent (p.147) to the graph at that point.

3) A tangent is a straight line that is parallel to the curve at that point.

4) The average speed at that point is equal to the gradient of the tangent.

Understanding motion graphs — it can be a real uphill struggle...

For practice, try sketching distance-time graphs for different situations. Like walking home or running from a bear.

Q1   Sketch a distance-time graph for an object that starts off travelling at a constant speed and then decelerates to a stop.

[2 marks]

Chapter P4 — Explaining Motion

Velocity-Time Graphs

Velocity-time graphs look a lot like the distance-time graphs. So be really careful not to mix them up.

Velocity-Time Graphs Can Be Used to Find Average Acceleration

Velocity-time graphs also describe the motion of an object.

1) The gradient (p.193) at any point gives the average acceleration of the object.
2) The steeper the graph, the greater the average acceleration.
3) Flat sections show a steady speed.
4) Uphill sections (/) are acceleration.
5) Downhill sections (\) are deceleration.
6) A curve means changing acceleration.
7) If the object is moving in a straight line (i.e. not changing direction) you can plot a speed-time graph instead.
8) These graphs have speed as the label on the y-axis, not velocity.
9) You can find the average acceleration of the object by finding the gradient of a speed-time graph.

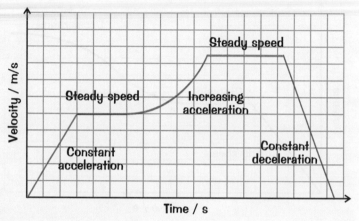

The Distance Travelled is the Area Under the Graph

1) The area under a speed-time (or velocity-time) graph is equal to the distance travelled by the object.
2) You can either calculate the area of the shape under the graph using a formula or by counting squares:

EXAMPLE: The graph shows an object travelling in a straight line with a constant acceleration. Find the distance travelled by the object in the first 10 s.

Finding the area of the shape under the graph
1) The area under the line is a triangle.
2) To work out the area of a triangle use the formula:
   area = ½ × base × height = (½ × 10 × 2) = 10 m

Finding the area by counting the squares
1) First, find the value of one square.
   The width of each square = 1 s
   The height of each square = 0.2 m/s
   So the value of each square = width × height = 1 × 0.2 = 0.2 m
2) Then count how many squares there are.
   Number of whole squares = 45 (in red), number of half squares = 10 (in blue)
   So total squares = 50
3) Calculate the distance travelled by multiplying the value of one square by the number of squares.
   Distance travelled = value of one square × number of squares = 0.2 × 50 = 10 m

Anyone up for a game of squares?

Make sure you know the differences between distance-time and velocity-time graphs, and how to read them.

Q1   A car accelerates from rest with a constant acceleration for 10 s until it reaches a speed of 20 m/s. It then travels at this speed for 20 s. Draw the velocity-time graph for this journey.   [2 marks]

Chapter P4 — Explaining Motion

Free Body Diagrams and Resultant Forces

A <u>free body diagram</u> is really useful for understanding <u>how</u> and <u>why</u> an object is <u>moving</u> or <u>not moving</u>.

Free Body Force Diagrams Show All the Forces Acting on an Object

1) Forces are <u>vectors</u> (see page 189) — they have a <u>size</u> and <u>direction</u>.
2) An <u>arrow</u> can be used to show the <u>direction</u> of a force. The <u>length</u> of the arrow shows its <u>size</u>.
3) <u>Free body diagrams</u> use arrows to show the <u>forces acting</u> on an <u>isolated object</u> or <u>system</u> (p.161).
4) This means they <u>only show</u> the forces <u>acting on</u> the object or system.
5) They <u>don't show</u> the forces the object or system <u>applies to the rest of the world</u>.

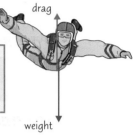

- For example, the image on the right shows a <u>free body diagram</u> of a skydiver.
- The skydiver's <u>weight</u> (p.188) acts on him, pulling him towards the ground.
- <u>Drag</u> (air resistance) also acts on him, in the <u>opposite direction</u> to his motion.

A Resultant Force is the Overall Force on a Point or Object

1) If <u>more than one force</u> acts at a single point, you can replace them with a <u>single force</u>.
2) This single force is called the <u>resultant force</u>.
3) It has the <u>same effect</u> as all the original forces (including their directions) <u>added together</u>.
4) You can work out if there is a <u>resultant force</u> on an object using a <u>free body diagram</u>.
5) Look at all the forces acting along the <u>same line</u> (e.g. <u>up and down</u>, <u>right and left</u>).
6) If the <u>total length</u> of arrows pointing in <u>one direction</u> is <u>bigger</u> to the <u>total length</u> pointing in the <u>opposite</u> direction, there is a <u>resultant force</u> in that direction. For example:

1) The <u>weight</u> of the apple is acting <u>downwards</u>.
2) The <u>normal contact force</u> from the table top is pushing <u>up</u> on the apple.
3) These two forces are <u>equal in size</u> and act in <u>opposite directions</u>.
4) This means there is a <u>zero resultant force</u>.
5) The object is said to be in <u>equilibrium</u> — <u>all</u> the forces are <u>balanced</u>.

1) The car's <u>weight</u> acts <u>downwards</u>. The <u>normal contact force</u> acts <u>upwards</u>.
2) The <u>arrows</u> for weight and the normal contact force are the <u>same length</u>. So these two forces are <u>balanced</u>.
3) <u>Air resistance</u> acts in the <u>opposite direction</u> to the <u>driving force</u>.
4) The driving force arrow is <u>longer</u> than the air resistance arrow.
5) So there is a <u>resultant force</u> in the direction of the driving force.

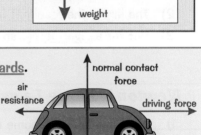

7) You can <u>calculate</u> the size of the resultant force by <u>adding together</u> the sizes of all the forces going in <u>one direction</u> and <u>subtracting</u> the sizes of all the forces going in the <u>opposite direction</u>.

Force yourself to revise this...

Free body diagrams can really help with force questions, so make sure you know how to draw them. If you're showing an object's weight (p.188) on a free body diagram, you should draw its arrow from the centre of the object.

Q1   Draw a free body diagram for a book with a weight of 10 N resting on a table.   [2 marks]

Newton's First and Second Laws

You met <u>Newton's Third Law</u> on page 187, and now it's time for the <u>rest</u> of Newton's incredibly useful laws.

Newton's First Law — A Force is Needed to Change Motion

1) <u>Newton's First Law says</u> that a <u>resultant force</u> is needed to <u>change the motion</u> of an object.

2) For <u>stationary</u> objects (objects that <u>aren't moving</u>), <u>Newton's First Law says</u>:

> If the resultant force on a <u>stationary</u> object
> is <u>zero</u>, the object will <u>remain stationary</u>.

3) And for <u>objects moving at</u> a <u>uniform velocity</u> (a <u>constant speed</u> in a <u>straight line</u>):

> If the <u>resultant force</u> on a moving object is <u>zero</u>, it will just
> carry on moving at a <u>constant speed</u> in a <u>straight line</u>.

4) If a <u>non-zero</u> resultant force acts on the object, the object can <u>change speed</u>, <u>change direction</u>, or <u>both</u>.

> 1) The object will <u>speed up</u> (accelerate) if the force is in the <u>same direction</u> as the object's <u>line of motion</u> (the <u>direction of travel</u>).
>
> 2) The object will <u>slow down</u> if the force is in the <u>opposite direction</u> to the object's line of motion.
>
> 3) The object will <u>change direction</u> if the force <u>isn't parallel</u> to the object's line of motion. (If the force doesn't act <u>in the same or opposite direction</u> as the direction the object is moving in.)

line of motion
resultant force
1
resultant force
2
3
resultant force

5) If a resultant force acts on a <u>stationary object</u>, the object will <u>start moving</u> in the direction of the force.

Newton's Second Law Connects Force, Mass and Acceleration

1) You also need to know <u>Newton's Second Law</u>:

> force (N) = mass (kg) × acceleration (m/s²)

2) The <u>larger</u> the <u>resultant force</u> acting on an object, the <u>more</u> the object accelerates.

3) But for a <u>given force</u>, an object with a <u>larger</u> mass will accelerate <u>less</u> than one with a smaller mass.

Newton's Three Laws Required Creativity

1) Newton's laws are some of the most <u>important</u> laws in physics.

2) Before Newton, lots of scientists had <u>observed</u> (looked at) and <u>discussed</u> many <u>different ideas</u> about <u>how objects moved</u>.

3) But Newton was the one who managed to <u>link them all together</u>.

4) Newton was able to create <u>general rules</u> for motion (his <u>three laws</u>) which could <u>describe</u> and <u>explain</u> what was going on in <u>any situation</u>.

5) Newton's laws of motion are great <u>examples</u> of needing lots of <u>imagination</u> to come up with a <u>scientific explanation</u> for what happens in experiments.

Newton's creation of the laws of motion was a big step forward in science, that really helped improve our understanding of the world.

Now you've started revising, you won't need a push to keep going...

Newton's First Law means that for an object at a steady speed, the forces acting on it are balanced.

Q1   Find the force needed for an 80.0 kg man on a 10.0 kg bike to accelerate at 0.25 m/s². [2 marks]

Reaction Times

Go long! You need fast <u>reaction times</u> to avoid getting hit in the face when playing catch.

A Typical Reaction Time is 0.2 s – 0.8 s

1) <u>Reaction time</u> is <u>how long</u> it takes your body to move after you notice something.
2) <u>Everyone's</u> reaction time is <u>different</u>.
3) A <u>typical</u> reaction time is between <u>0.2</u> and <u>0.8 s</u>.
4) You can do <u>simple experiments</u> to investigate your reaction time — more on these below.

You can Measure Reaction Times with a Computer or a Ruler

1) As reaction times are <u>so short</u>, you haven't got a chance of measuring one with a <u>stopwatch</u>.
2) One way of measuring reaction times is to use a <u>computer-based test</u>. For example, <u>clicking a mouse</u> when the screen changes colour.
3) Another method to measure reaction times is the <u>ruler drop test</u>.

The Ruler Drop Test

1) Sit with your arm resting on the edge of a table.
2) Get someone else to hold a ruler so it <u>hangs between</u> your thumb and forefinger, lined up with <u>zero</u>.
3) You may need a <u>third person</u> to be at <u>eye level with the ruler</u> to check it's lined up.
4) Without giving any warning, the person holding the ruler should <u>drop it</u>.
5) Close your thumb and finger to try to <u>catch the ruler as quickly as possible</u>.
6) The measurement on the ruler at the point where it is caught is <u>how far</u> the ruler dropped in the <u>time</u> it took you to <u>react</u>.
7) The <u>longer</u> the <u>distance</u>, the <u>longer</u> your <u>reaction time</u>.
8) A ruler will always fall at the <u>same rate</u>, so you can use a <u>ruler drop conversion</u> table to convert <u>distance caught</u> to <u>reaction time</u>.
9) For example, catching after <u>25 cm</u> is a reaction time of <u>0.23 s</u>.
10) You can also <u>calculate</u> your reaction time by <u>rearranging</u> the equation for <u>constant acceleration</u> (see p.191). This is because the <u>acceleration due to gravity is constant</u>.
11) It's <u>hard</u> to do this experiment <u>accurately</u>, but you can do a few things to <u>improve</u> your <u>results</u>.
   - Do a lot of <u>repeats</u> and calculate an <u>average</u> reaction time.
   - Add a <u>blob of modelling clay</u> to the bottom to help the ruler to fall <u>straight</u> down.
   - Make it a <u>fair test</u> — use the <u>same ruler</u> for each repeat, and have the <u>same person</u> dropping it.

ruler hanging between thumb and forefinger

finger in line with zero

ruler is dropped without warning

ruler caught between thumb and finger

distance fallen

Test a friend's reaction time by throwing this book at them...

Not really. Instead re-read this page and make sure you can describe the experiment. Much more fun.

Q1 State the typical reaction time of a person. [1 mark]

Q2 Give one way of measuring a person's reaction time. [1 mark]

Stopping Distances

This page is all about cars, but sadly it's not as fun as it sounds. It's even better — it's about car safety...

Stopping Distance = Reaction Distance + Braking Distance

1) In an emergency, a driver may perform an emergency stop.
2) During an emergency stop, the maximum force is applied by the brakes.
3) This is so the vehicle stops in the shortest possible distance.
4) The distance it takes for a vehicle to stop in an emergency is its stopping distance.

> Stopping Distance = Reaction Distance + Braking Distance

5) REACTION DISTANCE is how far the vehicle travels during the driver's reaction time.
6) The reaction time is the time between the driver seeing a hazard and applying the brakes.
7) BRAKING DISTANCE is the distance taken to stop under the braking force (once the brakes are applied).
8) The longer it takes to perform an emergency stop, the higher the risk of crashing into whatever's in front.
9) So the shorter a vehicle's stopping distance, the safer it is.
10) You need to be able to describe how different factors can affect the stopping distance of a vehicle.

Reaction Distance Depends on the Driver's Reactions and Speed

1) Reaction distance is affected by:
   - Your SPEED: the faster you're going, the further you'll travel during the time you take to react.
   - Your REACTION TIME: the longer your reaction time (see p.197), the longer your reaction distance.
2) A driver's reaction time can be increased by tiredness, drugs, alcohol and distractions.

Braking Distance Can be Affected by Many Different Factors

Braking distance is affected by:
1) Your SPEED: the faster a vehicle travels, the longer it takes to stop.
2) The MASS of your vehicle: a car full of stuff won't stop as quickly as an empty one.
3) The STATE of the ROAD:
   - If there is less grip between a vehicle's tyres and the road, it can cause the vehicle to skid.
   - Skidding increases the braking distance of a car.
   - Water, ice, oil or leaves on the road all reduce grip.
4) How good your TYRES are:
   - Bald tyres (ones that don't have any tread left) cannot get rid of water in wet conditions.
   - This leads to them skidding on top of the water.
5) How good your BRAKES are:
   - If brakes are worn or faulty (not working properly), they won't be able to apply as much force.
   - So the vehicle will take longer to stop for any given speed.
6) You need to think about what effect these factors can have on safety. For example:

> Icy conditions increase the chance of skidding. This increases the braking distance, which increases the stopping distance. So more room should be left between cars to avoid a crash if a car stops.

Stop right there — and learn this page...

Make sure you know how these factors affect the stopping distance and how this affects how safe it is to travel.

Q1   Explain why driving while tired is less safe than driving while well rested.   [2 marks]

Chapter P4 — Explaining Motion

Vehicle Safety

We're not done with safety yet, oh no. And there's even more about that fella Newton too, woo-hoo.

Large Decelerations can be Dangerous

1) According to Newton's Second Law (p.196), the larger the force on an object, the larger its acceleration.

2) Acceleration is the rate of change of speed (p.191).

3) So the larger the change of speed of an object, or the quicker this change happens, the larger the force on the object.

> Remember, deceleration is just negative acceleration.

4) So for events like car crashes, where the speed changes a lot in a short amount of time, the forces acting on the car and its passengers are very large. These large forces can cause injuries.

5) Vehicles also experience very large decelerations if they have to make an emergency stop (p.198).

6) This can be dangerous because it may cause the brakes to overheat. This makes the brakes work less well.

7) Large decelerations may also cause the vehicle to skid.

Vehicle Safety Features are Designed to Reduce Forces

Vehicle safety features reduce the forces acting on the vehicle and passengers. They do this by increasing the time it takes for them to slow down during an emergency stop or collision (crash).

Seat belts

- In vehicles (e.g. cars), the seat belts are designed to stretch slightly when a large force is applied to them.
- This slows passengers down over a longer period of time during a crash.
- This means the forces on the passengers during the crash are smaller, so the passengers are less likely to be harmed.

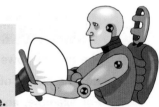

Air bags

- Air bags in cars quickly inflate (fill with air) if there's a collision.
- The passengers hit the squishy air bag instead of the solid dashboard.
- Like seat belts, this means passengers slow down over a longer period of time.

Crumple zones

- Crumple zones are areas at the front and back of a car which crumple up easily when they're hit.
- This increases the time taken for the whole car to stop, reducing the forces on the car and passengers.

Safety helmets

- Motorbike and bicycle helmets contain a layer of foam.
- In a collision, the foam is squashed, which increases the time taken for the cyclist's head to stop.
- This will reduce the force on a cyclist's head if they're in an accident.

1) We can make safety features like these thanks to our understanding of Newton's laws of motion.

2) Newton's laws have helped us to improve technology and produce new materials, which have allowed us to make all forms of travelling safer for people to use.

It's enough to put you off learning to drive, isn't it...

So there you go — why not amaze your friends with these fun safety facts next time you're popping a seat belt on? Make sure you can explain how each safety feature helps reduce the risk of passengers getting hurt.

Q1   Explain how bicycle helmets are designed to reduce the risk of a cyclist being injured in a crash. [2 marks]

Work Done and Power

It's time to talk about <u>work</u>. But not the kind you're already doing by reading this book. Oh no, this is all about our old friends <u>energy transfers</u> (have a look over at page 162 for more about these).

Work is Done When a Force Moves an Object

1) <u>Work done</u> and <u>energy transferred</u> are the <u>same thing</u>, p.162.

> When a <u>FORCE</u> makes an object <u>MOVE</u>, <u>ENERGY IS TRANSFERRED</u> and <u>WORK IS DONE</u>.

2) Whenever something begins to <u>move</u>, or <u>changes</u> how it's moving, a <u>force</u> must be acting on it (p.196).
3) If a <u>force</u> acts to <u>move</u> the object, you can say that <u>work</u> is done <u>by</u> the force <u>on</u> the object.
4) Energy is transferred <u>to</u> the object's energy stores.
5) If the force is trying to <u>stop the object moving</u> (e.g. friction), <u>work</u> is done <u>by</u> the object <u>against</u> the force.
6) In this case, energy is transferred <u>from</u> the object's energy stores.
7) The <u>formula</u> to calculate the <u>amount of work done</u> (or energy transferred) <u>by</u> a force is:

> work done (Nm or J) = force (N) × distance (m)

8) The <u>distance</u> in this equation is the <u>distance moved along the 'line of action' of a force</u>.
9) For work done <u>by</u> a force, this means the <u>distance</u> the object moves <u>in the direction of the force</u>.
10) For work done <u>against a force</u>, this means the <u>distance</u> moved in the <u>opposite direction</u> to the force.
11) <u>Work done</u> is sometimes given in newton-metres, <u>Nm</u>. Nm are the same as joules, <u>J</u>.
12) You need to be able to <u>convert</u> (change) between the two units. <u>1 Nm = 1 J</u>.

Power is the 'Rate of Energy Transfer' — i.e. How Much per Second

> <u>POWER</u> is the <u>RATE</u> at which <u>ENERGY IS TRANSFERRED</u> (or work is done) in a system.

1) The unit of power is the <u>watt</u> (<u>W</u>). <u>1 W = 1 J of energy transferred per second</u> (J/s).
2) So, the power of a <u>machine</u> is how much <u>energy is transferred</u> to it per second.
3) For example, an <u>electric drill</u> has a power of <u>700 W</u>.
4) This means it can transfer <u>700 J</u> of energy (or do 700 J of work) <u>every second</u>.
5) This is the <u>formula</u> for power:

> power (W) = energy transferred (J) ÷ time (s)

EXAMPLE: A motor transfers 4800 J of energy in 120 s. Find its power output.

<u>Substitute</u> the values into the power equation.
power = energy transferred ÷ time
= 4800 ÷ 120 = 40 W

6) If you <u>calculate</u> how much work is done to, e.g. <u>lift</u> a <u>heavy crate</u> or even just to <u>climb</u> a bunch of <u>stairs</u>, you'll see that it requires a <u>lot</u> of energy.
7) <u>Electrical appliances</u> can often transfer energy <u>much quicker</u> than people.
8) This is because they can have a much larger <u>power output</u>.
9) This makes them super useful, as it <u>reduces</u> the <u>time</u> taken to do loads of <u>everyday tasks</u>.

Energy transfers can be a lot of work...

Work done is just energy transferred. Make sure you remember how work done is related to motion and forces.

Q1 Calculate the work done when a 70 N force moves a box 0.5 m in the direction of the force. [2 marks]

Kinetic and Potential Energy Stores

This page covers two types of energy stores (p.161) and how to calculate how much energy is in them.

An Object at a Height has Energy in its Gravitational Potential Energy Store

1) When an object is at any height above the Earth's surface, it will have energy in its gravitational potential energy (g.p.e.) store.
2) When an object is raised, work is done by the lifting force against gravity.
3) This causes energy to be transferred to the object's gravitational potential energy store.
4) When an object is lowered, or falls, energy is transferred away from its gravitational potential energy store.
5) You can calculate the amount of energy in an object's g.p.e. store using the equation:

$$\text{gravitational potential energy} = \text{mass} \times \text{gravitational field strength} \times \text{height}$$
$$\text{(J)} \qquad \text{(kg)} \qquad \text{(N/kg)} \qquad \text{(m)}$$

A Moving Object has Energy in its Kinetic Energy Store

1) When an object is moving, it has energy in its kinetic energy store.
2) When a force causes an object to speed up, work is done by the force on the object.
3) This causes energy to be transferred to the object's kinetic energy store.
4) When a force causes an object to slow down, work is done by the object against the force.
5) This cause energy to be transferred away from the object's kinetic energy store.
6) You can find the energy in an object's kinetic energy store using:

$$\text{kinetic energy (J)} = 0.5 \times \text{mass (kg)} \times \text{speed}^2 \text{ (m/s)}^2$$

7) You need to be able to use this equation and the one above to calculate energy transfers between kinetic and gravitational potential energy stores.

EXAMPLE: A seagull is carrying a sandwich. It is flying at a height of 4.0 m above the ground. It drops the sandwich. The sandwich has a mass of 0.2 kg. The gravitational field strength is 10 N/kg. Calculate the energy in the kinetic energy store of the sandwich just before it reaches the ground. You can assume no air resistance acts on the sandwich.

1) Calculate the energy in gravitational potential energy (g.p.e.) store of the sandwich.

g.p.e = mass × gravitational field strength × height
= 0.2 × 10 × 4.0
= 8 J

2) As there is no air resistance, all the energy in the sandwich's g.p.e. store is transferred to its kinetic energy store.
3) So this amount equals the energy in the kinetic energy store of the sandwich.

energy in kinetic energy store = 8 J

There's potential for a joke here somewhere...

Ok people — don't forget that squared sign when you're working out the energy in an object's kinetic energy store. And remember, the energy in an object's kinetic energy store changes if its speed is changing.

Q1 A 2 kg object is raised from the ground to a height of 10 m. Calculate the amount of energy transferred to the gravitational potential energy store of the object. (Gravitational field strength = 10 N/kg.) [2 marks]

Q2 A cat running at 15 m/s has 450 J of energy in its kinetic energy store. Find the mass of the cat. [3 marks]

Describing Energy Transfers

That's right, it's time for even more on energy transfers. Lucky you, eh?

Energy is Always Conserved

1) You saw back on page 161 that for any process or event, energy is always conserved (see below).

2) You can use energy calculations to find out whether or not a process is possible (if it can happen).

3) If the energy before a process doesn't equal the energy after the process, that process can't happen.

4) If a process can happen, the formulas for work done (p.200) and the energy in certain stores (p.201) can be used to calculate what will happen. But they cannot explain why a process happens.

5) For example, if a force does work to increase an object's speed and there is no friction, the amount of energy transferred to its kinetic energy store will equal the work done on the object.

6) In most processes in the real world, some work must be done against frictional forces.

7) If there are frictional forces and work is done to increase an object's speed, the energy transferred to the object's kinetic energy store won't equal the work done on the object.

8) Some energy is dissipated by heating to the thermal energy stores of the object and its surroundings.

You Need to Know Some Examples of Energy Transfers

A BALL ROLLING UP A SLOPE:

The same energy transfers occur when a ball is thrown upwards.

- The ball does work against the gravitational force.
- So energy is transferred mechanically from the kinetic energy store of the ball to its gravitational potential energy store.
- Some work is done against frictional forces, so some energy is transferred mechanically to thermal energy stores.

A CAR SLOWING DOWN:

- When a car brakes, work is done on the wheels by friction between the brakes and the wheels.
- Energy is transferred mechanically from the kinetic energy store of the car to the thermal energy store of the brakes.
- Work is done by the car against the friction between the tyres and road.
- Energy is transferred mechanically from the kinetic energy store of the car to the thermal energy stores of the car and road.
- Energy is transferred by heating from these thermal energy stores to the thermal energy stores of the surroundings.
- Some energy is carried away by sound.

A BAT HITTING A BALL:

The same energy transfers often occur when any moving object hits an obstacle.

- The bat has energy in its kinetic energy store as it's swung.
- Work is done on the ball by the bat.
- Some energy is transferred mechanically to the ball's kinetic energy store.
- Some energy is also transferred mechanically to the thermal energy stores of the bat and the ball.
- This energy is then transferred to the surroundings by heating.
- The rest of the energy is carried away by sound.

A ROCK DROPPED FROM A CLIFF:

- Work is done by gravity on the rock as it falls towards the ground.
- Energy is transferred mechanically from the rock's gravitational potential energy store to the rock's kinetic energy store.
- Some work is done against air resistance.
- So some energy is transferred mechanically to the thermal energy stores of the rock and surroundings.

Energy transfers — a lot cheaper than football transfers...

You might be asked to explain what's happening in any of the situations above — make sure you understand them.

Q1   Describe the energy transfers that occur when a tennis racket is swung and hits a ball.   [4 marks]

Revision Questions for Chapter P4

Phew! It's the end of Chapter P4. Now it's time to see what you've got in the bag and what needs work.

- Try these questions and tick off each one when you get it right.
- When you've done all the questions for a topic and are completely happy with it, tick off the topic.

Forces (p.187-188) ☑

1) What is an interaction pair? ☑
2) What is Newton's Third Law of motion? Give an example of it in action. ☑
3) What are the differences between mass and weight? How can weight be calculated? ☑

Speed and Acceleration (p.189-194) ☑

4) True or false? Velocity is a scalar quantity. ☑
5) What is the equation for calculating the average speed of an object? ☑
6) State what is meant by acceleration. ☑
7) Describe an experiment to investigate the acceleration of a trolley down a ramp. ☑
8) How is the average speed of an object found from its distance-time graph? ☑
9) What does a flat section on a velocity-time graph represent? ☑
10) How is the distance travelled by an object found from its velocity-time graph? ☑

Newton's First and Second Laws (p.195-196) ☑

11) True or false? A free body diagram of an object only shows the forces that the act on the object. ☑
12) What is Newton's First Law of motion? ☑
13) Give the equation for Newton's Second Law of motion. ☑

Reaction Times and Stopping Distances (p.197-199) ☑

14) Describe the ruler drop test used to measure reaction times. ☑
15) What is meant by a driver's braking distance? ☑
16) State two factors which affect the reaction distance of a vehicle. ☑
17) Explain how crumple zones reduce the risk of injury in a crash. ☑

Energy Transfers (p.200-202) ☑

18) Give the equation for the work done on an object when it's moved a certain distance by a force. ☑
19) What is power? How is power calculated? ☑
20) How does the energy in an object's gravitational potential energy store change with height? ☑
21) Give the equation for the energy in the kinetic energy store of a moving object. ☑
22) Describe the energy transfers that occur when a ball is thrown upwards. ☑

The History of the Atom

Our ideas about atoms have changed a lot over time. You may have seen some of this stuff in chemistry (p.90) but you need to make sure you know all about models of the atom for your physics exam too.

Discovering the Electron Changed the Model of the Atom

1) In 1804, a man named John Dalton came up with a theory about what matter (stuff) was made of.

2) He thought that everything was made up of tiny spheres (atoms) that couldn't be broken up.

3) Dalton's theory was accepted for almost 100 years, until J. J. Thomson discovered particles called electrons. Thomson found that electrons could be removed from atoms.

4) This led scientists to think that atoms were small particles of positive matter with negative electrons spread through them like currants in a cake.

5) This model is the plum pudding model.

Rutherford Came Up with the First Nuclear Model

1) In the early 1900s, three scientists called Rutherford, Geiger and Marsden, carried out the Rutherford-Geiger-Marsden alpha particle scattering experiment.

2) In their experiment, alpha particles (p.206) were fired at a sheet of thin, gold foil.

3) Based on the plum pudding model, they expected:
   • Most of the alpha particles to go straight through the foil.
   • A small amount of them to change direction slightly.

4) But some of the results were different to what they expected.

   • Some alpha particles changed directions by large amounts.
   • So Rutherford said a gold atom must have a tiny region (area) at the centre of the atom that contains most of the atom's mass.
   • And the rest of the atom must be empty space.
   • The tiny area must be positively charged, as it repelled (pushed away) the positively charged alpha particles.

5) Rutherford called this tiny region the nucleus.

6) He came up with the first nuclear model of the atom in 1910:
   • There is a tiny, positively charged nucleus at the centre of the atom.
   • Most of the atom's mass is in the nucleus.
   • The nucleus is surrounded by a 'cloud' of negative electrons.
   • Most of the atom is empty space.

Bohr Changed Rutherford's Model

1) Electrons are negatively charged, and protons are positively charged (p.205).

2) So scientists realised that electrons in a 'cloud' around the nucleus of an atom would be attracted to the nucleus.

3) This would cause the atom to collapse (fall inwards).

4) Neils Bohr created a theory that fixed this. It said that electrons can only move around the nucleus at certain distances.

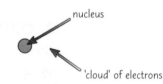

These models don't have anything on my toy trains...

That's a whole lot of history, considering this is a book about physics. It's all good, educational fun though.

Q1   Describe Dalton's theory of the atom.   [1 mark]

The Modern Model of the Atom

Now you've learnt all the bits leading up to it, it's time to learn what we <u>currently think</u> atoms are like.

Atoms are Made Up of Protons, Neutrons and Electrons

The <u>modern model</u> of the atom says that:

1) Atoms have a <u>nucleus</u> at their <u>centre</u>.

2) The <u>nucleus</u> is made up of <u>protons</u> and <u>neutrons</u>.

3) The <u>nucleus</u> contains <u>almost all of the mass</u> of the atom.

4) Electrons <u>surround</u> the nucleus at <u>different distances</u>.

5) The <u>radius</u> (the distance from the centre to the edge) of the <u>nucleus</u> is <u>much smaller</u> than the <u>radius</u> of the whole <u>atom</u>.

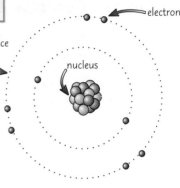
electron
fixed distance
nucleus

Protons and Electrons Have Equal but Opposite Charges

1) <u>Protons</u> are <u>positively charged</u>.

2) <u>Electrons</u> are <u>negatively charged</u>.

3) <u>Neutrons</u> are <u>neutral</u> (have <u>no charge</u>).

4) The <u>nucleus</u> is <u>positively charged</u>, because it is made of <u>protons</u> and <u>neutrons</u>.

5) <u>Atoms</u> are <u>neutrally charged</u>, because the <u>number of protons in an atom = the number of electrons in the atom</u>.

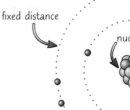
'Relative' just means compared to each other.

	Relative charge	Relative mass
Proton	+1	1
Neutron	0	1
Electron	-1	0

You Need to Know the Typical Sizes of Atoms and Small Molecules

1) Atoms are <u>small</u>. In fact, they're so small, we often use <u>standard form</u> (p.126) to talk about their size.

2) The <u>diameter</u> (the width) of an atom is about 1×10^{-10} m.

3) The <u>nucleus</u> is about <u>100 000 times smaller</u> than the <u>diameter</u> of the <u>atom</u>.

4) Atoms can <u>join together</u> to make <u>molecules</u>.

5) <u>Small molecules</u> are about the same size as atoms — they have a <u>diameter</u> of about 1×10^{-10} m.

Creating the Modern Model Took a lot of Imagination

1) The model of the atom has <u>changed a lot</u> over time (see p.203).

2) <u>Each time</u> an experiment was done that gave <u>unexpected results</u>, scientists had to use <u>reasoning</u> (thinking in clear <u>steps</u>) to come up with a <u>sensible explanation</u> for it.

3) This sometimes caused models to be <u>modified</u> (changed) or <u>added to</u>.

4) But sometimes it led to the <u>old</u> model being <u>rejected</u> completely for a <u>new one</u>.

5) For example, when the <u>plum pudding</u> model was <u>replaced</u> by Rutherford's <u>nuclear model</u>.

6) Rutherford's model is <u>very different</u> to all of the ones before it.

7) So he had to use his <u>imagination</u> to find an <u>explanation</u> that could explain <u>all</u> of the <u>evidence</u> he had.

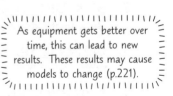
As equipment gets better over time, this can lead to new results. These results may cause models to change (p.221).

So atoms are teeny tiny, who knew...

Atoms make up everything, so they're pretty darn important. Make sure you learn all the facts about them — there's a nucleus in the middle, surrounded by electrons. A nucleus is made from protons and neutrons. All that fun stuff...

Q1   State and explain the charge of a nucleus.   [2 marks]

Isotopes and Radioactive Decay

There's a whole bunch of stuff to <u>learn</u> on this page. So read it <u>carefully</u> until it's all stuck in your head.

You can Describe Atoms Using their Charge and Mass

1) The <u>number of protons</u> in an atom is called its <u>atomic number</u> or <u>proton number</u>.
2) This tells you the <u>charge of the nucleus</u> (the <u>nuclear charge</u>).
3) The <u>mass number</u> of an atom is <u>the number of protons + the number of neutrons</u> in the atom.
4) This tells you the <u>mass of the nucleus</u> (the <u>nuclear mass</u>).
5) You can <u>describe</u> the <u>nucleus</u> of an atom like this:

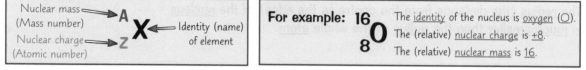

Nuclear mass (Mass number) → A

Nuclear charge → Z (Atomic number)

$^{A}_{Z}X$ ← Identity (name) of element

For example: $^{16}_{8}O$ — The <u>identity</u> of the nucleus is <u>oxygen</u> (<u>O</u>). The (relative) <u>nuclear charge</u> is <u>+8</u>. The (relative) <u>nuclear mass</u> is <u>16</u>.

6) The <u>nuclear charge</u> of an atom tells you <u>what element</u> it is.
7) Each <u>element</u> has a <u>characteristic positive charge</u> — a <u>particular</u> charge that is <u>different</u> for every element.

Isotopes are Different Forms of the Same Element

1) <u>Isotopes of an element</u> are <u>atoms</u> that have the <u>same number</u> of <u>protons</u>, but a <u>different</u> number of <u>neutrons</u>. So they have the <u>same nuclear charge</u>, but <u>different nuclear masses</u>.
2) For example, $^{12}_{6}C$, $^{13}_{6}C$ and $^{14}_{6}C$ are all <u>isotopes of carbon</u>.
3) <u>Some</u> isotopes are <u>unstable</u>.
4) <u>Unstable</u> nuclei <u>emit</u> (give out) <u>ionising radiation</u> (see below) which makes them <u>more stable</u>.
5) This is called <u>radioactive decay</u>.
6) A substance that <u>always</u> gives out <u>ionising radiation</u> is called <u>radioactive</u>.
7) A radioactive substance <u>contains atoms</u> of an <u>unstable isotope</u>.

Nuclei means more than one nucleus.

Unstable isotopes are sometimes called radioisotopes.

You Need to Know The Properties of Ionising Radiation

1) <u>Ionising radiation</u> is radiation that can <u>ionise</u> atoms (p.157). The types you need to know are:

1) <u>ALPHA PARTICLES</u>. An <u>alpha</u> particle (α) is <u>two neutrons</u> and <u>two protons</u> (the same as a <u>helium nucleus</u>). Alpha particles have a <u>relative mass of 4</u> and a <u>relative charge of +2</u>.

2) <u>BETA PARTICLES</u>. A <u>beta</u> particle (β) is identical to (the same as) an <u>electron</u>. Beta particles have <u>a relative mass of 0</u> and a <u>relative charge of –1</u>.

3) <u>GAMMA RAYS</u>. A <u>gamma ray</u> (γ) is a type of <u>electromagnetic radiation</u> (p.156), with a <u>very high frequency</u>. Gamma rays have <u>no mass</u> and <u>no charge</u>.

4) <u>NEUTRONS</u>. Neutrons have a <u>relative mass of 1</u> and a <u>relative charge of 0</u>.

2) How much radiation can <u>penetrate</u> a material is how <u>far</u> it can <u>travel through</u> the material before it's <u>absorbed</u> (<u>stopped</u>).
3) <u>Alpha particles</u> can't penetrate very far. They are stopped by a <u>thin sheet of paper</u>, <u>aluminium</u> or <u>lead</u>.
4) <u>Beta particles</u> can penetrate a <u>bit further</u>. They're stopped by a <u>thin sheet of aluminium</u> or <u>lead</u>.
5) <u>Gamma rays</u> penetrate the <u>furthest</u>. They're stopped by <u>thick sheets of lead</u>.

Ionising radiation — good for getting creases out of your clothes...

Learn what it takes to stop each kind of radiation — it might bag you some easy marks in the exam.

Q1 Which of the following are isotopes of the same element: $^{23}_{11}X$, $^{11}_{23}X$, $^{24}_{11}X$, $^{23}_{12}X$? [1 mark]

Nuclear Equations

Nuclear equations are all about making things balance, so stand on one leg and get practising.

Mass and Atomic Numbers Have to Balance in Nuclear Equations

1) Nuclear equations are a way of showing radioactive decay (p.206).

2) They're normally written like this:

   > nucleus before decay → nucleus after decay + radiation emitted

3) There is one golden rule to remember:

   > The total mass and atomic numbers must be equal on both sides of the arrow.

4) You need to be able to write balanced equations for any common radioactive decay.

5) These show the emissions of (giving out) alpha particles, beta particles, gamma rays or neutrons.

Watch out for a number before the type of radiation emitted. This shows how many of that type of radiation have been emitted.

Emitting an Alpha Particle

The nucleus emits 2 protons and 2 neutrons (an alpha particle), and:

- The mass of the nucleus (mass number) decreases by 4.
- The charge of the nucleus (atomic number) decreases by 2.

You write an alpha particle as $_2^4He$ as it's the same as a helium nucleus.

Radium decaying to radon:	$_{88}^{226}Ra \rightarrow _{86}^{222}Rn + _2^4He$		
mass number:	226 →	222 + 4	(= 226)
atomic number:	88 →	86 + 2	(= 88)

You can also write an alpha particle as $_2^4\alpha$.

Emitting a Beta Particle

In the nucleus, a neutron turns into a proton. The nucleus then emits an electron (a beta particle). When this happens:

- The mass of the nucleus doesn't change.
- The nuclear charge increases by 1.

You write a beta particle as $_{-1}^0e$ as it's the same as an electron.

Carbon decaying to nitrogen:	$_6^{14}C \rightarrow _7^{14}N + _{-1}^0e$		
mass number:	14 → 14 + 0	(= 14)	
atomic number:	6 → 7 + (–1)	(= 6)	

You may also see beta particles as $_{-1}^0\beta$.

Emitting a Gamma Ray

A gamma ray is emitted from a nucleus.

- The nuclear mass doesn't change.
- The nuclear charge doesn't change.

Iodine decaying to a more stable nucleus of iodine:	$_{53}^{130}I \rightarrow _{53}^{130}I + _0^0\gamma$		
mass number:	130 → 130 + 0	(= 130)	
atomic number:	53 → 53 + 0	(= 53)	

Emitting a Neutron

A neutron is given out by a nucleus.

- The nuclear mass decreases by 1.
- The nuclear charge doesn't change.

Helium decaying to a different isotope of helium:	$_2^5He \rightarrow _2^4He + _0^1n$		
mass number:	5 → 4 + 1	(= 5)	
atomic number:	2 → 2 + 0	(= 2)	

I think balancing equations is more fun than anything ever...

Right? Right?? *cough* I can't see your face, but I'm going to take a wild guess and say you don't believe me.

Q1 State the type of radiation given off in this decay: $_3^8Li \rightarrow _4^8Be +$ radiation. [1 mark]

Activity and Half-life

Isotopes <u>decay</u>, you just can't say exactly <u>when</u> they will. Which is why <u>half-lives</u> are really important...

The Activity of a Source is the Number of Decays per Second

1) The <u>activity</u> of a <u>radioactive source</u> is the <u>rate</u> at which it decays.
2) This means how many <u>unstable nuclei</u> decay <u>every second</u>.
3) Activity is measured in <u>becquerels</u>, <u>Bq</u>. 1 Bq is <u>1 decay per second</u>.

Radioactivity is a Totally Random Process

1) As radioactive decay is <u>random</u>, you <u>can't tell</u> exactly <u>which</u> unstable nucleus in a source will decay <u>next</u>.
2) You also <u>can't</u> say <u>when</u> any one of them will decay.
3) But for a <u>given radioactive isotope</u>, the <u>nuclei</u> all have a <u>fixed chance</u> of decaying. This chance is <u>different</u> for <u>different isotopes</u>.
4) So over a long enough period of <u>time</u>, some nuclei <u>will</u> decay.
5) This means that <u>over time</u>, the number of <u>undecayed</u> nuclei <u>decreases</u>.
6) There are <u>fewer nuclei left</u> to <u>decay</u>, so <u>less</u> nuclei decay <u>each second</u>.
7) So <u>over time</u>, the <u>activity</u> of a source <u>always decreases</u>.
8) To work out <u>how quickly</u> the activity decreases, you can use the <u>half-life of an isotope</u>:

> Half-life is also the average time taken for the number of radioactive nuclei of an isotope to halve.

> The <u>half-life</u> of an isotope is the <u>average time taken</u> for its <u>activity</u> to <u>halve</u>.

EXAMPLE: The half-life of a radioactive isotope is 30 minutes. Calculate how long it will take for the activity of the isotope to fall to one quarter of its starting value, A.

1) Keep <u>dividing the activity by 2</u>, until it reaches a <u>quarter</u> of its <u>starting value</u>.

At the start: after 1 half-life: after 2 half-lives:

$$A \quad (\div 2) \rightarrow \quad \frac{A}{2} \quad (\div 2) \rightarrow \quad \frac{A}{4}$$

So it takes 2 half-lives to get to a quarter of A.

2) <u>Count</u> how many <u>half-lives</u> this takes.

3) Multiply the <u>number of half-lives</u> by <u>how long</u> a half-life is to get the time.

2×30 minutes = 60 minutes
So time taken = 60 minutes (or 1 hour)

9) You can also <u>find the half-life</u> of an isotope using a <u>graph</u> of its <u>activity against time</u>:

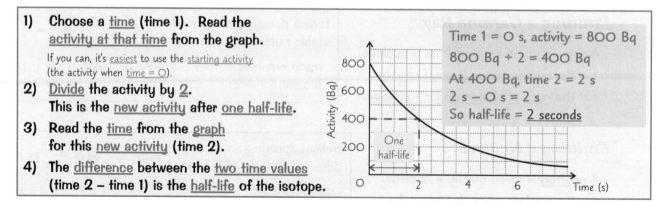

1) Choose a <u>time</u> (time 1). Read the <u>activity at that time</u> from the graph.
   If you can, it's <u>easiest</u> to use the <u>starting activity</u> (the activity when <u>time = 0</u>).
2) <u>Divide</u> the activity by <u>2</u>. This is the <u>new activity</u> after <u>one half-life</u>.
3) Read the <u>time</u> from the <u>graph</u> for this <u>new activity</u> (time 2).
4) The <u>difference</u> between the <u>two time values</u> (time 2 – time 1) is the <u>half-life</u> of the isotope.

Time 1 = 0 s, activity = 800 Bq
800 Bq ÷ 2 = 400 Bq
At 400 Bq, time 2 = 2 s
2 s – 0 s = 2 s
So half-life = <u>2 seconds</u>

The half-life of a box of chocolates is about five minutes...

Half-life questions aren't so bad once you get used to them. Have a practice with this question before moving on.

Q1   A radioactive isotope has a half-life of 2 years. The activity of a sample of this isotope is 100 Bq. Calculate the activity of the sample after 4 years.   [2 marks]

Dangers of Radioactivity

Time to find out about the <u>dangers</u> of <u>ionising radiation</u> and learn why being <u>safe</u> in a science lab is so important.

Ionising Radiation Can Damage Living Cells

1) <u>Ionising radiation</u> can have <u>hazardous</u> (<u>dangerous</u>) effects on the human body.

2) It can enter <u>living cells</u> and <u>damage</u> them.

3) The <u>amount of radiation</u> that a person <u>absorbs</u> is called the <u>radiation dose</u>.

4) <u>Lower doses</u> of ionising radiation <u>damage</u> cells.

5) This can make them <u>cancerous</u> (they can <u>cause cancer</u>).

6) <u>Higher doses</u> can <u>kill cells completely</u>.

7) If your body is <u>exposed to</u> radiation, that means radiation is <u>hitting</u> or <u>entering</u> your body.

8) The <u>more</u> radiation you're <u>exposed to</u>, the higher the <u>risk</u> (chance) that your cells will be <u>damaged</u>.

9) Radioactive sources must be <u>handled carefully</u> to try and <u>reduce the risk</u> of damage to your body.

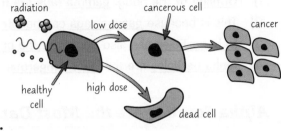

radiation   cancerous cell   cancer   low dose   healthy cell   high dose   dead cell

Exposure to Radiation from Outside of Your Body is called Irradiation

1) If <u>radiation</u> reaches your body from a radioactive source that is <u>away from your body</u>, you are being <u>irradiated</u>.

2) The <u>further</u> you are from a radioactive source, the <u>less radiation</u> will <u>reach</u> you.

3) To help <u>stop irradiation</u> when handling sources, you should:

- Stand behind <u>barriers</u> that will absorb radiation.
- Keep the source as <u>far away</u> from you as possible, e.g. hold it at arm's length.
- <u>Store</u> radioactive sources in <u>lead-lined boxes</u> when they're not being used.

Contamination is Radioactive Particles Getting On or Into Your Body

1) If <u>radioactive atoms</u> get <u>on</u> or <u>inside</u> your body, your body is <u>contaminated</u>.

2) These <u>contaminating atoms</u> might then decay and release <u>radiation</u> which could <u>harm</u> you.

3) To help <u>stop contamination</u> when handling sources, you should <u>wear gloves</u> and <u>use tongs</u> to hold them.

Contamination By a Source is More Dangerous than Irradiation

1) <u>Irradiation is temporary</u> — if the radioactive source is <u>taken away</u>, any irradiation it's causing <u>stops</u>.

2) You are <u>no longer</u> being <u>exposed</u> to ionising radiation.

3) <u>Contamination lasts longer</u> — if the source is <u>removed</u>, the contaminating atoms are <u>left behind</u>.

4) For example, if atoms <u>from a source</u> get on your hand and you accidentally <u>eat them</u>, <u>you are contaminated</u>. When the source is <u>removed</u>, those atoms are <u>still inside you</u>.

5) These atoms <u>will decay</u>, so you will <u>still be exposed</u> to ionising radiation.

6) This happens until the atoms <u>leave your body</u>.

7) So <u>contamination</u> by a <u>source</u> has a <u>higher risk</u> of damage than <u>irradiation</u> by the <u>same source</u>.

Unfortunately, you won't get superpowers if you're irradiated...

Being exposed to radiation doesn't mean you <u>will</u> get hurt. It just increases the chance of it. Remember that.

Q1   Explain what is meant by the term 'irradiation' when talking about radiation and the human body.   [1 mark]

More on the Dangers of Radioactivity

And we're not done yet. Time to learn even more about the <u>hazards</u> of <u>radioactive materials</u>.

Irradiation by a Gamma Source is the Most Dangerous

1) <u>Outside</u> of the body, <u>gamma</u> rays are the <u>most dangerous</u> type of <u>ionising radiation</u> (p.206).
2) This is because <u>gamma rays</u> can <u>penetrate far into</u> the body and get to <u>organs</u>.
3) <u>Beta particles</u> can also <u>penetrate the body</u> (but not as far).
4) <u>Alpha particles</u> are the <u>least dangerous</u> outside the body because they <u>can't pass through skin</u>.

Alpha Sources are the Most Dangerous to be Contaminated By

1) <u>Inside the body</u>, <u>alpha</u> particles are the <u>most</u> dangerous type of ionising radiation.
2) This be because they don't travel <u>far</u> before they are <u>absorbed</u>.
3) So cells near to the source <u>absorb a lot of radiation</u>, increasing their <u>risk of damage</u>.
4) <u>Beta</u> particles are <u>less damaging</u> inside the body, as they can <u>travel further</u> before they are <u>absorbed</u>.
5) This <u>reduces</u> the amount of radiation each cell is <u>exposed to</u>, so reduces the <u>risk of damage</u>.
6) <u>Gamma</u> rays are the <u>least dangerous</u> inside the body, as they mostly <u>pass straight out</u> without being absorbed.
7) They can still <u>do some damage</u> though.

The Hazards of a Radioactive Source Also Depend on its Half-Life

1) The <u>lower</u> the <u>activity</u> of a <u>radioactive source</u>, the <u>safer</u> it is to be around.
2) You can use the <u>half-life</u> (p.208) of a radioactive source to <u>work out</u> the <u>time it takes</u> for the source to become <u>relatively</u> (fairly) <u>safe</u>.

> **EXAMPLE:** A radioactive source has an activity of 3200 Bq. It is considered relatively safe when it has an activity of 400 Bq. The source has a half-life of 8 days. Calculate how long it will take for the source to become relatively safe.
>
> 1) Keep <u>dividing the starting activity by 2</u>, until it reaches 400 Bq.
>
> One half-life: 3200 Bq ÷ 2 = 1600 Bq
> Two half-lives: 1600 Bq ÷ 2 = 800 Bq
> Three half-lives: 800 Bq ÷ 2 = 400 Bq
>
> 2) Multiply the <u>number of half-lives</u> by <u>how long</u> one half-life is.   3 × 8 days = **24 days**

3) The <u>shorter</u> the <u>half-life</u> of a source, the <u>quicker</u> its <u>activity</u> will fall. And so the quicker it will be <u>safe</u> to be around.
4) You can use <u>half-lives</u> to <u>compare</u> the <u>safety</u> of sources that <u>emit the same type of radiation</u>. For example:

- Two sources both have the <u>same starting activity</u>.
- The source with the <u>longer</u> half-life will <u>always</u> be a <u>larger hazard</u> (it'll always be <u>more dangerous</u>).
- This is because after <u>any amount</u> of time, the activity of the source with the <u>shorter half-life</u> will be <u>lower</u> than the activity of the source with a <u>longer half-life</u>.

Top tip number 364 — if something is radioactive, don't lick it...

You need to be able to explain how the risk of danger from a source depends on both the type of radiation it releases and its half-life. Test yourself by trying out this question, then have a nice cuppa and a biscuit.

Q1   Explain why a gamma source is more dangerous to be irradiated by than an alpha source.   [2 marks]

Uses of Radiation

Ionising radiation isn't all doom and gloom — it has a few important <u>uses</u> in <u>medicine</u> that you need to learn.

Tracers in Medicine are Short Half-life Gamma Sources

1) <u>Tracers</u> are a way of using <u>ionising radiation</u> to see inside a patient's body.
2) They can be used to see <u>how well</u> a patient's <u>organs</u> are working.
3) Tracers are <u>injected into</u> or <u>eaten by</u> a patient.
4) The tracer <u>travels</u> through the body and <u>gives out radiation</u>.
5) Its path is followed on the outside of the body using a <u>radiation detector</u>.

Tracer inside body giving off radiation

Gamma rays

Radiation detector

- <u>Tracers</u> contain <u>gamma</u> sources (radioactive sources that emit <u>gamma rays</u>).
- This is because gamma rays can <u>pass out the body</u>, where they are <u>detected</u>.
- <u>Alpha</u> and <u>beta sources</u> aren't used as they <u>can't pass out</u> of the body, and they <u>cause more damage</u> than gamma sources (see the previous page).

6) <u>Tracers</u> need to get to the <u>correct part</u> of the body and still <u>give off</u> enough radiation to be <u>detected</u>.
7) They also need to <u>drop</u> to a <u>safe level</u> quite quickly, to reduce the radiation <u>dose</u> (p.209) to the patient.
8) So the <u>gamma source</u> in the tracer needs a fairly <u>short half-life</u> — e.g. <u>a few hours</u>.

Cancer Can be Treated Using Nuclear Radiation

1) Since high doses of radiation will <u>kill living cells</u> (p.209), radiation can be used to <u>kill cancerous cells</u>.
2) Radiation can be used to <u>remove</u> unwanted tissues (e.g. cancer) <u>completely</u> or to <u>control</u> them and <u>stop them spreading further</u>.
3) However, <u>damage</u> is often done to <u>normal cells</u> too, which makes the patient feel <u>very ill</u>.
4) So before ionising radiation is used to treat any disease, both the <u>patient</u> and <u>doctor</u> need to decide if the <u>benefits are worth the risks</u>.

<u>Gamma radiation treats cancer from outside the body</u>

1) A beam of <u>gamma rays</u> is <u>focused</u> on the tumour.
2) The gamma rays <u>pass through</u> the patient's body and <u>damage</u> the cells in the <u>tumour</u>.
3) This <u>also damages</u> some <u>healthy cells</u> nearby.

Source outside the body.

Gamma rays focused on tumour.

<u>Beta radation treats cancer from inside the body</u>

1) <u>Small containers</u> with <u>beta sources</u> inside are placed <u>next to</u> or <u>inside</u> the <u>tumour</u>.
2) The beta particles <u>damage the cells</u> in the <u>tumour</u>.
3) But they <u>can't travel too far</u> before they're absorbed, so <u>damage</u> to <u>healthy tissue</u> is <u>limited</u>.
4) If the half-life is <u>short</u> enough, the containers can be <u>left in</u>, as they will soon become <u>safe</u>.
5) Otherwise, the containers should be <u>removed</u> to <u>limit the damage</u> to healthy cells.

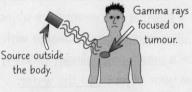

healthy cells

implant emitting radiation

tumour

<u>Alpha radiation treats cancer from inside the body</u>

1) An alpha source can be injected <u>straight into a tumour</u> to try and kill it.
2) This works because alpha particles do <u>lots</u> of <u>damage</u> to nearby cells (p.210).
3) The <u>half-life</u> of the source must be <u>short</u>, in case it <u>travels</u> to a <u>healthy</u> part of the body.

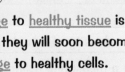

Once it's injected, the alpha source can't be removed.

So radiation is pretty handy in medicine...

Make sure you can describe the different ways of using radiation in medicine. Have a practice with this question.

Q1   Explain why gamma sources are used as medical tracers.   [2 marks]

Density

Time for some <u>maths</u> I'm afraid. But at least it comes with a fun experiment, so it's not all bad...

Density Measures How Close Together Particles Are

1) <u>Density</u> is <u>defined</u> as:

$$\text{density (kg/m}^3\text{)} = \text{mass (kg)} \div \text{volume (m}^3\text{)}$$

You'll get density in g/cm³ if you use the formula with a mass in g and a volume in cm³.

2) <u>Mass</u> is the <u>amount of matter</u> in an object, p.188.
3) An object's <u>volume</u> is the amount of <u>space</u> it takes up.
4) So <u>density</u> measures how <u>close together</u> the <u>particles</u> in an object are (p.213).

EXAMPLE: A 0.4 kg plank of wood has a volume of 0.8 m³. Calculate its density.

density = mass ÷ volume = 0.4 ÷ 0.8 = 0.5 kg/m³

You Need to be Able to Measure Density in Different Ways

PRACTICAL

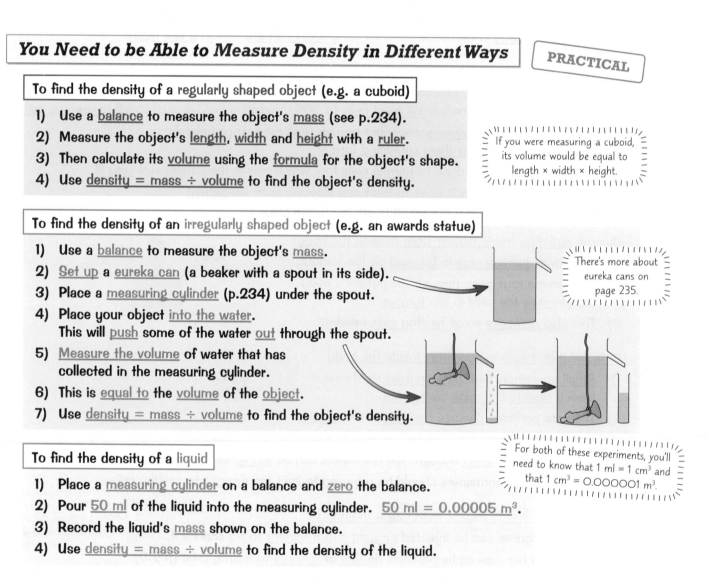

To find the density of a regularly shaped object (e.g. a cuboid)

1) Use a <u>balance</u> to measure the object's <u>mass</u> (see p.234).
2) Measure the object's <u>length</u>, <u>width</u> and <u>height</u> with a <u>ruler</u>.
3) Then calculate its <u>volume</u> using the <u>formula</u> for the object's shape.
4) Use <u>density = mass ÷ volume</u> to find the object's density.

If you were measuring a cuboid, its volume would be equal to length × width × height.

To find the density of an irregularly shaped object (e.g. an awards statue)

1) Use a <u>balance</u> to measure the object's <u>mass</u>.
2) <u>Set up</u> a <u>eureka can</u> (a beaker with a spout in its side).
3) Place a <u>measuring cylinder</u> (p.234) under the spout.
4) Place your object <u>into the water</u>.
   This will <u>push</u> some of the water <u>out</u> through the spout.
5) <u>Measure the volume</u> of water that has
   collected in the measuring cylinder.
6) This is <u>equal to</u> the <u>volume</u> of the <u>object</u>.
7) Use <u>density = mass ÷ volume</u> to find the object's density.

There's more about eureka cans on page 235.

To find the density of a liquid

1) Place a <u>measuring cylinder</u> on a balance and <u>zero</u> the balance.
2) Pour <u>50 ml</u> of the liquid into the measuring cylinder. <u>50 ml = 0.00005 m³</u>.
3) Record the liquid's <u>mass</u> shown on the balance.
4) Use <u>density = mass ÷ volume</u> to find the density of the liquid.

For both of these experiments, you'll need to know that 1 ml = 1 cm³ and that 1 cm³ = 0.000001 m³.

Learn this page. It is your density... I mean destiny...

Remember — density is all about how close together the particles in a substance are. Not too tricky in the end.

Q1　　Describe an experiment to find the density of an irregularly shaped solid object.　　　　[4 marks]

The Particle Model

There's lots to learn with the underlined particle model, but don't panic, take your time and read this page carefully...

The Particle Model is a Way of Describing Matter

> *Particles are the atoms or molecules that make up an object, p.205.*

1) The particle model of matter says:

- All matter is made up of tiny particles and there's nothing in between these particles.
- The particles of a certain substance are always the same, no matter the state of the substance.
- The particles of a substance have a particular mass. The mass is different for different substances.
- There are attractive forces between the particles. The size of the forces depends on the substance.

2) The particle model also describes how particles are arranged (laid out) and how they behave.

3) So it can be used to explain the differences between states of matter (solid, liquid and gas):

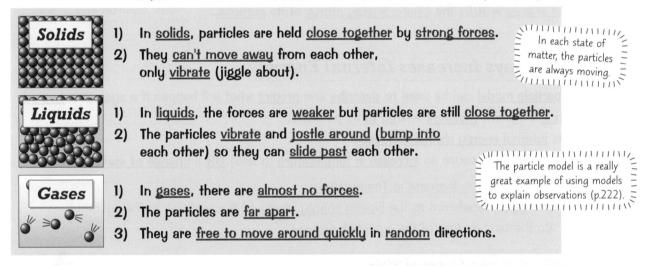

Solids
1) In solids, particles are held close together by strong forces.
2) They can't move away from each other, only vibrate (jiggle about).

> *In each state of matter, the particles are always moving.*

Liquids
1) In liquids, the forces are weaker but particles are still close together.
2) The particles vibrate and jostle around (bump into each other) so they can slide past each other.

> *The particle model is a really great example of using models to explain observations (p.222).*

Gases
1) In gases, there are almost no forces.
2) The particles are far apart.
3) They are free to move around quickly in random directions.

Mass Stays the Same but Density Changes in a Change of State

1) You need to know the names of the changes of state. These are:

1) Melting	2) Boiling/evaporating	3) Sublimating	4) Freezing	5) Condensing
(solid to liquid)	(liquid to gas)	(solid to gas)	(liquid to solid)	(gas to liquid)

2) A change of state is a physical change. This is different to a chemical change.

3) If you reverse a change of state, the substance gets back its original (starting) properties.

4) When a substance changes state:

- The particles of the substance don't change. They're just arranged in a different way.
- The number of particles stays the same, so the mass is conserved (the mass doesn't change).
- But the volume changes as the particles move closer together or further apart.
- As density = mass ÷ volume (p.212), and mass is constant, then density must change too.

1) Generally, solids are denser than liquids. And liquids are denser than gases.
2) Usually, the difference in density is very small between a solid and a liquid.
3) But the difference is very large between a liquid and a gas.
4) This is why a small volume of liquid produces a large volume of vapour (gas).

Particles can't be trusted — they make up everything...

The particle model explains a lot of what's coming up, so make sure you know it inside out.

Q1   Name three changes of state. For each, give the state before and after the change.   [3 marks]

More on the Particle Model

States of matter are <u>so</u> last page. Now it's time to use the <u>particle model</u> for <u>heating</u> and <u>gas pressure</u>...

Particles Store Energy in Kinetic and Potential Energy Stores

1) <u>Particles</u> have energy in:
   - Their <u>kinetic energy stores</u>, which is linked to how <u>fast</u> the particles are <u>moving</u>, p.201.
   - Their <u>potential energy stores</u>, which is linked to how <u>close together</u> the particles are.

2) You can <u>describe</u> the <u>energy</u> of a <u>system</u> in terms of the <u>energy stores</u> of its <u>particles</u>.

A system's <u>INTERNAL ENERGY</u> is the <u>total energy</u> in the <u>kinetic AND potential</u> energy stores of its <u>particles</u>.

The energy in a system's <u>THERMAL ENERGY STORE</u> is the <u>total energy</u> in <u>JUST</u> the <u>kinetic energy stores</u> of its <u>particles</u>.

So the hotter something is, the faster its particles move or vibrate.

Heating Always Increases Internal Energy

1) The <u>particle model</u> can be used to <u>describe</u> and <u>predict</u> what will happen if a system is <u>heated</u>.
2) <u>Heating</u> a system <u>transfers</u> energy <u>to</u> its particles.
3) So its <u>internal energy always increases</u>.
4) Heating will either cause an <u>increase in temperature</u> (p.215) <u>OR</u> a <u>change of state</u> (p.216).

<u>Heating Causing an Increase in Temperature:</u>
   - Energy is transferred to the <u>kinetic energy stores</u> of the particles in the system.
   - So the temperature of the system <u>increases</u>.

<u>Heating Causing a Change of State:</u>
   - Energy is transferred to the <u>potential energy stores</u> of the particles.
   - This is because the particles have moved <u>away from each other</u>.
   - Energy is <u>not</u> transferred to the <u>kinetic energy stores</u> of the particles (so the <u>temperature</u> of the system <u>doesn't change</u>).

5) <u>Cooling</u> a system <u>removes energy</u> from it. Energy is transferred <u>from</u> its particles.
6) This causes a <u>decrease in temperature</u> or a <u>change of state</u>.

The Particle Model Explains Gas Pressure

1) Particles in a gas are <u>free to move around</u> (p.213).
2) They <u>collide with</u> (bump into) each other and the sides of the <u>container</u> they're in.
3) When they hit something, they <u>apply a force</u> to it.
4) <u>Pressure</u> is <u>force over a given area</u>. So the gas particles create <u>pressure</u>.
5) <u>Increasing the temperature</u> of a gas <u>increases its pressure</u> — the <u>hotter</u> a gas is, the <u>faster</u> its particles <u>move</u>.
6) <u>Faster particles</u> cause <u>more collisions</u> in a <u>given time</u>, which causes a <u>larger force</u> on the container.
7) This <u>only</u> works if the <u>space</u> the gas takes up (the <u>volume</u>) <u>doesn't change</u>.

Gas particles need to watch where they're going...

As with many things in physics, it took lots of experiments and some maths to link a system's temperature to the kinetic energy stores of its particles. Good job they managed to, else you wouldn't get the fun of learning about it...

Q1 Explain why decreasing the temperature of a gas in a fixed container decreases its pressure. [3 marks]

Chapter P6 — Matter — Models and Explanations

Specific Heat Capacity

Specific heat capacity is really just a sciencey way of saying how hard it is to heat something up...

Specific Heat Capacity Links Temperature and Energy

1) Transferring energy to or from an object changes its internal energy (p.214).
2) This can change its temperature.
3) You can use this equation to find the energy transferred when an object heats up or cools down:

You can only use this if there's no change of state.

$$\text{Change in Internal Energy (J)} = \text{Mass (kg)} \times \text{Specific Heat Capacity (J/kg°C)} \times \text{Change in Temperature (°C)}$$

Specific heat capacity (SHC) is the energy stored by 1 kg of a material for a 1 °C temperature rise.

4) Different materials have different specific heat capacities.
5) So different materials store different amounts of energy per unit mass (kg) for a given temperature rise.
6) Materials with a high specific heat capacity store lots of energy.
7) It takes lots of energy to heat them up, and they release lots of energy when they cool down.

I have a high capacity for holiday-specific heat.

You can Find the Specific Heat Capacity of a Substance   PRACTICAL

You can use the following experiment to find the specific heat capacity of a liquid or a solid:

1) Use a balance to measure the mass of your substance.
2) Set up the experiment shown below.

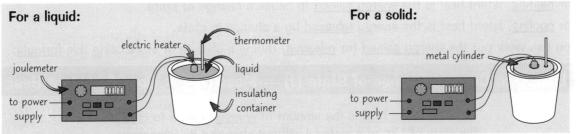

For a liquid:
electric heater, thermometer, joulemeter, liquid, to power supply, insulating container

For a solid:
metal cylinder, to power supply

3) Before starting the experiment make sure the joulemeter reads zero.
4) Measure the temperature of the substance, then turn on the power.
5) When the temperature has changed by a set amount (e.g. 10 °C), stop the experiment.
6) Record the amount of energy shown on the joulemeter. This is equal to the change in the internal energy of the substance.

A joulemeter measures the amount of energy used to heat the substance.

7) Rearrange the equation above to calculate the specific heat capacity of the substance:
specific heat capacity = energy on joulemeter ÷ (mass of substance × change in temperature).

Make sure that the apparatus is used safely in this experiment. For example:
• Let the equipment cool before touching it, to avoid burning yourself.
• And if you do have to move it before it's cool, wear insulated gloves.
• Put a lid on the container to stop the liquid spilling out of the container onto electronics.

I've eaten five sausages — I have a high specific meat capacity...

You can be tested on any part of it, so learn that experiment inside out. Ohh, and don't forget your oven gloves...

Q1   A 0.20 kg block of metal is heated. The metal has a specific heat capacity of 420 J/kg°C.
1680 J of energy is transferred to the block. Calculate the temperature change of the block.   [3 marks]

Specific Latent Heat

Specific latent heat sounds like specific heat capacity but it's very different. It's all to do with changing state.

Temperature is Constant During a Change of State

1) If you heat a solid enough, it will reach its melting point (the temperature at which the solid will melt).

2) Keep heating the solid and it will change state.

3) A liquid that's at its boiling point will begin to boil if it's heated.

4) Remember, when a substance changes state, energy is being transferred but the temperature of the substance stays the same (p.214).

If you keep cooling a gas it will condense, and if you keep cooling a liquid it will freeze.

5) You can see changes of state as flat spots on graphs of temperature against time:

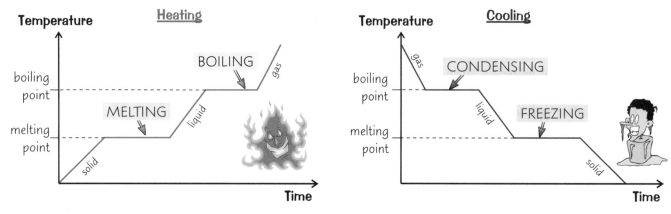

Latent Heat is the Energy Needed to Change State

1) The energy transferred during a change of state is called latent heat.

2) For heating, latent heat is the energy gained to cause a change of state.

3) For cooling, latent heat is the energy released by a change in state.

4) You can work out the energy gained (or released) during a change of state using this formula:

> **Energy to Cause a Change of State (J) = Mass (kg) × Specific Latent Heat (J/kg)**

Specific latent heat is the amount of energy needed to change the state of 1 kg of a material without changing its temperature.

Different substances have different specific latent heats.

5) Specific latent heat has different names for different changes of state:
   - For changing between a solid and a liquid it is called the specific latent heat of fusion.
   - For changing between a liquid and a gas it is called the specific latent heat of vaporisation.

EXAMPLE: The specific latent heat of vaporisation for water is 2 260 000 J/kg. How much energy is needed to completely boil 1.50 kg of water once it has reached its boiling point?

1) The mass and specific latent heat are in the right units, so just put them into the formula.

2) The units for the answer are joules because it's energy.

energy to cause a change of state
= mass × specific latent heat
= 1.50 × 2 260 000 = 3 390 000 J

6) Make sure you know the difference between specific latent heat and specific heat capacity (p.215). Specific heat capacity is to do with changes in temperature, not changes of state.

My specific latent heat of revision* is 500 J/kg...

Don't panic, the end is in sight. Only one more page about heating, then onto something new. Phew.

Q1   The specific latent heat of fusion for ice is 330 000 J/kg.
     How much energy is needed to melt 0.20 kg of ice if it is already at its melting point?   [2 marks]

Heating and Doing Work

Energy can be transferred in lots of different ways. Coming up, the fun of heating and working...

Heating and Work Done Both Mean 'Energy Transferred'

1) In the 18th and 19th centuries (1700-1900), scientists realised that heating and work (p.162) were both ways of transferring energy.

2) Joule was one of those scientists. He came up with experiments that showed that the same amount of mechanical work would always produce the same increase in temperature for a given object. ⟵

For example, Joule measured the work done to turn a paddle in some water. He then measured how much the temperature of the water changed.

Energy is Transferred When a System Changes

1) The energy transferred to raise the temperature of an object can be supplied in different ways.

2) For example, energy transferred by heating can be supplied by an electric heater or by burning a fuel.

> • In an electric kettle, energy is transferred electrically from the mains to the thermal energy store of the kettle's heating element.
> • It is then transferred by heating to the thermal energy store of the water.
> • This causes the water's temperature to rise.

3) And if mechanical work is done, energy is transferred (supplied) by the force doing the work:

> • When an object hits an obstacle (e.g. a wall) work is done by the normal contact force.
> • When an object slows down, work is done by friction.
> • In both these cases, the temperatures of the objects or their surroundings increase.

4) You've seen these examples before on p.202, but make sure you remember them for this chapter.

You Need to Know How to Calculate Energy Transfers

1) You need to be able to do energy transfer calculations for a system changing temperature or state.

2) So you'll need the equations for a change in temperature, p.215, and a change of state, p.216.

3) You'll need to know the equation for mechanical work done from page 200.

4) And you need to know equations for electrical energy transfers too, like the ones on p.177 and p.181.

> **EXAMPLE:** An electric heater is used to heat 0.40 kg of water. The electric heater has a power of 210 W. It is used to heat the water for 80 seconds. The specific heat capacity (SHC) of water is 4200 J/kg°C. Calculate the change in the temperature of the water.
>
> 1) Rearrange the power equation from page 181 to find out how much energy is transferred by the heater.
>
>   power = energy ÷ time,
>   energy = power × time
>   = 210 × 80 = 16 800 J
>
> 2) Rearrange the equation from page 215 for the change in temperature.
>
>   change in internal energy
>   = mass × SHC × change in temperature,
>
> 3) Then just put in your values.
>   The change in internal energy of the water is equal to the energy transferred to it by the heater.
>
>   So change in temperature
>   = change in internal energy ÷ (mass × SHC)
>   = 16 800 ÷ (0.40 × 4200) = 10 °C

Revise this page carefully or Joule regret it...

You're probably sick of them by now, but energy transfers are important, so make sure you can describe them.

Q1   A pan of water is heated on a gas hob.
     Describe the energy transfers that occur to cause a rise in temperature of the water.   [4 marks]

Forces and Elasticity

Elasticity involves lots of physics and pinging elastic bands at people. Ok, maybe not that last one.

A Deformation can be Elastic or Plastic

1) When you <u>apply more than one force</u> to a solid material it can be <u>stretched</u>, <u>compressed</u> or <u>twisted</u>.
2) These are types of <u>deformation</u> (changing shape).

> To <u>deform</u> an object, you need <u>at least two forces</u>. Think of a <u>spring</u> — if you just pull <u>one end</u> of it, and there's <u>no force</u> at the other end, you'll just <u>pull the spring along</u> rather than stretching it.

3) <u>Elastic deformation</u> is when an object <u>returns to its original shape</u> after the stretching forces are removed.
4) If the object <u>doesn't return</u> to its original shape, the deformation is <u>plastic</u>.
5) <u>Elastic objects</u> can be <u>elastically deformed</u>. <u>Plastic objects</u> are <u>plastically deformed</u>.
6) If the <u>forces</u> applied to an <u>elastic object</u> are <u>too big</u>, the object <u>won't</u> return to its original shape.
7) The object is said to have <u>become plastic</u> and it is <u>permanently distorted</u> (or <u>permanently deformed</u>).

Force and Extension are Linked

1) A <u>force</u> is applied to <u>both ends</u> of an object. The object <u>stretches</u>.
2) The <u>difference in length</u> between the <u>stretched</u> and the <u>unstretched</u> object is the <u>extension</u>.
3) If the object has been <u>compressed</u> (squished), the <u>difference in length</u> is the <u>compression</u>.

Hooke's Law Can be Used for Linear Systems

1) In <u>some cases</u>, the relationship between <u>force</u> and <u>extension</u> (or <u>compression</u>) is <u>linear</u>.
2) This is where the <u>extension</u> of the object is <u>proportional</u> (p.173) to the <u>force</u> applied to it.
3) In these cases, you can say the <u>object</u> is a <u>linear system</u>.
4) A <u>graph</u> of <u>force against extension</u> for a <u>linear system</u> is a <u>straight line</u>.

5) For <u>linear systems</u>, you can use <u>Hooke's law</u> to describe what's going on:

> **force exerted by a spring (N) = extension (m) × spring constant (N/m)**

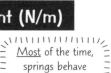

- You can use this equation to find the force exerted <u>on</u> OR <u>by</u> an object. (The force applied <u>to</u> a spring <u>equals</u> the force exerted <u>by</u> a spring, p.187.)
- The <u>spring constant</u> depends on the <u>material</u> that you are stretching.
- A <u>stiffer</u> material has a <u>greater</u> spring constant.

> <u>Most</u> of the time, springs behave linearly. This is why this equation talks about springs.

Systems Become Non-Linear if the Forces are Too Large

1) If the relationship between force and extension is <u>non-linear</u>, the object is a <u>non-linear system</u>.
2) Force is <u>not proportional</u> to extension and the force-extension graph is <u>not</u> a straight line.
3) <u>Most</u> objects are <u>linear systems</u> up to a <u>certain force</u>. <u>After</u> that force, they become <u>non-linear systems</u> (you can see this on the next page).

> Be careful — elastic objects **AREN'T** always <u>linear systems</u>. <u>Rubber bands</u> are <u>elastic objects</u>. They return to their <u>original shape</u> when released. But they are a <u>non-linear system</u>.

I hope this stuff isn't stretching you too much...

I can't say this enough — that equation ONLY works when the relationship between force and extension is linear.

Q1   A spring is linearly compressed 0.040 m by a 3.0 N force. Calculate its spring constant.   [3 marks]

Investigating Elasticity

More springs here, but now you actually get to do some experiments with them. Hip hip hooray.

You Can Calculate the Work Done to Deform an Object

1) When a force stretches or compresses an object, e.g. a spring, the force does work.
2) So energy is transferred to the object's elastic potential energy store (p.161).
3) When the force is removed, work is done by the object and this energy is transferred from the object.
4) You can find the energy transferred (or the work done) for any linear system using:

> energy stored in a stretched spring = ½ × spring constant × (extension)²
> (J)   (N/m)   (m)²

You Can Investigate the Link Between Force and Extension...

PRACTICAL

1) Set up the apparatus as shown in the diagram on the right.
2) Measure the original length of the spring (p.235).
3) Measure the mass of a mass (p.234).
4) Calculate its weight, p.188 (the force it will apply to the spring).
5) Add the mass to the spring and allow the spring to come to rest.
6) Write down the total force on the spring.
7) Measure the new length of the spring.
8) Find the extension (extension = new length − original length).
9) Repeat steps 3) to 8) until you've added all the masses.
10) Plot a force-extension graph of your results (see below).
11) Make sure you have at least 5 points where the line is straight.

Make sure you carry out the experiment safely. For example:
- Stand up so you can get out of the way quickly if the masses fall.
- Wear safety goggles to protect your eyes in case the spring snaps.

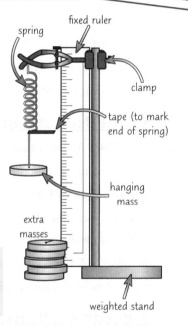

spring, fixed ruler, clamp, tape (to mark end of spring), hanging mass, extra masses, weighted stand

...And Use Your Results to Find Work Done

1) Your graph should look like the one on the right.
2) The spring will stretch linearly to begin with.
3) It will then start to stretch non-linearly if the force gets big enough.
4) This is why the graph curves. (Don't worry if yours doesn't though.)
5) You can use your force-extension graph to calculate the work done to stretch the spring.
6) Work done is equal to the area under the graph up to that extension.
7) You can find this area by calculating the area of the triangle or by counting squares (p.194).

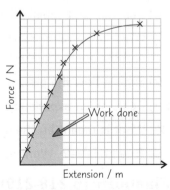

Force / N, Work done, Extension / m

Tell your parents you need to buy a trampoline for your revision...

Be careful with this experiment. If the weight on the end of the spring is too large, it could plastically deform.

Q1   Calculate the work done when a spring (spring constant = 54 N/m) extends linearly by 0.10 m.   [2 marks]

Revision Questions for Chapters P5 & P6

Well, that wraps up Chapter P6 — now let's see what you've managed to remember from the last two chapters.

*   Try these questions and tick off each one when you get it right.
*   When you've done all the questions for a topic and are completely happy with it, tick off the topic.

The Model of the Atom (p.204-205) ☑

1) Briefly explain how the model of the atom has changed over time. ☑
2) Describe the modern model of the atom. ☑
3) What is the typical diameter of an atom? ☑

Isotopes, Radioactive Decay and Half-life (p.206-208) ☑

4) What is the number of protons in an atom equal to: the nuclear charge or the nuclear mass? ☑
5) What is an isotope? ☑
6) True or false? Gamma radiation can be stopped by a thin sheet of aluminium. ☑
7) Draw the symbols for both alpha and beta radiation in nuclear equations. ☑
8) What type of radioactive decay doesn't change the mass or charge of the nucleus? ☑
9) What is meant by the activity of a source? What are its units? ☑
10) Explain what is meant by the term 'half-life'. ☑
11) Explain how you would find the half-life of a source from a graph of its activity against time. ☑

Dangers and Uses of Radiation (p.209-211) ☐

12) Give one effect ionising radiation can have on a person's body. ☑
13) What is meant when a body is said to be contaminated by a radioactive substance? ☑
14) Give one example of how to protect yourself against: a) irradiation,   b) contamination. ☑
15) Compare the hazards of being irradiated and contaminated by:
    a) an alpha source,   b) a gamma source. ☑
16) True or false? A radioactive source must have a long half-life in order to be used as a medical tracer. ☑
17) Apart from medical tracers, give one other way that ionising radiation is used in medicine. ☑

Density, Particles, Heating and Cooling (p.212-217) ☐

18) What is meant by the term 'density'? ☑
19) Describe solids, liquids and gases in terms of the movements of their particles. ☑
20) Describe and explain the usual change in density when a liquid is: a) boiled   b) frozen. ☑
21) What is the relationship between the temperature of a substance
    and the energy in the kinetic energy stores of its particles? ☑
22) Explain how the pressure of a gas at a constant volume will change if its temperature is increased. ☑
23) Describe an experiment to find the specific heat capacity of water. ☑
24) What is meant by the specific latent heat of fusion of a substance? ☑
25) True or false? Work done and heating are two ways of transferring energy. ☑

Elasticity (p.218-219) ☑

26) What is the difference between elastic deformation and plastic deformation? ☑
27) Give the equation that relates the force exerted by a spring to its linear extension and spring constant. ☑
28) Describe a simple experiment to investigate the relationship between force and extension. ☑

The Scientific Method

This section isn't about how to 'do' science — but it does show you the way most scientists work...

Scientists Come Up With Hypotheses — Then Test Them

Scientists try to explain things. There isn't a single scientific method that all scientists use to do this. But scientists often develop explanations by going through cycles of the following steps:

They make an observation.

1) Scientists OBSERVE (look at) something they don't understand, e.g. an illness.
2) They come up with a possible explanation for what they've observed.
3) This tentative (uncertain) explanation is called a HYPOTHESIS.

They test their hypothesis.

4) Next, they test whether the hypothesis is right or not.
5) They do this by making a PREDICTION — a statement based on the hypothesis that can be tested. E.g. a prediction could be that an increase in temperature will increase the rate of photosynthesis.
6) They then TEST this prediction by carrying out experiments.
7) If their prediction is right, this is EVIDENCE that their hypothesis might be right too.
8) It doesn't prove a hypothesis is correct though — evidence could still be found that disagrees with it.

Predictions can be written as statements or drawn as a diagram or a sketch graph.

Investigations must be designed so data can be collected in a safe, repeatable, accurate way — see pages 224-225.

Other scientists test the hypothesis too.

9) Other scientists check the evidence — for example, they check that the experiment was carried out in a sensible way. This is called PEER-REVIEW.
10) Scientists then share their results, e.g. in peer-reviewed journals.
11) Other scientists carry out more experiments to test the hypothesis.
12) They might try and get the original results. Or, they might do new experiments that test the hypothesis in a different way.
13) Sometimes these scientists will find more evidence that the hypothesis is RIGHT.
14) Sometimes they'll find evidence that shows the hypothesis is WRONG.
15) If the original results can't be reproduced (see p.223) then scientists won't trust them.
16) Sometimes new experiments will give unexpected results. These will also only be trusted if they can be repeated and reproduced.

The hypothesis is accepted or rejected.

17) If evidence from experiments backs up the prediction, it increases confidence in the hypothesis.
18) If all the evidence that's been found supports the hypothesis, it becomes an ACCEPTED THEORY. This is a widely accepted explanation that can be applied to lots of situations.
19) If the evidence from experiments doesn't fit with the hypothesis, then the results or the hypothesis must be wrong.
20) This decreases confidence in the hypothesis.

Sometimes new data doesn't support an accepted theory.

However, the theory will usually stick until a new and better theory is found. This is because the theory already explains loads of other observations really well.

The Scientific Method

Different Scientists Can Come Up With Different Explanations

1) Different scientists can look at the <u>same data</u> and explain it differently.

2) This is because different people can interpret data in <u>different ways</u>.

3) Sometimes a scientist's <u>background</u>, <u>experience</u> or <u>interests</u> will affect the way he or she thinks. For example, someone who studies <u>genetics</u> might use genetics to explain a particular <u>disease</u>. Someone else might think it's more about the <u>environment</u>.

4) The explanations are <u>tested</u> to see if one is <u>true</u>. Experiments are carried out to <u>collect data</u>.

5) The ways scientists can collect data have got better as <u>technology has developed</u>. New technology can allow scientists to make <u>new observations</u> and find <u>new evidence</u>.

6) New data can cause scientists to <u>change</u> their ideas and <u>hypotheses</u>. E.g. the <u>model of the atom</u> has changed because of <u>new observations</u> (see previous page).

Theories Can Involve Different Types of Models

1) A <u>model</u> is a <u>simple way</u> of <u>showing</u> what's going on in <u>real life</u>.

2) Models show the <u>key features</u> of a system or process, and the <u>rules</u> that control how the different features work together. They can be used to <u>explain ideas</u> and <u>make predictions</u>.

3) There are lots of <u>different types</u> of models. For example:

Representational models

- These are <u>simplified descriptions</u> or <u>pictures</u> of what's going on in real life.
- E.g. the <u>Bohr model</u> of an atom is a simple <u>picture</u> of what an atom looks like. (See p.90 for more.) It can be used to explain <u>trends</u> in the <u>periodic table</u>.

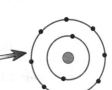

Spatial models

- These represent <u>physical space</u> and the <u>position of objects</u> within it.
- They can be used to predict things like the direction that a storm will move in.

Descriptive models

These are used to <u>describe</u> how things work. For example, describing the features of <u>sound waves</u> (p.150) can help to explain how sound travels through <u>materials</u>.

Mathematical models

- These use <u>patterns</u> found in <u>data</u> to <u>predict</u> what might happen in the <u>future</u>.
- They require lots of <u>calculations</u>.

Computational models

These are mathematical models that use computers (they can do calculations <u>more quickly</u>).

4) It can sometimes be quicker to use a model to test a hypothesis than an experiment. There are also fewer <u>ethical or practical problems</u> with using a model.

5) However, all models have a <u>limit</u> to what they can <u>explain</u> or <u>predict</u>.

I'm off to the zoo to test my hippo-thesis...

There's an awful lot to take in here. Make sure you understand it all before moving on. It's really important stuff.

Designing Investigations

Dig out your lab coat and dust down your badly-scratched safety glasses... it's <u>investigation time</u>.

Investigations Produce Evidence to Support or Disprove a Hypothesis

1) Scientists <u>observe</u> things and come up with <u>hypotheses</u> to explain them (see page 221). You need to be able to do the same. For example:

> <u>Observation</u>: People have big feet and spots. <u>Hypothesis</u>: Having big feet causes spots.

2) To <u>find out</u> if your hypothesis is <u>right</u>, you need to do an <u>investigation</u> to gather evidence.

3) To do this, you need to use your hypothesis to make a <u>prediction</u> — something you think <u>will happen</u> that you can <u>test</u>. E.g. people who have bigger feet will have more spots.

4) Investigations are used to see if there are <u>patterns</u> or <u>relationships</u> between <u>two variables</u>.

Evidence Needs to be Repeatable, Reproducible and Valid

1) <u>REPEATABLE</u> means that if the <u>same person</u> does the experiment again, they'll get <u>similar results</u>.

2) <u>REPRODUCIBLE</u> means that if <u>someone else</u> does the experiment, the results will still be <u>similar</u>.

3) <u>VALID results</u> come from experiments that were designed to be a <u>fair test</u>. They're also repeatable and reproducible.

To Make an Investigation a Fair Test You Have to Control the Variables

1) In a lab experiment you usually <u>change one variable</u> and <u>measure</u> how it affects <u>another variable</u>.

2) <u>Everything else</u> that could affect the results needs to <u>stay the same</u>. Then you know that the thing you're <u>changing</u> is the <u>only</u> thing that's affecting the results.

3) The variable you <u>change</u> is called the **INDEPENDENT VARIABLE**.

4) The variable you <u>measure</u> is the **DEPENDENT VARIABLE**.

5) Variables that you <u>keep the same</u> are called **CONTROL VARIABLES**.

> You could find how <u>temperature</u> affects <u>reaction rate</u> by measuring the <u>volume of gas</u> formed over time.
> * The <u>independent variable</u> is the <u>temperature</u>.
> * The <u>dependent variable</u> is the <u>volume of gas</u> produced.
> * <u>Control variables</u> include the <u>concentration</u> of reactants, the <u>time period</u> you measure, etc.

6) You need to be able to <u>suggest ways to control variables</u> in experiments. For example, you could use a <u>stop watch</u> to make sure you always measure the same time period.

7) Sometimes you can't control <u>all</u> the variables. So you can use a <u>control experiment</u> instead.

8) A control experiment is kept under the <u>same conditions</u> as the rest of the experiment, but <u>doesn't</u> have anything <u>done</u> to it. This is to see what happens when you don't change <u>anything</u>.

You Can Design Procedures to Produce or Characterise Substances

1) In some experiments you <u>produce</u> (make) or <u>characterise</u> (identify) a substance.

2) For example, when you carry out a reaction to make a <u>salt</u> (see p.141-142), you're <u>producing</u> a substance (<u>the salt</u>). And when you test a <u>gas</u> to work out its identity (see p.86), you're <u>characterising</u> a substance.

Designing Investigations

There Can be Hazards in Investigations

1) A hazard is something that could cause harm.

2) Hazards from science experiments include things like:

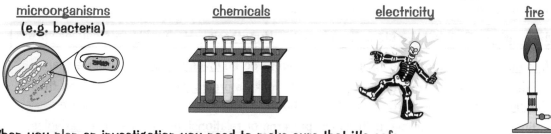

microorganisms
(e.g. bacteria)

chemicals

electricity

fire

3) When you plan an investigation you need to make sure that it's safe.

4) You should identify all the hazards that you might come across.

5) Then you should think of ways of reducing the risks. For example:

- If you're working with sulfuric acid, always wear gloves and safety goggles. This will reduce the risk of the acid burning your skin and eyes.

- If you're using a Bunsen burner, stand it on a heat proof mat. ⟹ This will reduce the risk of starting a fire.

A risk is the chance that a hazard will cause harm.

The Bigger the Sample Size the Better

1) Sample size is how many things you test in an investigation, e.g. 500 people or 20 types of metal.

2) The bigger the sample size the better — to reduce the chance of any weird results.

3) But scientists have to be realistic when choosing how big their sample should be. E.g. if you were studying how lifestyle affects weight it'd be great to study everyone in the UK (a huge sample), but it'd take ages and cost loads.

4) When you choose a sample of people, you need to make sure you've got a range of different people. For example, both men and women with a range of different ages.

5) This is so the sample represents the whole population.

Trial Runs Help Figure out the Details

1) A trial run is a quick version of your experiment.

2) They can be used to figure out what readings to take in the proper experiment.

For example, if you were investigating how temperature affects the rate of a reaction...
- You might do a trial run using temperatures of 10 °C, 20 °C, 30 °C, 40 °C and 50 °C.
- If there wasn't much difference in the results for 10 °C and 20 °C, you might just use 20-50 °C for the proper experiment.
- But jumping up by 10 °C each time might give you big changes in the rate of reaction. So, you might decide to use 5 °C jumps instead, e.g. 20, 25, 30, 35 °C...

This is no high street survey — it's a designer investigation...

You need to be able to plan your own investigations. You should also be able to look at someone else's plan and decide whether or not it needs improving. Those examiners are pretty demanding.

Chapter BCP7 — Ideas About Science

Collecting Data

You've designed the perfect investigation — now it's time to get your hands mucky and collect some data.

Your Data Should be Repeatable, Reproducible, Accurate and Precise

1) To check your results are repeatable, repeat the readings at least three times. Then check the repeat results are all similar.

2) To make sure your results are reproducible, get another person to do the experiment too.

3) ACCURATE results are results that are really close to the true answer.

4) The accuracy of your results usually depends on your method. You need to make sure you're measuring the right thing.

5) You also need to make sure you don't miss anything that should be included in the measurements. For example:

Repeat	Data set 1	Data set 2
1	12	11
2	14	17
3	13	14
Mean	13	14

> If you're measuring the volume of gas released by a reaction, make sure you collect all the gas.

Data set 1 is more precise than data set 2 — the results are all close to the mean (not spread out).

6) PRECISE results are ones where the data is all really close to the mean (average) of your repeated results.

Your Equipment has to be Right for the Job

1) The measuring equipment you use has to be able to accurately measure the chemicals you're using. E.g. if you need to measure out 11 cm³ of a liquid, use a measuring cylinder that can measure to 1 cm³ — not 5 or 10 cm³.

2) You also need to set up the equipment properly. For example, make sure your mass balance is set to zero before you start weighing things.

You Need to Look out for Errors and Outliers

1) The results of your experiment will always vary a bit because of RANDOM ERRORS — for example, mistakes you might make while measuring.

2) You can reduce the effect of random errors by taking repeat readings and finding the mean. This will make your results more precise.

3) If a measurement is wrong by the same amount every time, it's called a SYSTEMATIC ERROR. For example:

> If you measure from the very end of your ruler instead of from the 0 cm mark every time, all your measurements would be a bit small.

If there's no systematic error, then doing repeats and calculating a mean can make your results more accurate.

Always measure from here...
...not here.

4) If you know you've made a systematic error, you might be able to correct it. For example, by adding a bit on to all your measurements.

5) Sometimes you get a result that doesn't fit in with the rest. This is called an OUTLIER.

6) You should try to work out what happened. If you do (e.g. you find out you measured something wrong) you can ignore it when processing your results (see next page).

7) If nothing went wrong, then you should include outliers in your results.

Sleeping in the garden — the other kind of outlier...

Make sure you take lots of care when collecting data — there's plenty to watch out for, as you can see.

Processing and Presenting Data

Once you've got your <u>data</u>, you need to <u>interpret</u> it. This means doing a bit of <u>maths</u> to make it <u>more useful</u>.

Data Needs to be Organised and Processed

1) Tables are useful for <u>recording results</u> and <u>organising data</u>.
When you draw a table <u>use a ruler</u>. Make sure <u>each column</u> has a <u>heading</u> (including the <u>units</u>).

2) When you've done repeats of an experiment you should always calculate the <u>mean</u> (a type of average).
To do this, <u>add together</u> all the data values. Then <u>divide by</u> the total number of values in the sample.

3) You might also need to calculate the <u>range</u> (how spread out the data is).
To do this, find the <u>largest</u> number and <u>subtract</u> the <u>smallest</u> number from it.

Ignore outliers when calculating the mean and the range.

EXAMPLE: The results of an experiment to find the volume of gas produced in a reaction are shown below. Calculate the mean volume and the range.

Repeat 1 (cm³)	Repeat 2 (cm³)	Repeat 3 (cm³)	Mean (cm³)	Range (cm³)
28	37	32	(28 + 37 + 32) ÷ 3 = 32	37 − 28 = 9

4) Then you can display your data in a <u>chart</u> or <u>graph</u> to make it easier to see patterns.

You should be able to draw charts and plot graphs from results in a table.

If Your Data Comes in Categories, Present It in a Bar Chart

If the independent variable comes in <u>clear categories</u> (e.g. blood group, types of metal) or can be <u>counted exactly</u> (e.g. number of protons) you should use a <u>bar chart</u> to display the data. Here's what to do:

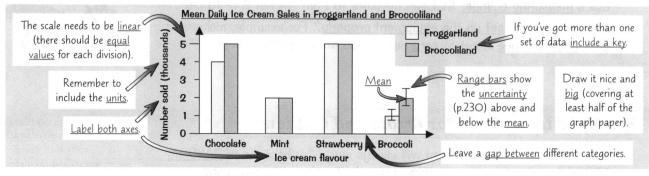

Mean Daily Ice Cream Sales in Froggartland and Broccoliland

The scale needs to be <u>linear</u> (there should be <u>equal values</u> for each division).

Remember to include the <u>units</u>.

<u>Label both axes</u>.

If you've got more than one set of data <u>include a key</u>.

<u>Range bars</u> show the <u>uncertainty</u> (p.230) above and below the <u>mean</u>.

Draw it nice and <u>big</u> (covering at least half of the graph paper).

Leave a <u>gap between</u> different categories.

If Your Data is Continuous, Plot a Graph

If both variables can have any value <u>within a range</u> (e.g. length, volume) use a <u>graph</u> to display the data.

Here are the rules for plotting points on a graph:

Graph to Show Product Formed Against Time

Use the biggest data values you've got to draw a <u>sensible scale</u> on your axes.

The <u>dependent</u> variable goes on the <u>y-axis</u> (the <u>vertical</u> one).

outlying result

The <u>independent</u> variable goes on the <u>x-axis</u> (the <u>horizontal</u> one).

To plot points, use a sharp pencil and make <u>neat little crosses</u> (don't do blobs).

nice clear mark / smudged unclear marks

To draw a <u>line</u> (or <u>curve</u>) of <u>best fit</u>, draw a line <u>through</u>, or as <u>near</u> to, as <u>many points as possible</u>. Ignore any <u>outliers</u>. <u>Don't</u> join the crosses up.

Draw it <u>big</u> (covering at least two thirds of the graph paper).

Remember to include the <u>units</u>.

Chapter BCP7 — Ideas About Science

Processing and Presenting Data

Graphs Can Give You a Lot of Information About Your Data

1) This is the <u>formula</u> you need to calculate the <u>gradient</u> (slope) of a graph:

2) You can use it to work out a rate, e.g. the <u>rate of a reaction</u> (how <u>quickly</u> the reaction happens).

$$\text{gradient} = \frac{\text{change in } y}{\text{change in } x}$$

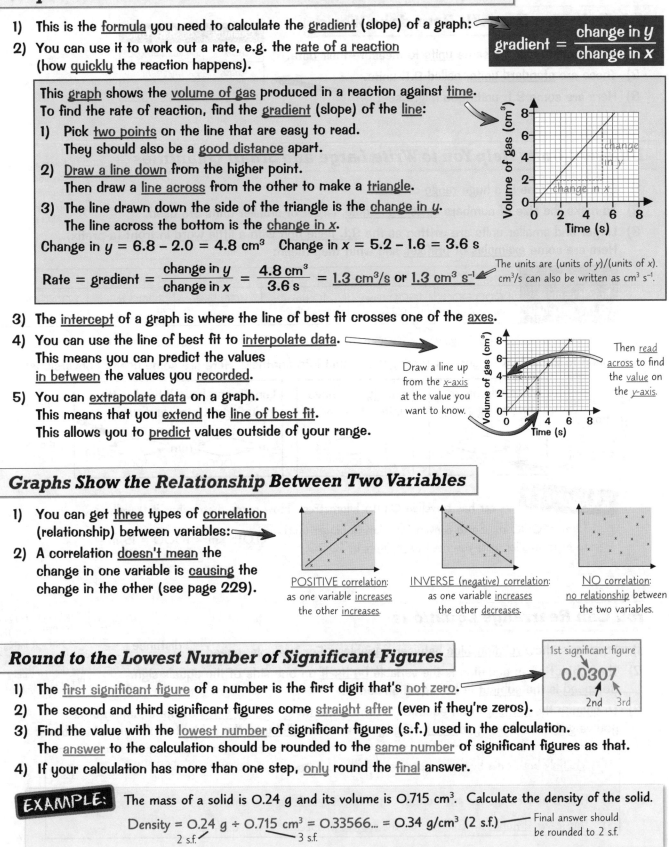

This <u>graph</u> shows the <u>volume of gas</u> produced in a reaction against <u>time</u>.
To find the rate of reaction, find the <u>gradient</u> (slope) of the <u>line</u>:

1) Pick <u>two points</u> on the line that are easy to read.
   They should also be a <u>good distance</u> apart.

2) <u>Draw a line down</u> from the higher point.
   Then draw a <u>line across</u> from the other to make a <u>triangle</u>.

3) The line drawn down the side of the triangle is the <u>change in y</u>.
   The line across the bottom is the <u>change in x</u>.

Change in y = 6.8 − 2.0 = 4.8 cm³   Change in x = 5.2 − 1.6 = 3.6 s

$$\text{Rate} = \text{gradient} = \frac{\text{change in } y}{\text{change in } x} = \frac{4.8 \text{ cm}^3}{3.6 \text{ s}} = \underline{1.3 \text{ cm}^3/\text{s}} \text{ or } \underline{1.3 \text{ cm}^3 \text{ s}^{-1}}$$

The units are (units of y)/(units of x). cm³/s can also be written as cm³ s⁻¹.

3) The <u>intercept</u> of a graph is where the line of best fit crosses one of the <u>axes</u>.

4) You can use the line of best fit to <u>interpolate</u> data.
   This means you can predict the values
   <u>in between</u> the values you <u>recorded</u>.

5) You can <u>extrapolate</u> data on a graph.
   This means that you <u>extend</u> the <u>line of best fit</u>.
   This allows you to <u>predict</u> values outside of your range.

Draw a line up from the <u>x-axis</u> at the value you want to know.

Then <u>read across</u> to find the <u>value</u> on the <u>y-axis</u>.

Graphs Show the Relationship Between Two Variables

1) You can get <u>three</u> types of <u>correlation</u> (relationship) between variables:

2) A correlation <u>doesn't mean</u> the change in one variable is <u>causing</u> the change in the other (see page 229).

<u>POSITIVE</u> correlation: as one variable <u>increases</u> the other <u>increases</u>.

<u>INVERSE</u> (negative) correlation: as one variable <u>increases</u> the other <u>decreases</u>.

<u>NO</u> correlation: <u>no relationship</u> between the two variables.

Round to the Lowest Number of Significant Figures

1) The <u>first significant figure</u> of a number is the first digit that's <u>not zero</u>.

1st significant figure
0.0307
2nd   3rd

2) The second and third significant figures come <u>straight after</u> (even if they're zeros).

3) Find the value with the <u>lowest number</u> of significant figures (s.f.) used in the calculation.
   The <u>answer</u> to the calculation should be rounded to the <u>same number</u> of significant figures as that.

4) If your calculation has more than one step, <u>only</u> round the <u>final</u> answer.

EXAMPLE: The mass of a solid is 0.24 g and its volume is 0.715 cm³. Calculate the density of the solid.

Density = 0.24 g ÷ 0.715 cm³ = 0.33566... = 0.34 g/cm³ (2 s.f.)
2 s.f.   3 s.f.

Final answer should be rounded to 2 s.f.

I love eating apples — I call it core elation...

Science is all about finding relationships between things. And I don't mean that chemists gather together in corners to discuss whether or not Devini and Sebastian might be a couple... though they probably do that too.

Units and Equations

Graphs and maths skills are all very well, but the numbers don't mean much if you can't get the <u>units</u> right.

S.I. Units Are Used All Round the World

1) All scientists use the same <u>units</u> to measure their data.

2) These are <u>standard units</u>, called S.I. units.

3) Here are some S.I. units you might see:

Quantity	S.I. Base Unit
mass	kilogram, kg
length	metre, m
time	second, s

Different Units Help You to Write Large and Small Quantities

Kilogram is an exception. It's an S.I. unit with the prefix already on it.

1) Quantities come in a huge <u>range</u> of sizes.

2) To make the size of numbers <u>easier to handle</u>, larger or smaller units are used.

3) Larger and smaller units are written as the <u>S.I. base unit</u> with a <u>little word</u> in <u>front</u> (a prefix). Here are some <u>examples</u> of <u>prefixes</u> and what they mean:

prefix	mega (M)	kilo (k)	deci (d)	centi (c)	milli (m)	micro (μ)
how it compares to the base unit	1 000 000 times bigger	1000 times bigger	10 times smaller	100 times smaller	1000 times smaller	1 000 000 times smaller

E.g. 1 <u>kilo</u>metre is <u>1000</u> metres.

E.g. there are <u>1000</u> <u>milli</u>metres in 1 metre.

You need to know how to <u>convert</u> (change) one unit into another. Here are some useful conversions:

DIVIDE to go from a <u>smaller unit</u> to a <u>bigger unit</u>.

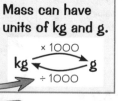

Mass can have units of kg and g.

$$kg \xrightarrow{\times 1000} g$$
$$kg \xleftarrow{\div 1000} g$$

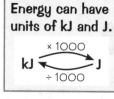

Energy can have units of kJ and J.

$$kJ \xrightarrow{\times 1000} J$$
$$kJ \xleftarrow{\div 1000} J$$

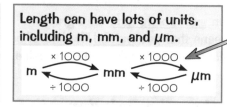

Length can have lots of units, including m, mm, and μm.

$$m \xrightarrow{\times 1000} mm \xrightarrow{\times 1000} \mu m$$
$$m \xleftarrow{\div 1000} mm \xleftarrow{\div 1000} \mu m$$

MULTIPLY to go from a <u>bigger unit</u> to a <u>smaller unit</u>.

EXAMPLE: A car has travelled 0.015 kilometres. How many metres has it travelled?

1 km = 1000 m. So to convert from km (a bigger unit) to m (a smaller unit) you need to <u>multiply</u> by 1000.

0.015 km × 1000 = 15 m

You Can Rearrange Equations

Always make sure the values you put into an equation or formula have the right units.

1) Equations show <u>relationships</u> between <u>variables</u>. For example, $speed = \dfrac{distance}{time}$.

2) The <u>subject</u> of an equation is the variable <u>by itself</u> on one side of the equals sign. So <u>speed</u> is the <u>subject</u> in the equation above.

3) To <u>change</u> the <u>subject</u> of an equation do the same thing to <u>both sides</u> of the equation until you've got the subject you <u>want</u>. E.g. you can make <u>distance</u> the subject of the equation above:

1) <u>Multiply</u> both sides by <u>time</u>: $speed = \dfrac{distance}{time} \longrightarrow speed \times time = \dfrac{distance \times time}{time}$

2) Time is now on the top <u>and</u> bottom of the fraction, so it cancels out: $speed \times time = \dfrac{distance \times \cancel{time}}{\cancel{time}}$

3) This leaves <u>distance</u> by itself. So it's the <u>subject</u>: $speed \times time = distance$

I wasn't sure I liked units, but now I'm converted...

It's easy to get in a muddle when converting between units, but there's a handy way to check you've done it right. If you're moving from a smaller unit to a larger unit (e.g. g to kg) the number should get smaller, and vice versa.

Drawing Conclusions

Congratulations — you're nearly at the end of a gruelling investigation, time to draw conclusions.

You Can Only Conclude What the Data Shows and NO MORE

1) To come to a conclusion, look at your data and say what pattern you see between the variables.

The table on the right shows the rate of a reaction in the presence of two different catalysts:	Catalyst	Rate of reaction (cm³/s)	CONCLUSION: Catalyst **B** makes this reaction go faster than catalyst A.
	A	13.5	
	B	19.5	
	No catalyst	5.5	

2) It's important that the conclusion matches the data it's based on — it shouldn't go any further.

> You can't conclude that catalyst B increases the rate of any other reaction more than catalyst A — the results might be completely different.

3) You also need to be able to use your results to justify your conclusion (i.e. back it up).

> Catalyst B made the rate of reaction on average 6.5 cm³/s faster than catalyst A.

4) When writing a conclusion you need to say whether or not the data supports the original hypothesis:

> The hypothesis for this experiment might have been that catalyst B would make the reaction go quicker than catalyst A. If so, the data supports the hypothesis.

Correlation DOES NOT Mean Cause

If two things are correlated, there's a relationship between them — see page 227. But a correlation doesn't always mean that the factor causes the outcome. There are several reasons for this:

1) Sometimes two things can show a correlation by chance. This is why one case on its own isn't enough to show that a factor causes an outcome. Repeatable, reproducible data must be collected.

> E.g. there may be a correlation between a person's hair colour and how good they are at throwing a frisbee in a school. But another scientist wouldn't get the same results in another school.

2) A lot of the time it may look as if a factor is causing an outcome but it isn't — another, hidden factor links them both.

> E.g. there's a correlation between water temperature and shark attacks. They're linked by a third variable — the number of people swimming (more people swim when the water's hotter, which means you get more shark attacks).

3) Sometimes a correlation is just when a factor makes an outcome more likely — not certain to happen.

> E.g. if you eat a diet high in saturated fat, it increases your risk of heart disease. It doesn't mean you will get it. That's because there are lots of different factors that work together to affect the outcome.

4) Scientists don't usually accept that a factor causes an outcome unless they can work out a possible mechanism that links the two things.

> E.g. there's a correlation between increased carbon dioxide levels in the atmosphere and global warming. Carbon dioxide can absorb energy so that it's not lost into space, and the Earth heats up. This is the mechanism.

I conclude that this page is a bit dull...

...but just because I find it dull doesn't mean that I can conclude it's dull. Stick with this page and it'll make sense.

Uncertainties and Evaluations

You can never be certain that your data is 100% correct. You need to decide how confident you are in it...

Uncertainty is the Amount of Error Your Measurements Might Have

1) Measurements you make will have some uncertainty in them (i.e. they won't be completely perfect).

2) This can be due to random errors (see page 225). It can also be due to limits in what your measuring equipment can measure.

The range is the largest value minus the smallest value (p.226).

$$\text{uncertainty} = \frac{\text{range}}{2}$$

3) This means that the mean of your results will have some uncertainty to it.

4) You can calculate the uncertainty of a mean result using this equation:

5) The less precise your results are, the higher the uncertainty will be.

6) Uncertainties are shown using the '±' symbol.

 EXAMPLE:

The table below shows the results of an experiment to find the speed of a trolley. Calculate the uncertainty of the mean.

Repeat	1	2	3	mean
Speed (m/s)	2.02	1.98	2.00	2.00

1) First work out the range:
   Range = 2.02 − 1.98
   = 0.04 m/s

2) Use the range to find the uncertainty:
   Uncertainty = range ÷ 2 = 0.04 ÷ 2 = 0.02 m/s   So, uncertainty of the mean = 2.00 ± 0.02 m/s

Evaluations — Describe How it Could be Improved

In an evaluation you look back over the whole investigation.

1) You should comment on the method — was it valid? Did you control all the other variables to make it a fair test?

2) Comment on the quality of the results — was there enough evidence to reach a valid conclusion? Were the results repeatable, reproducible, accurate and precise?

3) Were there any outliers? If there were none then say so. If there were any, try to explain them — were they caused by errors in measurement?

4) You should comment on the level of uncertainty in your results too.

5) Thinking about these things lets you say how confident you are that your conclusion is right.

6) Then you can suggest any changes to the method that would improve the quality of the results, so you could have more confidence in your conclusion.

7) For example, taking measurements in smaller intervals could give you a more accurate result. E.g.

- Say you do an experiment to find the temperature at which an enzyme works best.
- You take measurements at 30 °C, 40 °C and 50 °C. The results show that the enzyme works best at 40 °C.
- To get a more accurate result, you could repeat the experiment and take more measurements around 40 °C. You might then find that the enzyme actually works best at 42 °C.

8) You could also make more predictions based on your conclusion. You could then carry out further experiments to test the new predictions.

Evaluation — next time, I'll make sure I don't burn the lab down...

By now you should have realised how important trustworthy evidence is (even more important than a good supply of spot cream). Evaluations are a good way to assess evidence and see how things can be improved in the future.

New Technologies and Risk

By reading this page you are agreeing to the risk of a paper cut...

Scientific Technology Usually Has Benefits and Negative Impacts

1) Scientists have created loads of new technologies that could improve our lives.
   For example, these developments in nanoscience:

   - Using nanotubes to carry drug molecules to specific parts of the body.
   - Developing new and better catalysts.

2) However, sometimes new technology can have unwanted impacts.
   It can affect our quality of life or the environment. For example:

   - Nanoparticles are very small so could get into our cells.
     They could cause side effects that haven't been discovered.
   - Nanoparticles might not get filtered out of waste water when they get washed away.
     This could mean they might end up in rivers, where they could harm plants or animals.

3) Scientists try to find ways to reduce these impacts on people and the environment.

Nothing is Completely Risk-Free

Risks can affect an individual or a whole group of people.

1) Remember, a hazard is something that could cause harm — see page 224.

2) All hazards have a risk attached to them — this is the chance that the hazard will cause harm.

3) The risks of some things seem pretty obvious. Or we might have known about them
   for a while, like the risk of causing acid rain by polluting the atmosphere.

4) New technology can bring new risks. E.g. scientists are creating technology to capture and store
   carbon dioxide. But if the carbon dioxide leaked out it could damage soil or water supplies. These risks
   need to be considered alongside the benefits of the technology, e.g. lower greenhouse gas emissions.

5) You can estimate the size of a risk by finding how many times something
   happens in a big sample over a given period of time. For example:

6) To make a decision about activities that involve hazards,
   we need to think about:

   - the chance of the hazard causing harm,
   - how bad the outcome (consequences) would be if it did.

> You could estimate the risk of a driver crashing by finding how many people in a group of 100 000 drivers crashed their cars in a year.

People Make Their Own Decisions About Risk

1) Not all risks have the same consequences. For example, if you chop veg with
   a sharp knife you risk cutting your finger, but if you go scuba-diving you risk death.

2) Most people are happier to accept a risk if the consequences don't last long and aren't serious.

3) People are also usually happy to accept a risk if it's something they have chosen to do, rather
   than not having had a choice.

Not revising — an unacceptable exam risk...

All activities pose some sort of risk. It's just a case of deciding whether that risk is worth it in the long run.

Communication and Issues Created by Science

Scientific developments can be great, but they can sometimes <u>raise more questions</u> than they answer...

It's Important to Tell People About Scientific Discoveries

1) Scientific discoveries can make a big difference to <u>people's lives</u>.
2) So scientists need to <u>tell the world</u> about their discoveries.
3) They might need to tell people to <u>change their habits</u>, e.g. stop smoking to protect against lung cancer.
4) They might also need to tell people about new <u>technologies</u>. For example:

> • New technology is being developed to generate <u>renewable energy</u>.
> • Information about this needs to be given to <u>politicians</u>.
> • They can then <u>decide</u> whether to <u>allow</u> the development.
> • Information should also be given to the <u>public</u>, who will be <u>affected</u>.

5) Scientific discoveries can be communicated to the public by the <u>media</u> (e.g. newspapers or television).
6) <u>Reports</u> about scientific discoveries in the <u>media</u> can be <u>misleading</u>.
7) The data might be <u>presented</u> in a way that's <u>not quite right</u> — or it might be <u>oversimplified</u>.
8) This means that people may not <u>properly understand</u> what the scientists found out.
9) People who want to make a point can also sometimes <u>present data</u> in a <u>biased way</u> (in a way that's <u>unfair</u> or <u>ignores</u> one side of the argument). For example:

> • A <u>scientist</u> may talk a lot about <u>one particular relationship</u> in the data (and not mention others).
> • A <u>newspaper article</u> might describe data <u>supporting</u> an idea without giving any evidence <u>against</u> it.

Scientific Developments are Great, but they can Raise Issues

1) Scientific developments include <u>new technologies</u> and <u>new advice</u>.
2) These developments can create <u>issues</u>. For example:

<u>Economic (money) issues:</u> Society <u>can't</u> always <u>afford</u> to do things scientists recommend, like spend money on green energy resources.

<u>Social (people) issues:</u> Decisions based on scientific evidence affect <u>people</u> — e.g. should alcohol be banned (to prevent health problems)?

<u>Personal issues:</u> Some decisions will affect <u>individuals</u> — e.g. people may be upset if a <u>wind farm</u> is built next to their house.

<u>Environmental issues:</u> <u>Human activity</u> often affects the <u>environment</u> — e.g. some people think that <u>genetically modified crops</u> (see page 7) could cause <u>environmental problems</u>.

Science Can't Answer Every Question — Especially Ethical Ones

1) At the moment scientists <u>don't agree</u> on some things — like what the universe is made of.
2) This is because there <u>isn't</u> enough <u>data</u> to <u>support</u> the scientists' hypotheses.
3) But <u>eventually</u>, we probably <u>will</u> be able to answer these questions once and for all.
4) Experiments <u>can't tell us</u> whether something is <u>ethically right or wrong</u>. For example, whether it's right for people to use new drugs to help them do better in exams.
5) The best we can do is make a decision that <u>most people</u> are more or less happy to live by.

Tea to milk or milk to tea? — Totally unanswerable by science...

Science can't tell you whether or not you <u>should</u> do something. That's for you and society to decide. But there are tons of questions science might be able to answer, like where life came from and where my superhero socks are.

Revision Questions for Chapter BCP7

That's all for <u>Chapter BCP7</u> — time to conclude and evaluate what you've learnt.

- Try these questions and <u>tick off each one</u> when you <u>get it right</u>.
- When you've done <u>all the questions</u> under a heading and are <u>completely happy</u>, tick it off.

<u>The Scientific Method (p.221-222)</u> ☑

1) What is a hypothesis? ☑
2) Briefly explain how the peer-review process works. ☑
3) True or false? "Scientific theories are explanations that still need to be accepted." ☑
4) Give two reasons why scientists may come up with different explanations for the same observation. ☑
5) Give one advantage of using models. ☑

<u>Designing Investigations and Collecting Data (p.223-225)</u> ☑

6) What is meant by the term 'valid result'? ☑
7) How could a scientist try to make their investigation a fair test? ☑
8) Why is a control experiment important in an investigation? ☑
9) Give a potential hazard in an experiment where a Bunsen burner is used.
   Explain what you would do to reduce the risk. ☑
10) Give one reason why it is better to have a large sample size than a small sample size in an investigation. ☑
11) What are precise results? ☑
12) What type of error is caused if a measurement is wrong by the same amount every time? ☑

<u>Processing and Presenting Data, Units and Equations (p.226-228)</u> ☑

13) How would you calculate: a) the mean of a set of results, b) the range of results? ☑
14) What type of data would you present on a bar chart? ☑
15) What is the intercept of a graph? ☑
16) Sketch a graph showing: a) a positive correlation, b) a negative correlation. ☑
17) Which of the following prefixes is used for a smaller unit: nano or micro? ☑
18) How would you convert a value that has units of J so that it has units of kJ? ☑

<u>Conclusions, Uncertainties and Evaluations (p.229-230)</u> ☑

19) What does it mean if two things are correlated with each other? ☑
20) Why is one set of results on its own not enough to suggest a correlation? ☑
21) How can you calculate the uncertainty of a mean result? ☑
22) Give four things you should consider when evaluating the quality of data. ☑

<u>New Technologies and Risk (p.231)</u> ☑

23) Give one example of a new technology that has improved people's lives. ☑
24) Give one reason why a person might be willing to accept a particular risk. ☑

<u>Communication and Issues Created by Science (p.232)</u> ☑

25) Give an example of how information could be presented in a biased way. ☑
26) State four types of issues that might be created by new scientific developments. ☑

Measuring Techniques

- <u>Chapter BCP8</u> covers <u>practical skills</u> you'll need to know about
  for the course (including at least 15% of your exams).
- You have to do experiments to cover at least <u>16 Practical Activity Groups</u>.
  These are covered in <u>Chapters B1-B6</u>, <u>C1-C6</u> and <u>P1-P6</u> earlier in
  the book. They're <u>highlighted</u> with <u>practical stamps</u> like this one. → **PRACTICAL**
- The following pages cover some <u>extra bits and bobs</u> you need to know
  about practical work. First up, some <u>measuring techniques</u>...

Mass Should Be Measured Using a Balance

1) To measure mass, put the <u>container</u> you're measuring the substance <u>into</u> on the <u>balance</u>.

2) Set the balance to exactly <u>zero</u>. Then <u>add</u> your substance and <u>read off</u> the <u>mass</u>.

3) If you want to transfer the substance to a new container, you need to make sure that the mass you <u>transfer</u> is the <u>same</u> as the mass you <u>measured</u>.

4) There are different ways you can do this. For example:

  - If you're <u>dissolving</u> a mass of a solid in a solvent to make a <u>solution</u>,
    you could <u>wash</u> any remaining solid into the new container using the <u>solvent</u>.

  - You could set the balance <u>to zero</u> before you put your <u>weighing container</u> on the balance.
    Then <u>reweigh</u> the weighing container <u>after</u> you've transferred the substance.
    Use the <u>difference</u> in mass to work out <u>exactly</u> how much substance you've transferred.

Three Ways to Measure Liquids

1) There are a few methods you might use to transfer a volume of liquid:

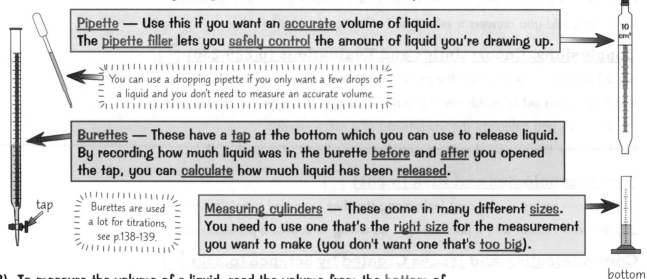

pipette filler

> <u>Pipette</u> — Use this if you want an <u>accurate</u> volume of liquid.
> The <u>pipette filler</u> lets you <u>safely control</u> the amount of liquid you're drawing up.

> You can use a dropping pipette if you only want a few drops of
> a liquid and you don't need to measure an accurate volume.

> <u>Burettes</u> — These have a <u>tap</u> at the bottom which you can use to release liquid.
> By recording how much liquid was in the burette <u>before</u> and <u>after</u> you opened
> the tap, you can <u>calculate</u> how much liquid has been <u>released</u>.

tap

> Burettes are used
> a lot for titrations,
> see p.138-139.

> <u>Measuring cylinders</u> — These come in many different <u>sizes</u>.
> You need to use one that's the <u>right size</u> for the measurement
> you want to make (you don't want one that's <u>too big</u>).

2) To measure the volume of a liquid, read the volume from the <u>bottom</u> of
   the <u>meniscus</u> (the curved upper surface of the liquid) when it's at <u>eye level</u>.

bottom of the meniscus

Measuring Techniques

You Can Measure Gas Volumes

There are a few ways you can measure the volume of a gas:

1) <u>Gas syringe</u> — this is the <u>most accurate</u> way to measure gas volume.

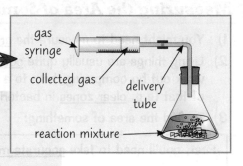

- Make sure the plunger moves <u>smoothly</u>.
- Read the volume from the <u>scale</u> on the syringe.
- <u>Temperature</u> and <u>pressure</u> affect the <u>volume</u> of a gas, so take your readings at <u>room temperature</u> and <u>pressure</u>.
- Make sure the gas syringe is the <u>right size</u> for your measurements.

2) <u>Upturned measuring cylinder</u> filled with <u>water</u> — read more about this on page 239.

3) <u>Counting the bubbles</u> produced.

- This method is <u>less accurate</u>.
- But it will give you <u>results</u> that you can <u>compare</u>.

Always make sure your equipment is <u>sealed</u> so no gas can escape. This will make your results more <u>accurate</u>.

Eureka Cans Measure the Volumes of Solids

1) A <u>eureka can</u> is a <u>beaker with a spout</u>.

2) It's used with a <u>measuring cylinder</u> to find the <u>volume</u> of an <u>irregularly shaped solid object</u> (p.212).

3) Here are a few things you need to do when you <u>use</u> one:

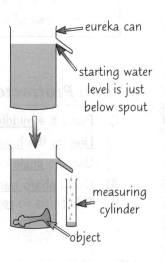

- Fill it with water so the water level is <u>above the spout</u>.
- Let the water <u>drain</u> from the spout, leaving the water level <u>just below</u> the start of the spout. <u>Throw away</u> the water that's drained out.
- Place a clean, dry measuring cylinder underneath the <u>spout</u>. (This means <u>all</u> the water moved by an object goes into the measuring cylinder.)
- After adding the object, wait until the spout·has <u>stopped dripping</u> before measuring the volume. This will give you a more <u>accurate</u> result.

Measure Most Lengths with a Ruler

1) Make sure you <u>choose</u> the <u>right ruler</u> to measure length:
   - In most cases a <u>centimetre ruler</u> can be used.
   - <u>Metre rulers</u> are handy for <u>large</u> distances.
   - <u>Micrometers</u> are used for measuring <u>tiny</u> things (e.g. the <u>diameter of a wire</u>).

2) The ruler should always be <u>alongside</u> what you want to measure.

3) It may be <u>tricky</u> to measure just <u>one</u> of something (e.g. water ripples, p.152). Instead, you can measure the length of <u>ten</u> of them together. Then <u>divide by ten</u> to find the <u>length of one</u>.

4) You might need to take <u>lots of measurements</u> of the <u>same</u> object (e.g. a spring). If so, make sure you always measure from the <u>same point</u> on the object. Draw or stick small <u>markers</u> onto the object to line your ruler up against.

5) Make sure the ruler and the object are always at <u>eye level</u> when you take a reading.

Measuring Techniques

Measuring the Area of Something

1) You might need to measure the <u>area</u> of something (e.g. part of a habitat, a living thing).

2) Living things are usually quite <u>complex shapes</u>. You can make their area easier to work out by comparing them to a <u>simpler shape</u>. You can then work out the area of that (e.g. <u>clear zones</u> in bacterial lawns are roughly <u>circular</u> — see pages 16-17).

3) To find the area of something:

First, you'll need to take <u>accurate measurements</u> of its dimensions.

If you want to <u>measure</u> the area of a <u>field</u> that is <u>rectangular</u>, use a <u>tape measure</u> or a <u>trundle wheel</u> to measure the <u>length</u> and <u>width</u> of the field. Record your readings in metres.

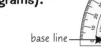

55 m

30 m

Area = 1650 m²

Then you can <u>calculate</u> its <u>area</u>.

Area of a <u>rectangle</u> = <u>length</u> × <u>width</u>.
If your field is 30 m by 55 m, the <u>area</u> would be 30 × 55 = <u>1650 m²</u>.

Here are some examples of other area formulas that may come in useful:

- Area of a triangle = ½ × base × height
- Area of a circle = πr^2

Don't forget the units of area are always something squared, e.g. mm².

Use a Protractor to Find Angles

1) Place the <u>middle</u> of the protractor on the <u>pointy bit</u> of the angle.

2) <u>Line up</u> the <u>base line</u> of the protractor with one line of the angle.

3) Use the <u>scale</u> on the protractor to measure the angle of the other line.

4) Use a <u>sharp pencil</u> to draw lines at an <u>angle</u> (e.g. in ray diagrams). This helps to <u>reduce errors</u> when measuring the angles.

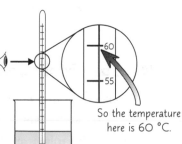

base line

Measure Temperature Using a Thermometer

1) Make sure the <u>bulb</u> of your thermometer is <u>completely under the surface</u> of the substance.

2) If you're taking a <u>starting temperature</u>, you should wait for the temperature to <u>stop changing</u>.

3) Read your measurement off the <u>scale</u> at <u>eye level</u>.

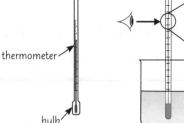

thermometer

bulb

60
55

So the temperature here is 60 °C.

You May Have to Measure the Time Taken for a Change

1) You should use a <u>stopwatch</u> to <u>time</u> experiments. These measure to the nearest <u>0.1 s</u>.

2) Always make sure you <u>start</u> and <u>stop</u> the stopwatch at exactly the right time.

3) You can set an <u>alarm</u> on the stopwatch so you know exactly when to stop an experiment or take a reading.

4) You might be able to use a <u>light gate</u> instead (p.241). This will <u>reduce the errors</u> in your experiment.

stop watch

Chapter BCP8 — Practical Skills

Measuring Techniques and Drawing Apparatus

Measure pH to Find Out How Acidic or Alkaline a Solution Is

You need to be able to decide the best method for <u>measuring pH</u>, depending on what your experiment is.

Indicators

- Indicators are <u>dyes</u> that <u>change colour</u>. They can be used to <u>estimate pH</u>.
- Add a <u>couple of drops</u> of the indicator to the solution you want to test.
- It will <u>change colour</u> depending on if it's in an <u>acid</u> or an <u>alkali</u> (see p.140).

> <u>Universal indicator</u> is a <u>mixture</u> of indicators.
> It changes colour <u>gradually</u> as pH changes.
> It can be used to <u>estimate</u> the pH of a solution based on its colour.

Indicator paper

- There are also <u>paper indicators</u>. These are <u>strips of paper</u> that contain indicator. If you <u>spot</u> some solution onto indicator paper, the paper will <u>change colour</u> to show the pH.

> <u>Litmus paper</u> turns <u>red</u> in acidic conditions and <u>blue</u> in basic conditions.
> <u>Universal indicator paper</u> can be used to <u>estimate</u> the pH based on its colour.

- Indicator paper is <u>useful</u> when:
  1) You <u>don't</u> want to change the colour of <u>all</u> of the substance.
  2) The substance is <u>already</u> coloured (so it might <u>hide</u> the colour of the indicator).
  3) You want to find the pH of a <u>gas</u> — hold a piece of <u>damp indicator paper</u> in a <u>gas sample</u>.

pH probes

- <u>pH probes</u> measure pH <u>electronically</u> (see page 140).
- They are more <u>accurate</u> than indicators.

Make Sure You Can Draw Diagrams of Your Equipment

1) Once you know what <u>apparatus</u> you will use in an experiment, you should write a <u>method</u>.
2) Your <u>method</u> should include a <u>labelled diagram</u> of how your equipment will be <u>set up</u>.
3) Use <u>scientific drawings</u> — each piece of equipment is drawn as if you're looking at it <u>from the side</u>.
4) For example:

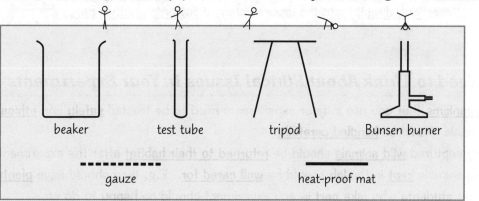

beaker   test tube   tripod   Bunsen burner

gauze   heat-proof mat

5) The <u>beaker</u> and <u>test tube</u> above <u>aren't sealed</u>. To show them <u>sealed</u>, draw a <u>bung</u> in the top.

Experimentus apparatus...

It's too bad, but being a wizard won't help you here. Make sure you get your head down and learn these techniques inside out. They need to be second nature when it comes to any practicals.

Safety and Ethics

<u>Before</u> you start any experiment, you need to know what <u>safety measures</u> you should be taking. They depend on your <u>method</u>, your <u>equipment</u> and the <u>chemicals</u> you're using.

To Make Sure You're Working Safely in the Lab You Need to...

1) Wear <u>sensible clothing</u> (e.g. shoes that will protect your feet from spillages). Also:

   • Wear a <u>lab coat</u> to protect your <u>skin</u> and <u>clothing</u>.

   • Wear <u>safety goggles</u> to protect your <u>eyes</u>, and <u>gloves</u> to protect your <u>hands</u>.

2) Be aware of <u>general safety</u> in the lab. E.g. don't touch any <u>hot equipment</u>.

3) Follow any <u>instructions</u> that your teacher gives you <u>carefully</u>.

4) <u>Chemicals</u> and <u>equipment</u> can be <u>hazardous</u> (dangerous). E.g. some chemicals are <u>flammable</u> (they <u>catch fire easily</u>) — this means you must be careful <u>not</u> to use a <u>Bunsen burner</u> near them.

5) Here are some <u>tips</u> for working with <u>chemicals</u> and <u>equipment</u> safely...

Working with chemicals

1) Make sure you're working in an area that's <u>well ventilated</u> (has a good flow of air).

2) If you're doing an experiment that produces nasty <u>gases</u> (such as chlorine), carry out the experiment in a <u>fume hood</u>. This means the gas <u>can't escape</u> out into the room you're working in.

3) Never <u>touch</u> any chemicals (even if you're wearing gloves):
   • Use a <u>spatula</u> to transfer <u>solids</u> between containers.
   • Carefully <u>pour</u> liquids between containers using a <u>funnel</u>. This will help <u>prevent spillages</u>.

4) Be careful when you're <u>mixing</u> chemicals, as a reaction might occur. E.g. if you're <u>diluting</u> a liquid, always add the <u>concentrated substance</u> to the <u>water</u>. This stops it getting <u>hot</u>.

Working with equipment

1) Use <u>clamp stands</u> to stop masses and equipment falling.

2) Make sure <u>masses</u> are <u>not too heavy</u> (so they <u>don't break</u> the equipment they're used with).

3) Let hot materials <u>cool</u> before moving them. Or wear <u>insulated gloves</u> while handling them.

4) If you're using an <u>immersion heater</u>, you should always let it <u>dry out</u> in air. This is just in case any liquid has <u>leaked</u> inside the heater.

5) When working with electronics, make sure you use a <u>low voltage</u> and <u>current</u>. This prevents the wires <u>overheating</u>. It also stops <u>damage to components</u>.

6) If you're using a <u>laser</u>, you should always wear <u>laser safety goggles</u>. Never <u>look directly into</u> the laser or shine it <u>towards another person</u>.

You Need to Think About Ethical Issues In Your Experiments

Any <u>organisms</u> that you use in your experiments need to be treated <u>safely</u> and <u>ethically</u>. This means:

1) Animals should be <u>handled carefully</u>.

2) Any captured <u>wild animals</u> should be <u>returned to their habitat</u> after the experiment.

3) Any animals <u>kept</u> in the <u>lab</u> should be <u>well cared for</u>. E.g. they should have <u>plenty of space</u>.

4) Other <u>students</u> who <u>take part</u> in any experiment should be <u>happy</u> to do so.

Safety first...

I know — lab safety isn't the most exciting topic. But it's mega important. Not only will it stop you from blowing your eyebrows off, it'll help you pick up more marks in the exam. And that IS worth getting excited about...

Setting Up Experiments

Setting up the equipment for an experiment in the right way is <u>important</u>.

You Can Collect a Gas in a Measuring Cylinder

1) The most accurate way to measure the volume of gas produced is to collect it in a <u>gas syringe</u> (p.235).

2) You can also use a <u>measuring cylinder</u> turned <u>upside down</u> and filled with <u>water</u> to <u>collect gas</u>.

3) Then you can <u>measure</u> the <u>gas volume</u>. Here's how you do it:

- <u>Set up</u> the <u>equipment</u> like in the <u>diagram</u>.
- Record the <u>starting level</u> of the water in the measuring cylinder.
- Any gas from the reaction will pass <u>through</u> the delivery tube and <u>into</u> the <u>measuring cylinder</u>.
- The gas will <u>push the water out</u> of the measuring cylinder.
- Record the <u>end level</u> of water in the measuring cylinder.
- Calculate the <u>volume</u> of gas produced — <u>subtract</u> the <u>end level</u> of water from the <u>starting level</u> of water.

delivery tube

collected gas

measuring cylinder filled with water

reaction mixture

beaker of water

Make sure the delivery tube is inside the measuring cylinder. This stops the gas escaping out into the air.

4) You can use the method above to collect a <u>gas sample</u> to <u>test</u>.

- Use a <u>test tube</u> instead of a measuring cylinder.
- When the test tube is full of gas, you can <u>put a bung in it</u>. This lets you <u>store</u> the gas for later.

You Can Identify the Products of Electrolysis

There's more about electrolysis on p.110-111.

1) When you <u>electrolyse</u> a <u>salt solution</u>:

- At the <u>cathode</u>, you'll get a <u>pure metal</u> coating the electrode OR bubbles of <u>hydrogen gas</u>.
- At the <u>anode</u>, you'll get bubbles of <u>oxygen gas</u> OR <u>chlorine</u> if chloride ions are present.

2) You may have to <u>do some tests</u> to find out what's been <u>made</u>.

3) To do this, you need to <u>set up the equipment</u> correctly to <u>collect</u> any <u>gas</u> that's produced. The easiest way to collect the gas is in a <u>test tube</u>.

4) Here's how to set up the equipment...

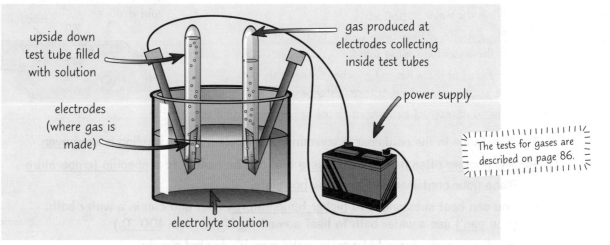

upside down test tube filled with solution

gas produced at electrodes collecting inside test tubes

electrodes (where gas is made)

power supply

electrolyte solution

The tests for gases are described on page 86.

I set up my equipment — they had a blind date at the cinema...

Being good at setting up experiments won't just make your investigations more reliable. You might also be asked to comment on how an experiment's been set up in the exam. So best get learning. You'll thank me for it...

Heating Substances

You need to be able to decide on the <u>best</u> and <u>safest</u> method for heating a substance...

Bunsen Burners Have a Naked Flame

Bunsen burners can heat things <u>quickly</u>. You can easily <u>change</u> how <u>strongly</u> they heat things. You shouldn't use them to heat things that are <u>flammable</u>, in case they <u>catch fire</u>.

Here's how to <u>use</u> a Bunsen burner...

1) Connect the Bunsen burner to a <u>gas tap</u>. Check that the <u>hole</u> is <u>closed</u>.

2) Place the Bunsen burner on a <u>heat-proof mat</u>.

3) Light a <u>splint</u> and hold it over the Bunsen burner.

4) Now, <u>turn on</u> the gas. The Bunsen burner should light with a <u>yellow flame</u>.

5) <u>Open</u> the <u>hole</u> to turn the flame <u>blue</u>. The <u>more open</u> the hole, the <u>hotter</u> the flame.

6) Heat things <u>just above</u> the <u>blue cone</u> — this is the <u>hottest</u> part of the flame.

7) When the Bunsen burner <u>isn't heating</u> anything, <u>close</u> the hole. This makes the flame <u>yellow</u> and <u>easy to see</u>.

8) If you're heating a container (with your substance in it) <u>in</u> the flame, hold it at the <u>top</u> with a pair of <u>tongs</u>.

9) If you're heating a substance in a <u>test tube</u>, make sure that the test tube is <u>pointing away from you</u>.

10) If you're heating a container <u>over</u> the flame, put a <u>tripod and gauze</u> over the Bunsen burner before you light it. Then place the container on the gauze.

splint

Heat-proof mat

Hole is closed

to gas

Hottest part of the flame

Hole is open

to gas

Water Baths & Electric Heaters Have Set Temperatures

1) A <u>water bath</u> is a <u>container</u> filled with <u>water</u>. It can be heated to a <u>specific temperature</u>.

2) A <u>simple</u> water bath can be made by heating a <u>beaker of water</u> over a <u>Bunsen burner</u>.
   - The temperature is checked with a <u>thermometer</u>.
   - However, it's <u>hard</u> to keep the temperature of the water <u>constant</u>.

3) An <u>electric water bath</u> will <u>check</u> and <u>change</u> the temperature for you. Here's how you use one:

   - <u>Set</u> the <u>temperature</u> on the water bath.
   - Allow the water to <u>heat up</u>.
   - Place your container (with your substance in it) in the water bath using <u>tongs</u>.
   - The level of the water <u>outside</u> the container should be <u>just above</u> the level of the substance <u>inside</u> it.
   - The substance will be warmed to the <u>same temperature</u> as the water.

   A water bath

   rubber duck

   reaction container

   temperature control

   The substance in the container is surrounded by water, so the heating is very <u>even</u>.

4) <u>Electric heaters</u> often have a metal <u>plate</u> that can be heated to a <u>specific temperature</u>.
   - Place your container on <u>top</u> of the <u>hot plate</u>.
   - You can heat substances to <u>higher temperatures</u> than you can in a water bath. (You <u>can't</u> use a water bath to heat something higher than <u>100 °C</u>.)
   - You have to <u>stir</u> the substance to make sure it's <u>heated evenly</u>.

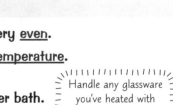
Handle any glassware you've heated with tongs until you're sure it's cooled down.

A bath and an electric heater — how I spend my January nights...

My science teacher used to play power ballads when the Bunsens were alight. Then he'd sway like he was at a gig.

Working with Electronics

Electrical devices are used in loads of experiments. Make sure you know how to use them.

You Have to Interpret Circuit Diagrams

1) You can plan and build a circuit using a circuit diagram.
2) To make a circuit diagram, you need to know all of the circuit symbols on page 172.

There Are a Few Ways to Measure Potential Difference and Current

Voltmeters Measure Potential Difference

1) Connect the voltmeter in parallel (p.179) across the component you want to test.
2) The wires that come with a voltmeter are usually red (positive) and black (negative). These go into the red and black coloured ports on the voltmeter.
3) Then read the potential difference from the scale (or from the screen if the voltmeter is digital).

Ammeters Measure Current

1) Connect the ammeter in series (p.178) with the component you want to test.
2) Ammeters usually have red and black ports to show you where to connect your wires.
3) Read off the current shown on the scale (or screen).

Turn your circuit off between readings. This stops wires overheating and affecting your results.

Multimeters Measure Both

1) Multimeters measure a range of things — usually potential difference, current and resistance.
2) To find potential difference, plug the red wire into the port that has a 'V' (for volts).
3) To find the current, use the port labelled 'A' (for amps).
4) The dial on the multimeter should then be turned to the relevant section — for example, to measure the current in amps, turn the dial to 'A'.
5) The screen will display the value you're measuring.

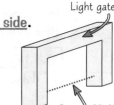

Light Gates Measure Time, Speed and Acceleration

1) A light gate sends a beam of light from one side of the gate to a detector on the other side.
2) When something passes through the gate, the light beam is interrupted.
3) The gate measures when the beam was interrupted and how long it was interrupted for.
4) Light gates can be connected to a computer.
5) To find the speed of an object, type the length of the object into the computer. The computer will calculate the speed of the object as it passes through the beam.
6) To measure acceleration, use an object that interrupts the signal twice, e.g. a piece of card with a gap cut into the middle.
7) The light gate measures the speed for each section of the object. It uses this to calculate the object's acceleration. This can then be read from the computer screen.
8) Light gates can be used instead of a stop watch. This will reduce the errors in your experiment.

Light gate

Beam of light

Piece of card

Have a look at page 192 for an example of a light gate being used.

A light gate is better than a heavy one...

After finishing this page, you should be able to take on any electrical experiment that they throw at you... ouch.

Investigating Ecosystems Data

Pages 41-42 show you how to <u>investigate ecosystems</u> — here's how you can get the <u>most</u> from your <u>data</u>.

Organisms Should Be Sampled At Random Sites in an Area

1) If you want to know the <u>distribution</u> of an organism in an area, or its <u>population size</u>, you can take population samples using <u>quadrats</u> or <u>transects</u> (see pages 40-42).

2) If you only take samples from <u>one part</u> of the area, your results will be <u>biased</u> — they may not <u>accurately represent</u> the <u>whole area</u>.

3) To make sure that your sampling isn't <u>biased</u>, it should be <u>random</u>. For example:

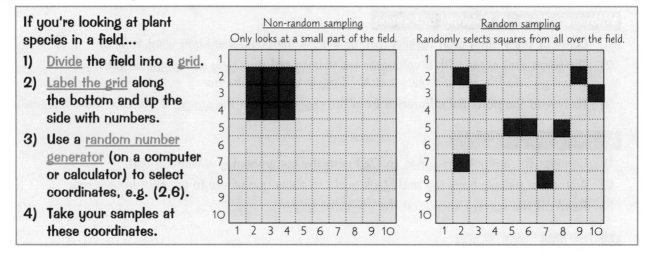

If you're looking at plant species in a field...

1) <u>Divide</u> the field into a <u>grid</u>.

2) <u>Label the grid</u> along the bottom and up the side with numbers.

3) Use a <u>random number generator</u> (on a computer or calculator) to select coordinates, e.g. (2,6).

4) Take your samples at these coordinates.

<u>Non-random sampling</u>
Only looks at a small part of the field.

<u>Random sampling</u>
Randomly selects squares from all over the field.

Percentiles Tell you Where in Your Data Set a Data Point Lies

1) Percentiles divide a data set into <u>one hundred equal chunks</u>.

2) Each chunk is <u>one percentile</u>. This means it represents <u>one percent</u> of the data.

3) The <u>value of a percentile</u> tells you <u>what percentage</u> of the data set has a <u>lower value</u> than the data points in that percentile.

4) E.g. an <u>oak tree</u> is in the <u>90th percentile</u> for <u>height</u> in a forest. This means that <u>90%</u> of the <u>trees</u> in the forest are <u>shorter</u> than the oak tree.

5) Percentiles can be used to give a <u>better idea</u> of the <u>spread</u> of data than the <u>range</u> (the difference between the lowest and highest values — see page 226). For example:

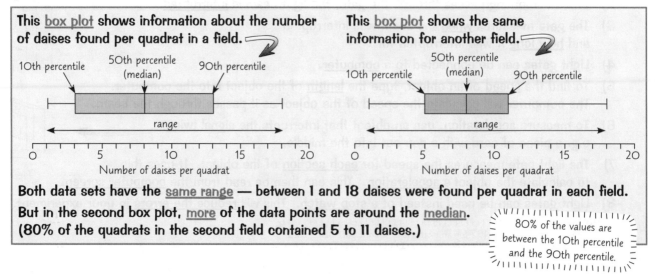

This <u>box plot</u> shows information about the number of daises found per quadrat in a field.

10th percentile
50th percentile (median)
90th percentile
range
Number of daises per quadrat

This <u>box plot</u> shows the same information for another field.

50th percentile (median)
10th percentile
90th percentile
range
Number of daises per quadrat

Both data sets have the <u>same range</u> — between 1 and 18 daises were found per quadrat in each field.

But in the second box plot, <u>more</u> of the data points are around the <u>median</u>. (80% of the quadrats in the second field contained 5 to 11 daises.)

80% of the values are between the 10th percentile and the 90th percentile.

Purrcentiles tell you where the cat lies in the data set...

Sampling is an important part of an investigation. It needs to be done randomly, or the data won't be worth much.

Answers

p.1 — Cells and Genetic Material
Q1 As one long circular strand of DNA *[1 mark]* or in a plasmid *[1 mark]*.

p.2 — Cells and Microscopes
Q1 Select the objective lens with the lowest power *[1 mark]* and move the stage up so the slide is just underneath the objective lens *[1 mark]*. Looking through the eyepiece, move the stage downwards until the specimen is nearly in focus *[1 mark]*. Move the fine adjustment knob until you get a clear image *[1 mark]*.

p.3 — DNA and Characteristics
Q1 Its entire genetic material *[1 mark]*.
Q2 a) An organism's genotype is the combination of alleles it has for each gene *[1 mark]*.
b) An organism's phenotype is the characteristics that it displays *[1 mark]*.

p.4 — Genetic Diagrams
Q1 Tt *[1 mark]*

p.5 — More Genetic Diagrams
Q1 A carrier is someone who has a copy of the (recessive) allele that causes the genetic disorder, but doesn't actually have the disorder *[1 mark]*.

p.6 — Genome Research and Testing
Q1 E.g. the amniotic fluid could be sampled *[1 mark]* to get some of the fetus' DNA, which could be tested for genetic variants linked to a disorder *[1 mark]*.

p.7 — Genetic Engineering
Q1 It can improve the yield of the crop *[1 mark]*, because herbicide-resistant crops can be sprayed with herbicides to kill weeds without the crop being damaged *[1 mark]*.

p.8 — Health and Disease
Q1 A disease that cannot be passed from one organism to another *[1 mark]*.

p.9 — How Disease Spreads
Q1 It's spread when infected leaves rub against healthy leaves *[1 mark]*.

p.10 — More on How Disease Spreads
Q1 a bacterium *[1 mark]*

p.11 — Defending Against Pathogens
Q1 Platelets prevent microorganisms from entering the blood through wounds in the skin *[1 mark]* by clumping together to form blood clots that plug/seal the wound *[1 mark]*.

p.12 — The Human Immune System
Q1 E.g. antibodies disable the pathogen / antibodies 'tag' the pathogens, which helps other white blood cells to find them and destroy them *[1 mark]*.
Q2 Memory cells remain in the blood after the first infection with a pathogen *[1 mark]*. If the same pathogen enters the body again, the memory cells will quickly make the antibodies to kill it *[1 mark]*.

p.13 — Reducing and Preventing the Spread of Disease
Q1 It helps to reduce the spread of diseases that are spread in water *[1 mark]*. / It helps to reduce the spread of pathogens present in urine / faeces *[1 mark]*.

p.14 — Reducing and Preventing the Spread of Disease
Q1 Benefit: e.g. crop rotation stops pathogen populations getting too big *[1 mark]*. Cost: e.g. it can be costly for farms if they have to grow different crops every year *[1 mark]*.

p.15 — Vaccinations
Q1 antibodies *[1 mark]*

p.16 — Culturing Microorganisms
Q1 To show that any difference in the growth of the bacteria is only due to the effect of the antibiotic used *[1 mark]*.

p.17 — Culturing Microorganisms
Q1 a) A *[1 mark]*
b) diameter = 13 mm
radius = 13 ÷ 2 = 6.5 mm
$\pi r^2 = \pi \times 6.5^2$ *[1 mark]*
= 132.7... = 133 mm² *[1 mark]*

p.18 — Non-Communicable Diseases
Q1 E.g. eating too much *[1 mark]*, not exercising *[1 mark]*.

p.19 — More on Non-Communicable Diseases
Q1 Any two from: e.g. cirrhosis / CVD / cancer. *[2 marks — 1 mark for each correct answer.]*

p.20 — Interpreting Data on Disease
Q1 A bigger sample size makes it more likely that more of the different characteristics present in the whole population will be included in the sample *[1 mark]*.

p.21 — Investigating Pulse Rate
Q1 The time taken for the heart rate to return to its normal resting rate after exercise *[1 mark]*.

p.22 — Treating Disease
Q1 bacteria *[1 mark]*

p.23 — Treating Cardiovascular Disease
Q1 E.g. risk of infection / losing a lot of blood *[1 mark]*.

p.24 — Developing New Medicines
Q1 In a double-blind trial, patients are randomly put into two groups — one group receives the drug and the other receives a placebo *[1 mark]*. Neither the patient nor the doctor knows whether the patient is getting the drug or a placebo until all of the results have been gathered *[1 mark]*.

p.27 — Enzymes
Q1 33 ÷ 60 = 0.55 cm³/second *[1 mark]*

p.28 — Photosynthesis
Q1 If it gets too hot, the enzymes that control photosynthesis might denature *[1 mark]* so the plants might not be able to photosynthesise any more *[1 mark]*.

p.29 — Investigating Photosynthesis
Q1 a) The leaf would turn blue-black *[1 mark]*.
b) The plant would have been photosynthesising whilst in the light *[1 mark]*. So it would have produced starch, which makes iodine solution turn blue-black *[1 mark]*.

p.30 — Investigating the Rate of Photosynthesis
Q1 Keep the distance from the light source the same for the plant at each temperature *[1 mark]*.

p.31 — Diffusion, Osmosis and Active Transport
Q1 E.g. active transport requires energy and diffusion doesn't *[1 mark]*. Active transport moves particles from an area of lower concentration to an area of higher concentration, but diffusion moves particles from an area of higher concentration to an area of lower concentration *[1 mark]*.

p.32 — Transport in Plants and Prokaryotes
Q1 Each branch of a plant's roots is covered in millions of root hair cells *[1 mark]*, which gives the plant a big surface area for absorbing water and mineral ions from the soil *[1 mark]*.

p.34 — Investigating Diffusion and Osmosis
Q1 percentage change $= \dfrac{11.4 - 13.3}{13.3} \times 100$
= –14.3% *[2 marks for correct answer, 1 mark for correct answer without minus sign.]*
Q2 That it is also 0.3 mol/dm³ *[1 mark]*.

p.35 — Xylem and Phloem
Q1 Xylem is made up of dead cells joined together *[1 mark]* with no end walls between them and a hole down the middle *[1 mark]*. It is strengthened by lignin *[1 mark]*.

p.36 — Stomata
Q1 They open during the day to let carbon dioxide and oxygen in and out *[1 mark]* and to let water vapour out *[1 mark]*.

p.37 — Transpiration Rate
Q1 When there is more air movement, transpiration is faster *[1 mark]*. This is because water vapour around the leaf is swept away more quickly *[1 mark]*. This means that there's a higher concentration of water vapour inside the leaf compared to outside *[1 mark]* and so water moves out of the leaf quickly by diffusion *[1 mark]*.

p.38 — Using a Potometer
Q1 E.g. temperature, air movement *[2 marks — 1 mark for each correct answer.]*

p.39 — Ecosystems and Interactions Between Organisms
Q1 Any two from: e.g. availability of food / number of predators / presence of pathogens / competition *[2 marks — 1 mark for each correct answer.]*

p.40 — Abiotic Factors and Investigating Distribution
Q1 This is when toxic chemicals build up the further along a food chain you go *[1 mark]*.

p.41 — Investigating Ecosystems
Q1 Population size = (number in first sample × number in second sample) ÷ number in second sample previously marked
= (22 × 26) ÷ 4
= 143 crabs *[2 marks for correct answer, otherwise 1 mark for correct working.]*

p.42 — More on Investigating Ecosystems
Q1 Mark out a line in the area you want to study using a tape measure *[1 mark]*. Place quadrats at intervals / next to each other along the line *[1 mark]*. Count and record the organisms in each quadrat *[1 mark]*.

244

Answers

p.43 — Investigating Factors Affecting Distribution

Q1 The presence of many species of lichen indicates the air is clean *[1 mark]* because some species of lichen are sensitive to pollution in the air *[1 mark]*.

p.44 — Food Chains and Food Webs

Q1 The number of hawks might increase because there will be more mice for them to eat *[1 mark]*.

p.45 — Making and Breaking Biological Molecules

Q1 a) simple sugars *[1 mark]*
b) amino acids *[1 mark]*

p.46 — Testing for Biological Molecules

Q1 Protein is present *[1 mark]*.

p.47 — Cycles in Ecosystems

Q1 Any two from: e.g. respiration / combustion / decomposition *[2 marks — 1 mark for each correct answer.]*

p.48 — More on Cycles in Ecosystems

Q1 By evaporation / transpiration *[1 mark]*.

p.50 — Respiration

Q1 glucose + oxygen → carbon dioxide + water *[1 mark for correct reactants, 1 mark for correct products.]*

p.51 — More on Respiration

Q1 Ethanol and carbon dioxide *[1 mark]*.

p.52 — The Cell Cycle and Mitosis

Q1 E.g. the cell grows *[1 mark]*, increases the amount of its sub-cellular structures *[1 mark]* and copies its DNA *[1 mark]*.

p.53 — Microscopy

Q1 They've allowed us to see cells in more detail *[1 mark]*, which has allowed scientists to understand how the internal structures of sub-cellular structures are related to their functions *[1 mark]*.

p.54 — More Microscopy

Q1 actual size = measured size ÷ magnification *[1 mark]*
= 0.7 mm ÷ 400 = 0.00175 mm *[1 mark]*
0.00175 mm × 1000 = 1.75 μm *[1 mark]*

p.55 — Sexual Reproduction and Meiosis

Q1 During fertilisation, a male gamete fuses with a female gamete to form a zygote *[1 mark]*. Gametes need half the chromosome number so that the zygote ends up with the full number of chromosomes *[1 mark]*.

p.56 — Stem Cells

Q1 The tips of plant shoots contain meristem tissue *[1 mark]*. Meristems produce stem cells that are able to divide and form any cell type in the plant *[1 mark]*. This means the plant is able to produce all the different specialised cells it needs in order to grow into a new plant *[1 mark]*.

p.58 — Exchange of Materials

Q1 Surface area:
$(1 \times 1) \times 2 = 2$
$(2 \times 1) \times 4 = 8$
$2 + 8 = 10$ μm² *[1 mark]*
Volume:
$1 \times 1 \times 2 = 2$ μm³ *[1 mark]*
So the surface area to volume ratio is 10 : 2, which is 5 : 1 in its simplest form *[1 mark]*.

p.59 — Human Exchange Surfaces

Q1 E.g. they have a large surface area / they have very thin walls / they have a good blood supply *[1 mark]*.

p.60 — The Circulatory System

Q1 the right ventricle *[1 mark]*

p.61 — Blood Vessels

Q1 They have a big lumen to help the blood flow even though the pressure is low *[1 mark]*. They have valves to stop the blood flowing backwards *[1 mark]*.

Q2 E.g. capillaries have permeable walls, so that substances can diffuse in and out of them *[1 mark]*. Their walls are only one cell thick, so substances can diffuse in and out quickly *[1 mark]*.

p.62 — Blood

Q1 haemoglobin *[1 mark]*

Q2 Any three from: e.g. red blood cells have a large surface area for absorbing oxygen. / They don't have a nucleus, which allows more room for carrying oxygen. / They contain haemoglobin, which allows them to carry oxygen. / They're small and flexible so they can easily pass through tiny capillaries.
[3 marks — 1 mark for each correct answer.]

p.63 — The Nervous System

Q1 brain *[1 mark]*, spinal cord *[1 mark]*

p.64 — Reflexes

Q1 The stimulus is detected by sensory receptors *[1 mark]*, which send impulses along a sensory neurone to the CNS *[1 mark]*. The impulse is sent along a relay neurone *[1 mark]*. It is then passed on to a motor neurone and travels along it to the effector *[1 mark]*.

p.65 — Hormones in Reproduction

Q1 FSH/follicle-stimulating hormone *[1 mark]*

p.66 — Contraception

Q1 E.g. oral contraceptives can have unpleasant side-effects. / She might find it difficult to take her pills regularly *[1 mark]*.

p.67 — Homeostasis and Blood Sugar Level

Q1 When the blood glucose level is too high, the pancreas releases insulin *[1 mark]*. Insulin causes glucose to move into cells *[1 mark]*. Glucose is converted to glycogen in liver and muscle cells *[1 mark]*.

p.68 — Natural Selection and Evolution

Q1 Some of the musk oxen may have had a genetic variant/allele which gave them thicker fur *[1 mark]*. Those musk oxen would have been more likely to survive and reproduce *[1 mark]* and so pass on their genetic variants/alleles for thicker fur *[1 mark]*. Thicker fur may have become more common in the population over time *[1 mark]*.

p.69 — Evidence for Evolution

Q1 Fossils can show what organisms that lived a long time ago looked like *[1 mark]*. Arranging them in date order shows how organisms gradually changed/developed *[1 mark]*.

p.70 — Selective Breeding

Q1 He should choose the bean plants that are best at surviving the drought *[1 mark]* and breed them with each other *[1 mark]*. He should then continue this process over several generations *[1 mark]*.

p.71 — Classification

Q1 E.g. organisms may look very similar but have very different DNA sequences *[1 mark]*.

p.72 — Biodiversity

Q1 E.g. chemicals used in farming may pollute lakes, rivers and oceans *[1 mark]*, affecting plants and animals that live in the water *[1 mark]*.

p.73 — More on Biodiversity

Q1 The Siberian tigers could be bred in zoos and then released back into the wild *[1 mark]*.

p.74 — Maintaining Biodiversity

Q1 E.g. undiscovered plant species may contain new chemicals that we could use in medicines *[1 mark]*. If these plants become extinct we could miss out on new medicines *[1 mark]*.

p.76 — States of Matter

Q1 In a solid there are strong forces of attraction between particles *[1 mark]*. In a liquid the forces of attraction between particles are weaker than in a solid *[1 mark]*. In a gas there are no forces of attraction between particles *[1 mark]*.

p.77 — Changing State

Q1 a) solid *[1 mark]*
b) liquid *[1 mark]*
c) liquid *[1 mark]*
d) gas *[1 mark]*

p.78 — Chemical Formulas

Q1 5 *[1 mark]*

p.79 — Chemical Equations

Q1 $2Fe + 3Cl_2 \rightarrow 2FeCl_3$ *[1 mark]*

p.80 — Endothermic and Exothermic Reactions

Q1 a) endothermic *[1 mark]*
b) The temperature will decrease *[1 mark]*.

p.81 — Bond Energies

Q1 It is an exothermic process *[1 mark]*, because energy is released to the surroundings when bonds are made *[1 mark]*.

p.82 — The Evolution of the Atmosphere

Q1 Any two from: e.g. carbon dioxide dissolved in the oceans *[1 mark]* / green plants and algae used carbon dioxide for photosynthesis *[1 mark]* / dead sea creatures formed sedimentary rocks, oil and gas which trapped carbon *[1 mark]*.

p.83 — Combustion and Greenhouse Gases

Q1 carbon dioxide/CO_2 *[1 mark]*, water/H_2O *[1 mark]*, carbon monoxide/CO *[1 mark]*, soot/carbon *[1 mark]*

p.84 — Climate Change

Q1 Any three from: e.g. polar ice caps melting / sea levels rising / changing rainfall patterns / some regions may have too much or too little water / it may be difficult to produce food / there may be an increase in the frequency and severity of storms *[3 marks — 1 mark for each correct answer]*.

p.85 — Reducing Greenhouse Gas Emissions

Q1 E.g. governments can put a cap on the amount of greenhouse gases that a business can emit and issue licences for set amounts of emissions up to this point *[1 mark]*. Governments can tax companies according to the amount of greenhouse gases that they emit *[1 mark]*.

Answers

p.86 — Pollutants and Tests for Gases
Q1 E.g. acid gas scrubbers fitted to power stations can remove nitrogen oxide before they are released into the atmosphere *[1 mark]*. Catalytic converters fitted to cars also remove some of the nitrogen oxides from exhaust fumes *[1 mark]*.

p.87 — Water Treatment
Q1 E.g. to force dissolved gases out of the water *[1 mark]* and to remove ions that react with oxygen to form solid oxides *[1 mark]*.

p.88 — More on Water Treatment
Q1 E.g. the seawater is passed through a membrane that only lets water molecules through *[1 mark]*. Ions and other molecules cannot pass through the membrane and are separated from the water *[1 mark]*.

p.90 — The History of the Atom
Q1 In the plum pudding model, the atom is a ball of positive charge with electrons stuck in *[1 mark]*.

p.91 — The Atom
Q1 In the nucleus *[1 mark]*.
Q2 nucleus, atomic diameter, simple molecule, nanoparticle *[2 marks for all 4 correct, 1 mark if up to 2 are incorrect]*.

p.92 — Atoms and Isotopes
Q1 Bromine-79: 35 protons, 35 electrons and (79 − 35 =) 44 neutrons *[1 mark]*. Bromine-81: 35 protons, 35 electrons and (81 − 35 =) 46 neutrons *[1 mark]*.

p.93 — The Periodic Table
Q1 2 *[1 mark]*

p.94 — Electronic Structure
Q1 2, 8, 8, 1 or
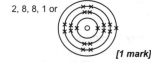
[1 mark]

p.95 — Metals and Non-Metals
Q1 At the far right of the periodic table *[1 mark]*.
Q2 Any three from: e.g. metals tend to be shiny / good conductors of heat / good at conducting electricity / have high melting/boiling points / usually solid at room temperature / form compounds with ionic or metallic bonds / tend to have high densities *[1 mark for each, up to 3 marks]*.

p.96 — Group 1 Elements
Q1 As you go further down the group, the outer electron is further away from the nucleus *[1 mark]*. This means the attraction between the nucleus and the electron decreases *[1 mark]*, so the electron is more easily removed and reactivity increases *[1 mark]*.

p.97 — Reactions of Group 1 Elements
Q1 lithium *[1 mark]*

p.98 — More Reactions of Group 1 Elements
Q1 $2Rb + 2H_2O \rightarrow 2RbOH + H_2$ *[1 mark for correct reactants and products, 1 mark for correctly balanced equation.]*

p.99 — Group 7 Elements
Q1 Bromine would be a solid at this temperature *[1 mark]*. The melting points of the halogens increase as you go down the group, so at the melting point of chlorine, bromine would still be solid *[1 mark]*.

p.100 — Displacement Reactions of Group 7
Q1 The chlorine displaced the iodine from the solution *[1 mark]*.

p.101 — Group 0 Elements
Q1 Xenon has a higher boiling point than neon *[1 mark]*.
Q2 Argon has a full outer shell *[1 mark]* which is very stable *[1 mark]*.

p.102 — Ions
Q1 18 *[1 mark]*

p.103 — Ionic Bonding
Q1
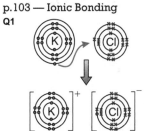
[1 mark for arrow showing electron transferred from potassium to chlorine, 1 mark for correct outer shell electron configurations, 1 mark for correct charges.]

p.104 — Ionic Compounds
Q1 Li_2O *[1 mark]*

p.106 — Metallic Bonding
Q1 a) E.g. It contains free electrons which are able to carry an electrical current *[1 mark]*.
b) The layers of ions in a metal can slide over each other without the metallic bonds breaking *[1 mark]*.

p.107 — Reactivity and Reactions of Metals
Q1 Lead would not displace zinc from zinc chloride solution *[1 mark]*, as it's lower than zinc in the reactivity series/it's less reactive than zinc *[1 mark]*.

p.108 — More Reactions of Metals
Q1 E.g. copper / silver *[1 mark]*

p.109 — Extracting Metals
Q1 Iron is less reactive than carbon *[1 mark]* so you could extract iron from its ore by reducing it with carbon *[1 mark]*.

p.110 — Electrolysis
Q1 a) chlorine/Cl_2 *[1 mark]*
b) sodium atoms/Na *[1 mark]*

p.111 — Electrolysis of Aqueous Solutions
Q1 chlorine gas *[1 mark]*

p.112 — Covalent Bonding
Q1 NH_3 *[1 mark]*

p.113 — Simple Covalent Substances
Q1 O_2 is a small molecule, so the intermolecular forces between molecules of O_2 are weak *[1 mark]* and don't need much energy to break, so oxygen has a low boiling point *[1 mark]*.

p.114 — Empirical Formulas
Q1 The smallest whole number ratio of atoms in a compound *[1 mark]*.
Q2 The largest number that divides into both 8 and 18 is 2.
C: 8 ÷ 2 = 4
H: 18 ÷ 2 = 9
Empirical formula = C_4H_9 *[1 mark]*

p.115 — Homologous Series and Alkanes
Q1 a) E.g. $C_{10}H_{22}$ is more viscous than C_5H_{12} / C_5H_{12} is less viscous than $C_{10}H_{22}$ *[1 mark]*.
b) E.g. $C_{10}H_{22}$ has a higher boiling point than C_5H_{12} / C_5H_{12} has a lower boiling point than $C_{10}H_{22}$ *[1 mark]*.
c) E.g. $C_{10}H_{22}$ is less flammable than C_5H_{12} / C_5H_{12} is more flammable than $C_{10}H_{22}$ *[1 mark]*.

p.116 — Fractional Distillation of Crude Oil
Q1 At the bottom *[1 mark]*.

p.117 — Uses of Crude Oil
Q1 E.g. the short chain hydrocarbon products can be used as fuels / long chain hydrocarbons will not be wasted / without cracking we would need more crude oil to meet the demands for petrol *[1 mark]*.

p.119 — Polymers
Q1 E.g. doesn't soften when heated, strong, hard, stiff *[1 mark for each, up to 4 marks]*.

p.120 — Giant Covalent Structures
Q1 Any two from, e.g. giant covalent structure / covalent bonding / high melting point *[1 mark for each similarity, up to 2 marks]*.

p.121 — Bulk Properties of Materials
Q1 Charged particles/electrons or ions that are free to move *[1 mark]*.

p.122 — Types of Materials
Q1 e.g. concrete / carbon fibre *[1 mark]*

p.123 — Materials and their Uses
Q1 E.g. glass would be the best choice *[1 mark]*. The equipment shouldn't soften or melt below 300 °C, so poly(propene) is a poor choice *[1 mark]*. Aluminium is fairly reactive, so could react with the chemicals *[1 mark]*.

p.124 — Reuse and Recycling
Q1 Recycling PET uses fewer resources and less energy than making 'new' PET *[1 mark]*.

p.125 — Life Cycle Assessments
Q1 Any two from: e.g. the energy required to extract the raw materials / whether the raw materials are renewable or not / whether other harmful emissions are produced / whether the waste products are harmful or not / how environmentally friendly the cars are to dispose of *[1 mark for each, up to 2 marks]*.

p.126 — Nanoparticles
Q1 The molecule with a diameter of 0.2 nm *[1 mark]*.

p.127 — Uses of Nanoparticles
Q1 Any two from: e.g. catalysts / to deliver drugs / stronger plastics / molecular sieves *[1 mark for each, up to 2 marks]*.

p.129 — Purity and Mixtures
Q1 The sample melts over a range of temperatures *[1 mark]*. The melting point is lower than that of pure aspirin *[1 mark]*.

p.130 — Chromatography
Q1 filter paper *[1 mark]*

p.131 — Interpreting Chromatograms
Q1 $Rf = \dfrac{\text{distance travelled by solute}}{\text{distance travelled by solvent front}} = \dfrac{4.8}{6.0}$ *[1 mark]*
= 0.80 *[1 mark]*

Answers

p.132 — Distillation
Q1 Liquid B will be collected in the first fraction *[1 mark]* because it has the lowest boiling point *[1 mark]*.

p.133 — Separating Mixtures
Q1 E.g. gently heat the solution to evaporate off some of the water *[1 mark]*. Stop heating once about half of the water has evaporated / once copper sulfate crystals start to form *[1 mark]*. Allow the solution to cool *[1 mark]*. Filter the crystals out of the solution *[1 mark]* and dry them in a warm place / desiccator / drying oven *[1 mark]*.

p.134 — Relative Mass
Q1 a) A_r of H = 1.0 and A_r of O = 16.0
M_r of H_2O = (2 × 1.0) + 16.0 = 18.0 *[1 mark]*
b) A_r of Li = 6.9, A_r of O = 16.0 and A_r of H = 1.0
So M_r of LiOH = 6.9 + 16.0 + 1.0 = 23.9 *[1 mark]*
c) A_r of H = 1.0, A_r of S = 32.1 and A_r of O = 16.0
M_r of H_2SO_4 = (2 × 1.0) + 32.1 + (4 × 16.0) = 98.1 *[1 mark]*
Q2 A_r of K = 39.1, A_r of O = 16.0 and A_r of H = 1.0
M_r of KOH = 39.1 + 16.0 + 1.0 = 56.1 *[1 mark]*
$\frac{39.1}{56.1}$ × 100 = 69.7% *[1 mark]*

p.135 — Conservation of Mass
Q1 Total mass of reactants = 6.00 g
Known mass of products = 3.36 g
Mass of CO_2 = 6.00 − 3.36 *[1 mark]*
= 2.64 g *[1 mark]*

p.136 — More on Conservation of Mass
Q1 One of the reactants is a gas *[1 mark]* and the products are solid, liquid or aqueous *[1 mark]*.
Q2 The mass will decrease *[1 mark]*.

p.137 — Acids, Alkalis and Standard Solutions
Q1 sulfuric acid + sodium hydroxide → sodium sulfate + water *[1 mark]*

p.138 — Titrations
Q1 The indicator changes colour *[1 mark]*.

p.139 — Evaluating Titration Data
Q1 Mean = (16.40 + 16.45 + 16.35) ÷ 3
= 49.20 ÷ 3 = 16.40 cm³ *[1 mark]*

p.140 — Acids, Alkalis and pH
Q1 a) acidic *[1 mark]*
b) red *[1 mark]*

p.141 — Reactions of Acids
Q1 sodium chloride/NaCl *[1 mark]* and hydrogen/H_2 *[1 mark]*

p.142 — Making Salts
Q1 E.g. add the carbonate to the acid *[1 mark]*. The reaction has finished when the excess solid sinks to the bottom of the flask *[1 mark]*. Filter off the excess solid *[1 mark]*. Gently heat the solution to evaporate off some of the water, then leave it to cool and form crystals *[1 mark]*. Filter off the solid and leave it to dry *[1 mark]*.

p.143 — Rates of Reactions
Q1 It will increase the rate of the reaction *[1 mark]*.

p.144 — Reaction Rates and Catalysts
Q1 A catalyst is a substance that increases the rate of a reaction *[1 mark]*, without being changed or used up in the reaction *[1 mark]*.

p.145 — Measuring Reaction Rates
Q1 E.g. using a gas syringe / bubbling into an upturned measuring cylinder filled with water *[1 mark]*.

p.146 — Finding Reaction Rates from Graphs
Q1 Volume of gas produced after 10 s = 12 cm³ *[1 mark]*.
Change in time = 10 s, so
reaction rate = 12 cm³ ÷ 10 s = 1.2 cm³/s *[1 mark]*.

p.147 — Using Tangents to Find Reaction Rates
Q1 a) E.g.

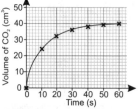

[1 mark for correctly plotting all seven points, 1 mark for drawing a line of best fit.]

b) E.g.

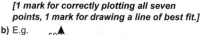
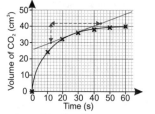

change in y = 42 − 30 = 12
change in x = 44 − 12 = 32
rate = (change in y) ÷ (change in x) = 12 ÷ 32
= 0.38 cm³/s
[1 mark for drawing a tangent at 26 s. 1 mark for correctly finding a change in y from the tangent. 1 mark for correctly finding a change in x from the tangent. 1 mark for a final answer between 0.28 cm³/s and 0.48 cm³/s.]

p.148 — Dynamic Equilibrium
Q1 E.g. a reversible reaction is one where the products can react with each other to produce the reactants *[1 mark]*.
Q2 Temperature, *[1 mark]* pressure *[1 mark]* and concentration *[1 mark]*.

p.150 — Wave Basics
Q1 The wavelength is the distance between one point on a wave (one disturbance) and the same point on the next wave (the next disturbance) *[1 mark]*.

p.151 — Wave Speed
Q1 wave speed = frequency × wavelength, so
frequency = wave speed ÷ wavelength *[1 mark]*
= 0.15 ÷ 0.75 *[1 mark]*
= 0.2 Hz *[1 mark]*

p.152 — Wave Experiments
Q1 E.g. create waves in the ripple tank by attaching a signal generator to the ripple tank's dipper *[1 mark]*. Float a cork in the ripple tank. When the cork is at the top of a 'bob', start the stopwatch. Time how long the cork takes to complete 10 bobs *[1 mark]*. Divide this time by 10 to find the period *[1 mark]*. Calculate the frequency using frequency = 1 ÷ period *[1 mark]*.

p.153 — Reflection
Q1 27° *[1 mark]*

p.154 — Refraction
Q1 Refraction is when a wave changes direction as it crosses a boundary between two different materials *[1 mark]*.

p.155 — Investigating Refraction
Q1 E.g. draw around a glass block on a piece of paper and shine a light ray into the side of the glass block at an angle *[1 mark]*. Trace the incident ray and mark where the ray exits from the block. Remove the block and join up the rays that you have drawn with a straight line *[1 mark]*. Measure the angle of incidence and angle of refraction for where the light entered the block *[1 mark]*.

p.156 — The Electromagnetic Spectrum
Q1 Radio waves *[1 mark]*

p.157 — Energy Levels in Atoms
Q1 Any two from: (high energy) ultraviolet / X-rays / gamma rays *[2 marks — 1 mark for each correct answer]*

p.158 — Uses of EM Radiation
Q1 E.g. sending TV / radio signals *[1 mark]*.

p.159 — More Uses of EM Radiation
Q1 Any two from: e.g. seeing broken bones / seeing through objects / treating cancer *[2 marks — 1 mark for each correct answer]*

p.160 — Temperature and Radiation
Q1 It will decrease *[1 mark]*.

p.161 — Energy Stores and Conservation of Energy
Q1 Elastic energy store *[1 mark]*

p.162 — Energy Transfers
Q1 Energy is transferred electrically *[1 mark]* from the chemical energy store of the battery *[1 mark]* to the kinetic energy store of the motor *[1 mark]*.

p.163 — Efficiency and Power
Q1 convert 4.8 kJ into J = 4.8 × 1000 = 4800 J *[1 mark]*
energy transferred = power × time
so, power = energy transferred ÷ time
= 4800 ÷ 120 *[1 mark]*
= 40 W *[1 mark]*

p.164 — Reducing Unwanted Energy Transfers
Q1 E.g. lubricate the moving parts *[1 mark]*

p.165 — Energy Resources
Q1 Fossil fuels are burnt to heat water and produce steam *[1 mark]*. The steam causes the turbine to turn *[1 mark]*. The turbine drives the generator and turns a magnet near a wire which generates electricity *[1 mark]*.

p.166 — Renewable Energy Resources
Q1 Any two from: E.g. biofuels / wind power / the sun/solar / hydroelectricity / the tides *[1 mark for each, up to 2 marks]*
Q2 Any two from: E.g. spoil the view / noisy / only work when it's windy / high set-up cost *[1 mark for each correct answer]*

Answers

p.167 — More on Energy Resources
Q1 Advantage — E.g. no pollution once running *[1 mark]*
Disadvantage — E.g. high initial costs / only generate electricity during the day / can't make more electricity for increased demand *[1 mark]*.
Q2 E.g. hydroelectric plants usually involve flooding a valley, which makes lots of plants and animals lose their habitats/homes *[1 mark]*. The rotting plants in the flooded valley release greenhouse gases, which lead to global warming *[1 mark]*.

p.168 — Trends in Energy Use
Q1 Any two from: e.g. it is a clean energy resource / it is reliable / it provides lots of jobs
[1 mark for each, correct answer]

p.169 — The National Grid
Q1 An alternating voltage constantly changes direction *[1 mark]*. A direct voltage is always in the same direction *[1 mark]*.
Q2 Live — 230 V *[1 mark]*, Neutral — 0 V *[1 mark]*, Earth — 0 V *[1 mark]*.

p.171 — Current, Potential Difference and Resistance
Q1 charge = current × time
Rearrange for current:
current = charge ÷ time *[1 mark]*
= 1500 ÷ 500 *[1 mark]*
= 3 A *[1 mark]*

p.172 — Describing and Drawing Circuits
Q1 potential difference = current × resistance
Rearrange the equation for resistance:
resistance = potential difference ÷ current
[1 mark]
= 32 ÷ 4 *[1 mark]*
= 8 Ω *[1 mark]*

p.173 — Investigating Resistance
Q1 E.g.

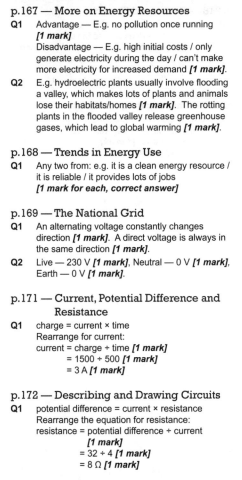

[1 mark for all circuit symbols correct, 1 mark for battery, test wire and ammeter connected in series, 1 mark for voltmeter connected in parallel with the test wire]

You'll still get the marks if you didn't include a switch in your circuit — but it's useful to help you control your experiment.

p.174 — LDRs and Thermistors
Q1 The greater the light intensity, the lower the resistance *[1 mark]*.

p.175 — *I-V* Characteristics
Q1 It stays constant *[1 mark]*.

p.176 — Circuit Devices and *I-V* Characteristics
Q1 a)

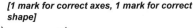

[1 mark for correct axes, 1 mark for correct shape]

b)

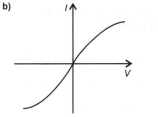

[1 mark for correct axes, 1 mark for correct shape]

p.177 — Energy in Circuits
Q1 potential difference = work done ÷ charge
= 810 ÷ 90 *[1 mark]*
= 9 V *[1 mark]*

p.178 — Series Circuits
Q1 net resistance = 3 + 3 *[1 mark]* = 6 Ω *[1 mark]*

p.179 — Parallel Circuits
Q1 3.5 V *[1 mark]*

p.180 — Investigating Series and Parallel Circuits
Q1 The brightness of each bulb decreases as more bulbs are connected in series *[1 mark]*.

p.181 — Electrical Power
Q1 power = potential difference × current
= 230 × 3.0 *[1 mark]*
= 690 W *[1 mark]*

p.182 — Transformers
Q1 power input = potential difference across primary coil × current in primary coil
so:
potential difference in primary coil
= power input ÷ current in primary coil.
power input = power output, so:
potential difference in primary coil
= power output ÷ current in primary coil *[1 mark]*
= 320 ÷ 160 *[1 mark]*
= 2.0 V *[1 mark]*

p.183 — Permanent and Induced Magnets
Q1 At the poles *[1 mark]*.
Q2 E.g. permanent magnets always produce their own magnetic fields but induced magnets only become magnets when they're inside another magnetic field *[1 mark]*.

p.184 — Magnetism and Electromagnetism
Q1 E.g.

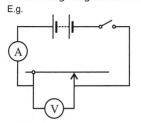

[1 mark for circles getting larger and further apart with wire at centre, 1 mark for arrows on field lines in the correct direction.]

p.185 — Solenoids and Electromagnets
Q1 Any two from: e.g. increase the current through the coil / increase the number of turns but keep the length the same / decrease the cross-sectional area of the coil.
[2 marks — 1 mark for each correct]

p.187 — Forces and Newton's Third Law
Q1 10 N *[1 mark]*

p.188 — Mass and Weight
Q1 weight = mass × gravitational field strength
mass = weight ÷ gravitational field strength
[1 mark]
= 820 ÷ 10 *[1 mark]* = 82 kg *[1 mark]*

p.189 — Distance, Displacement, Speed and Velocity
Q1 average speed = distance ÷ time
= 600 ÷ 120 *[1 mark]*
= 5 m/s *[1 mark]*

p.190 — Measuring and Converting Units
Q1 Multiply the speed by 3600 to convert from m/s to m/h:
speed = 2 × 3600 = 7200 m/h *[1 mark]*
Divide the speed by 1000 to convert from m/h to km/h:
speed = 7200 ÷ 1000 *[1 mark]*
= 7.2 km/h *[1 mark]*

p.191 — Acceleration
Q1 initial speed = 4 m/s, final speed = 10 m/s, distance = 10 m
acceleration = (final speed^2 − initial speed^2) ÷ (2 × distance) *[1 mark]*
= (10^2 − 4^2) ÷ (2 × 10) *[1 mark]*
= (100 − 16) ÷ (2 × 10)
= 4.2 m/s^2 *[1 mark]*

p.192 — Investigating Motion
Q1 Use the light gates to time how long it takes the object to pass between the two light gates *[1 mark]*. Measure the distance between the two light gates *[1 mark]*. Divide the distance by the time taken for the object to travel between the two light gates *[1 mark]*.

p.193 — Distance-Time Graphs
Q1 E.g.

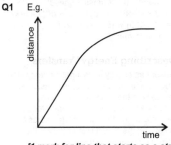

[1 mark for line that starts as a straight line with an upwards slope, 1 mark for the line then curving downwards until it becomes flat]

p.194 — Velocity-Time Graphs
Q1

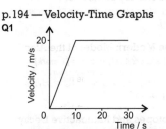

[1 mark for a straight line with an upwards slope to 20 m/s in 10 s, 1 mark for a straight, flat line at 20 m/s for the next 20 s]

Answers

p.195 — Free Body Diagrams and Resultant Forces

Q1

[1 mark for arrows pointing in the right direction and labelled correctly, 1 mark for arrows being the same length.]

p.196 — Newton's First and Second Laws

Q1 Find the total mass of the man and the bike:
mass = 80.0 + 10.0 = 90.0 kg
force = mass × acceleration
= 90.0 × 0.25 *[1 mark]*
= 22.5 N *[1 mark]*

p.197 — Reaction Times

Q1 0.2 - 0.8 s *[1 mark]*

Q2 E.g. using the ruler drop test / using a computer-based test *[1 mark]*.

p.198 — Stopping Distances

Q1 Tiredness increases your reaction time, and so your reaction distance *[1 mark]*. This makes you less likely to stop in time before a hazard, and so more likely to have a collision *[1 mark]*

p.199 — Vehicle Safety

Q1 The foam in the helmet squashes when the cyclist's head hits something. This increases the time it takes for the cyclist's head to come a stop *[1 mark]*. This reduces the force acting on the cyclist's head, which reduces the risk of injury *[1 mark]*.

p.200 — Work Done and Power

Q1 work done = force × distance
work done = 70 ÷ 0.5 *[1 mark]*
= 35 J *[1 mark]*

p.201 — Kinetic and Potential Energy Stores

Q1 gravitational potential energy
= mass × gravitational field strength × height
= 2 × 10 × 10 *[1 mark]* = 200 J *[1 mark]*

Q2 kinetic energy = 0.5 × mass × speed^2
mass = (2 × kinetic energy) ÷ speed^2 *[1 mark]*
= (2 × 450) ÷ 15.0^2 *[1 mark]*
= 4 kg *[1 mark]*

p.202 — Describing Energy Transfers

Q1 The racket has energy in its kinetic energy store *[1 mark]*. Some of this energy is transferred mechanically to the ball's kinetic energy store *[1 mark]*. Some energy is transferred mechanically to the thermal energy stores of the racket and the ball. (This energy is then transferred by heating to the surroundings.) *[1 mark]* The rest is carried away by sound *[1 mark]*.

p.204 — The History of the Atom

Q1 Atoms are tiny spheres that can't be broken up *[1 mark]*.

p.205 — The Modern Model of the Atom

Q1 A nucleus is positively charged *[1 mark]* because it is made up of protons which are positively charged, and neutrons which are neutral *[1 mark]*.

p.206 — Isotopes and Radioactive Decay

Q1 $^{23}_{11}X$ and $^{24}_{11}X$ *[1 mark]*

p.207 — Nuclear Equations

Q1 beta radiation *[1 mark]*

p.208 — Activity and Half-life

Q1 First, find out how many half-lives occur in 4 years:
4 years ÷ 2 years = 2 *[1 mark]*
After one half-life:
Activity = 100 ÷ 2 = 50 Bq
After two half-lives:
Activity = 50 ÷ 2 = 25 Bq.
So the activity after 4 years is 25 Bq *[1 mark]*.

p.209 — Dangers of Radioactivity

Q1 Irradiation is where radiation from a radioactive source away from the body reaches the body *[1 mark]*.

p.210 — More on the Dangers of Radioactivity

Q1 E.g. gamma rays can penetrate into your body and cause harm to organs *[1 mark]*. But alpha particles don't travel as far/are stopped by skin, so they can't damage your organs and so are less dangerous than gamma rays *[1 mark]*.

p.211 — Uses of Radiation

Q1 Gamma radiation is very penetrating *[1 mark]*, so it can be detected outside the body with the radiation detector *[1 mark]*.

p.212 — Density

Q1 E.g. use a balance to find the mass of the object *[1 mark]*. Set up a eureka can and place the object into the can *[1 mark]*. Collect the water pushed out by the object in a measuring cylinder and record its volume *[1 mark]*. Then calculate the density of the object using density = mass ÷ volume *[1 mark]*.

p.213 — The Particle Model

Q1 Any three from: melting, solid to liquid / boiling/evaporating, liquid to gas / sublimating, solid to gas / freezing, liquid to solid / condensing, gas to liquid.
[3 marks — 1 mark for each correct answer]

p.214 — More on the Particle Model

Q1 Decreasing the temperature of the gas means that the gas particles have less energy in their kinetic energy stores *[1 mark]*. They hit the container walls less often so the total force applied is lower *[1 mark]*. A lower force means a lower pressure *[1 mark]*.

p.215 — Specific Heat Capacity

Q1 change in internal energy
= mass × specific heat capacity × change in temperature, so:
change in temperature
= change in internal energy ÷ (mass × specific heat capacity) *[1 mark]*
= 1680 ÷ (0.20 × 420) *[1 mark]*
= 20 °C *[1 mark]*

p.216 — Specific Latent Heat

Q1 energy to cause a change of state
= mass × specific latent heat
= 0.20 × 330 000 *[1 mark]*
= 66 000 J *[1 mark]*

p.217 — Heating and Doing Work

Q1 E.g. energy is transferred from the chemical energy store of the gas to the thermal energy store of the pan *[1 mark]* by heating *[1 mark]*. Energy is then transferred by heating *[1 mark]* from the thermal energy store of the pan to the thermal energy store of the water *[1 mark]*.

p.218 — Forces and Elasticity

Q1 Rearrange force exerted by a spring
= extension × spring constant
So spring constant = force exerted by a spring ÷ extension *[1 mark]*
= 3.0 ÷ 0.040 *[1 mark]*
= 75 N/m *[1 mark]*

p.219 — Investigating Elasticity

Q1 energy stored in a stretched spring
= ½ × spring constant × (extension)^2
= ½ × 54 × 0.10^2 *[1 mark]*
= 0.27 J *[1 mark]*

Index

Index

Index

Index